Physics of
CRYSTALLINE DIELECTRICS
Volume 1
Crystallography and
Spontaneous Polarization

Physics of

CRYSTALLINE DIELECTRICS

Volume 1

Crystallography and Spontaneous Polarization

I. S. Zheludev
Institute of Crystallography of the
Academy of Sciences of the USSR
Moscow, USSR

Translated from Russian by
Albin Tybulewicz
Editor, *Soviet Physics — Semiconductors*

ℚ PLENUM PRESS • NEW YORK-LONDON • 1971

Prof. Ivan Stepanovich Zheludev was born in 1921. He was graduated in 1950 from the Physics Department (Radiophysics Section) of the Moscow State University. The following year he joined the Crystallography Institute of the Academy of Sciences of the USSR and in 1960 became Head of the Laboratory of Electrical Properties of Crystals at this Institute. He was awarded the degree of Candidate of Physico-Mathematical Sciences in 1954 and won his doctorate in 1961. His scientific research has always been concerned with the properties of dielectrics (particularly ferroelectrics, piezoelectrics, and pyroelectrics) in relation to their structure and symmetry. Professor Zheludev has published extensively. He is the coauthor (with V. M. Fridkin) of the monograph *Photo-electrets and the Electrophotographic Process* published in 1960 and translated into English (Consultants Bureau, New York, 1961). Zheludev taught first as a lecturer and then as a professor at the Moscow State University (1955–61); at the Indian Institute of Sciences, Bangalore (1962–63); and at the Voronezh University (1964–66). Since 1966 he has held the temporary appointment of Deputy General Director of the International Atomic Energy Agency in Vienna.

The original Russian text, published in one volume by Nauka Press in Moscow in 1968, has been corrected by the author for this edition. Volume 1 of the present edition is comprised of pages 1–236, inclusive, of the original edition and Volume 2 of pages 237–425, inclusive. Pages 426–461 are not included in the present edition. The English translation is published under an agreement with Mezhdunarodnaya Kniga, the Soviet book export agency.

Желудев Иван Степанович

ФИЗИКА КРИСТАЛЛИЧЕСКИХ ДИЭЛЕКТРИКОВ

FIZIKA KRISTALLICHESKIKH DIELEKTRIKOV

Library of Congress Catalog Card Number 79-138522
SBN 306-37781-0

© 1971 Plenum Press, New York
A Division of Plenum Publishing Corporation
227 West 17th Street, New York, N. Y. 10011

United Kingdom edition published by Plenum Press, London
A Division of Plenum Publishing Company, Ltd.
Donington House, 30 Norfolk Street, London W.C. 2, England

Preface to the American Edition

Research in solid-state physics in general and in the physics of dielectrics in particular has grown rapidly in scope and quantity in the last twenty-five years. In the fifties and early sixties, there was an upsurge of interest in ferroelectricity, piezoelectricity, and pyroelectricity. The classical physics of dielectrics, represented by books of H. Fröhlich, C. P. Smyth, G. I. Skanavi, and A. von Hippel, is now unthinkable without ferroelectricity. The structure and properties of ferroelectrics have been described in a number of books and reviews, including those of W. Känzig, H. D. Megaw, F. Jona and G. Shirane, W. J. Merz and E. Fatuzzo.

The present work deals with the physics of crystalline dielectrics and is based on the investigations carried out by scientists throughout the world. But, understandably, the emphasis is on the research done in the USSR, particularly in the author's laboratory. A special feature of this two-volume treatise is the prominent place given to the symmetry and structure of dielectrics and to the importance of spontaneous electric polarization in many properties of crystals. In fact, these aspects take up the whole of the first volume. The second volume is concerned mainly with various properties and phenomena whose nature is illustrated by considering specific crystals. Thus, for example, the phenomena of polarization, piezoelectricity, electrostriction, etc., are first discussed in detail. Then follow descriptions of these phenomena in specific compounds. This approach seems to be more systematic and it is hoped that the book will be useful to a wide range of readers.

I. S. Zheludev

v

Preface to the Russian Edition

This book is an extended treatment of various aspects of the structure and electrical properties of dielectric crystals. It is the outgrowth of several lecture courses given by the author in the last decade to research workers, postgraduate students, and undergraduates at the Crystallography Institute of the Academy of Sciences of the USSR, at the Moscow and Voronezh State Universities, and at the Indian Institute of Science at Bangalore.

Since the main stress is laid on the properties of crystals, the traditional subjects of the physics of isotropic dielectrics (polarization, electrical conductivity, and dielectric losses) are supplemented by chapters or sections dealing with pyroelectric and piezoelectric properties, electrocaloric phenomena, electrostriction, etc. Since the spontaneous polarization plays an exceptionally important role in many properties of crystals, the atomic and domain structure of dielectrics and the theory of spontaneous polarization are given special treatment in this book.

Sections 1 and 2 of Chapter III were written mainly by A. S. Sonin; Section 1 of Chapter VI was contributed by V. V. Gladkii. G. A. Zheludeva and L. P. Pashkova helped the author considerably in the preparation of the manuscript for press.

The author is most grateful to all those who helped him in writing and revising the manuscript as well as in publishing this book.

I. S. Zheludev

General Introduction

The physics of crystalline dielectrics deals with all the phenomena and properties which are related in some way to the electric polarization of crystals. The physics of dielectrics covered in this book includes the phenomena and properties resulting from the application of an external electric field or those resulting from the spontaneous polarization observed in some crystals, as well as the electric polarization phenomena due to mechanical strain or stress (piezoelectric polarization).

Even until fairly recently, the physics of dielectrics consisted mainly of the following subjects: electric polarization, electrical conductivity, dielectric losses, and electric strength of isotropic dielectrics (capacitor and insulation materials) widely used in technology.

Recent developments in technology have been characterized by extensive use of crystals. Thus, the successful development of quantum electronics, piezoelectric techniques, electroacoustics, metrology, etc., would be impossible without the use of crystals. Moreover, crystals are widely used in the well established branches of electrical and radio engineering, such as capacitor manufacture and electric insulation technology. These applications of crystals have led to the emergence and rapid development of new subjects in the physics of dielectrics: pyroelectricity, piezoelectricity, electrostriction, etc. But only when we are armed with full knowledge of the properties of a given dielectric, including its polarizability, electrical conductivity, electric strength, pyroelectric and piezoelectric properties, and elastic and electrostriction parameters, can we realize all the possible technological applications of this material.

The establishment of the physics of dielectrics as an independent branch of physics is closely related to the work of Soviet scientists, particularly A. F. Ioffe, I. V. Kurchatov, Ya. I. Frenkel' (J. Frenkel), B. M. Vul, A. K. Val'ter, P. P. Kobeko, G. I. Skanavi, N. P. Bogoroditskii, and A. A. Vorob'ev. The development of the physics of dielectrics during the last three or four decades has resulted in the establishment of industrial and research organizations and institutions which are supplying Soviet electrical and radio engineering industries with the necessary dielectric materials.

The modern physics of dielectrics is basically the physics of ferroelectrics and antiferroelectrics, as well as of piezoelectric and pyroelectric materials. The milestones in the development of this new physics of dielectrics are the investigations of ferroelectrics, carried out in the nineteen-thirties by I. V. Kurchatov and his colleagues, the studies of B. M. Vul and others which led to the discovery (in 1944) of the most important ferroelectric material, barium titanate, as well as the work of V. L. Ginzburg on the theory of ferroelectricity.

Important results relating to piezoelectric and ferroelectric crystals were obtained by A. V. Shubnikov and his colleagues. G. A. Smolenskii and his team had many successes in the preparation of new oxygen-octahedral ferroelectrics and in the study of their properties. A key place in the investigations of the structure of ferroelectrics is occupied by the work of G. S. Zhdanov and his colleagues.

The physics of dielectrics is part of solid-state physics. Consequently, further development of the physics of dielectrics will depend on the extensive use of diffraction methods for structure investigation (x-ray, neutron, and electron diffraction methods), resonance methods for the investigation of the structure of crystals and the fields in them (nuclear magnetic resonance, quadrupole resonance, Mössbauer effect), and on the many varieties of spectral investigations covering a wide range of electromagnetic wavelengths from the visible right down to the millimeter region.

The promising directions of investigation in the physics of dielectrics are those concerned with materials exhibiting simultaneously several properties: these materials include photoconducting ferroelectric and piezoelectric substances, semiconducting piezoelectric materials, materials exhibiting magnetic and electric ordering of their structure, and so on.

Introduction to Volume 1

Since a crystal is an anisotropic medium, its physical (particularly electrical) properties can be described satisfactorily only if one adopts some of the crystallographic concepts and data, particularly those belonging to physical crystallography. Chapter I deals with the topics in crystallography which will be required in subsequent chapters.

A crystal is a continuous medium with a three-dimensional periodic distribution of matter (a "uniform discontinuum"). All the properties of a crystal are governed by its composition and structure. However, in many cases, the macroscopic properties of a crystal (for example, pyroelectric, piezoelectric, and other properties) can be described by representing the crystal as a continuous uniform anisotropic medium. The concept of continuity does not require further comment. A uniform medium is a medium in which a given property is the same at all points in the medium. A medium is anisotropic if a given property varies with the direction. The nature of the anisotropy is governed by the symmetry of the medium.

There are two aspects of symmetry. One is the point symmetry. In this case, a crystal is regarded as a finite three-dimensional figure. Symmetrical transformations of such a figure by point-symmetry operations leave at least one point of the figure unaltered. This point is known as special and the symmetry groups corresponding to these symmetry transformations are known as the point groups. We can also consider a crystal as an infinite body with a periodic structure. The symmetry of such a body is described by the space groups of symmetry.

The anisotropy of continuous uniform media can be considered satisfactorily using the concept of point symmetry. However, the descriptions of such properties and processes as the polarizability, the appearance and disappearance of the spontaneous polarization, etc., require the knowledge of the space symmetry. Consequently, we shall discuss the fundamentals of both point and space symmetry.

Since a discussion of electrical properties requires some knowledge of crystallography (such as the selection of the system of coordinates, face indices, etc.), we shall present this information in a concise form.

Some problems associated with electrical properties can be discussed only using special ideas of symmetry and physical crystallography (Curie's principle, Neumann's principle, etc.). These ideas are also discussed in Chap. I.

The problem of spontaneous electric polarization is one of the most important in modern solid-state physics. Apart from the scientific aspects, the importance of spontaneous polarization is primarily due to the extensive technological applications of substances exhibiting this property. Many of the basic properties and processes in dielectrics (polarization, pyroelectric phenomena, piezoelectric effect, electrostriction, electrical conductivity, etc.) are closely related to the presence of spontaneous polarization and its changes under the action of external agents (heating or cooling, deformation, electric fields, etc.). The spontaneous electric polarization of ferroelectrics and antiferroelectrics governs all the physical properties of these materials.

There have been many theoretical and experimental investigations of spontaneous electric polarization. Particularly important are the studies of the structure and physical properties, whose aim is to elucidate the temperature dependence of the spontaneous polarization. Unfortunately, the nature of the spontaneous polarization has not yet been fully determined.

In the final analysis, spontaneous polarization is governed by the structure and nature of the bonds between the particles forming a crystal. In view of this, special attention will be paid to investigations of the structure of ferroelectrics and antiferroelectrics (Chaps. II and III). The spontaneous polarization domains

and their behavior as a function of temperature are discussed in
Chap. IV.

The thermal, pyroelectric, and other properties of crystals,
closely related to the spontaneous polarization of linear and nonlinear dielectrics, are dealt with in Chap. V. Chapter VI is concerned with the theory of the spontaneous electric polarization.

For the convenience of the reader, a foldout containing a conversion table for the Shubnikov, Schoenflies, and International crystallographic systems has been included at the rear of the book,
between pages 330 and 331.

Contents of Volume 1

Contents of Volume 2

Chapter I

Symmetry. Fundamentals of Crystallography

§1. Point Symmetry

A. Definitions and Basic Concepts. Symmetry is the property of geometrical figures which have identical and regularly distributed parts. We shall consider only finite figures although there is, in general, no limitation to the size of a figure in point symmetry. The laws governing the uniform distribution of equal parts in a figure are given by symmetry operations or symmetry transformations. The science of symmetry shows that symmetry transformations of three-dimensional figures are simple (proper) rotation and rotation accompanied by reflection (improper or reflection rotation).*

The operation of simple rotation is self-evident and does not require special comment. Examples of figures, parts of which can be made to coincide by simple rotation, are shown in Fig. 1.† The rotation axes of these figures are known as n-fold symmetry axes, where n is the number of coincidences encountered in rotation through 360°.

The coincidence of the parts of figures in operations involving rotation and reflection is shown in Fig. 2. In this case, coincidence is achieved by a complex operation consisting of rotation followed

---

*Instead of mirror reflections accompanied by rotation, we can use also the rotation-inversion operation.

†Here, the parts of a figure are general (irregular) tetrahedra, as discussed by Shubnikov [7]. In those cases when the fourth vertex of a tetrahedron lies below the plane of the paper, the tetrahedron is represented simply by a triangle.

1

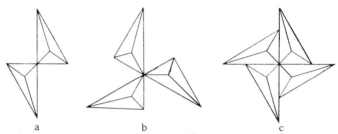

Fig. 1. Examples of figures with twofold (a), threefold (b), and fourfold (c) axes.

by reflection of the parts of the figures in some plane. In Fig. 2a,
this plane is perpendicular to the plane of the figure and directed
vertically. Here, the parts of the figure can be made to coincide
by rotation through 360° (the onefold axis is horizontal and lies in
the plane of the figure) and reflection. Such an operation is usually
called reflection (strictly, reflection rotation) and the corresponding symmetry element is known as the plane of symmetry and is
denoted by the letter m. In Fig. 2d, the rotation takes place about
the axes perpendicular to the plane of the figure, and is followed
by reflection in the plane of the figure. Such reflection transforms
"right-handed" tetrahedra into "left-handed" figures, and conversely. (This operation is similar to the "transformation" of the right
hand into the left hand by a mirror.) In this case, as in the case of
simple rotation, the figure in the new position (reached after the
symmetry transformation) is completely identical with the figure
in the original position. This means, of course, that the transformations considered are symmetrical. The axes in reflection-ro-
tation operations are simply called n-fold reflection axes. The

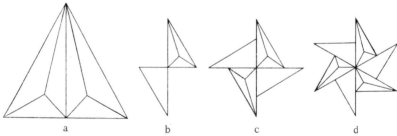

Fig. 2. Examples of figures with onefold (a, reflection plane), twofold (b, inversion
center), fourfold (c), and sixfold (d) rotation-reflection axes.

order of an axis is equal to the number of coincidences of the figure encountered in rotation through 360°.

The order of symmetry axes, both rotation and reflection, can be arbitrary. Simple rotation axes are usually denoted by numbers, 1, 2, 3, 4, 5, 6, 7, 8, ..., ∞, which indicate the order of the axes; reflection axes are denoted by barred numbers, which also indicate the order of the axes: $\bar{1}, \bar{2}, \bar{3}, \bar{4}, \bar{5}, \bar{6}, \bar{7}, \bar{8}, \bar{9}, ..., \bar{\infty}$.

Each of the figures shown in Fig. 1 has a point which remains invariant under rotation. This is the point of intersection of the rotation axis with the plane of Fig. 1. Such a point is known as special. The same property, i.e., invariance in symmetry operations, can be exhibited also by a line, a plane, or a three-dimensional body. In Fig. 2a the vertical line lying in the plane of Fig. 2 is special. We can easily imagine a figure which has a special plane; such a figure would consist of two tetrahedra which are in contact along reflection-equivalent faces. When one of the tetrahedra in Fig. 1 or Fig. 2 is considered as an independent figure, such a figure can be a special body: all its points are invariant in symmetry operations (in fact, we can perform only operation 1, i.e., the figure has a onefold symmetry axis).

Symmetry operations are regarded as equivalent, i.e., identical, if they result in the same regrouping of parts of the figure. Thus, rotations by 180° to the right and left are identical and rotation by 60° to the left (right) is identical with rotation by 120° to the right (left).

We must consider separately inversion and identity operations. The inversion operation consists of the reflection of a figure at a point. Let us denote the point at which reflection takes place by the letter O. The inversion operation consists of the translation, along lines passing through the point O, of all points in the figure to the opposite side of O, in such a way that the new distances of all these points from the point O are equal to the original distances. If a figure can be brought into self-coincidence by inversion at a given point, this point is known as the inversion center or center of symmetry and we then say that the figure has an inversion center (C). We can easily show that the inversion operation is equivalent to reflection and rotation by 180° (C = $\bar{2}$). Figures 2b and 2d have inversion centers. We can also show that if a figure has a symmetry axis of even order and a plane of symmetry perpendicular to this axis, it must have an inversion center.

The unity or identity operation is the operation whereby a figure is transformed into itself by leaving it at its original place. The identity operation is denoted by the number 1 which corresponds to the onefold symmetry axis.

To clarify the definition of symmetry given at the beginning of this section, we shall now consider the concept of the equivalence of figures and their parts.

The concept of equivalence is closely related to the concept of symmetry transformations. When we consider the parts of a figure, we conclude that equivalent figures are those which transform into each other, i.e., which exchange places after being subjected to symmetry transformations. We can distinguish two types of equivalence of the parts of a symmetrical figure: reflection equivalence and congruent equivalence. The parts of a figure related by reflection equivalence are transformed into one another by rotation and reflection, while the congruently equivalent parts can be transformed into one another by simple rotation. Sometimes, the operation of simple rotation is called an operation of the first kind, and the operation of rotation and reflection is called an operation of the second kind.

The concept of equivalence can be applied not only to the parts of a figure but also to the figure itself. Thus, we may have figures which are equivalent to each other only in the congruent sense (for example, the two tetrahedra shown in Fig. 1 are considered as separate units); or we may have figures which exhibit only the reflection equivalence (for example, the pair of octahedra shown in Fig. 2a when regarded as separate entities). We may also have figures which are equivalent to each other in the congruent and reflection senses. If the equivalence is only of the reflection type, the corresponding figures are called enantiomorphous with respect to each other. One of the enantiomorphous figures is regarded as left-handed and the other as right-handed. Two enantiomorphous figures are shown in Fig. 3.

Every symmetry transformation can be repeated as many times as we please. Operations which consist of two, three, etc., repetitions of some operation are called ranks of that operation. If the

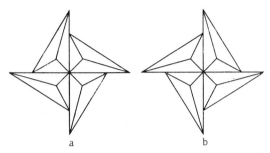

Fig. 3. Example of the reflection (enantiomorphous) equivalence of figures, each of which consists only of right-handed (a) or left-handed (b) parts.

original operation is denoted by M, these ranks are denoted by M^2, M^3, M^4, etc.

An operation equivalent to two consecutive operations is called the product of these operations and is denoted by the two symbols of these operations standing side by side. It must be stressed that the result of two consecutive symmetry transformations may depend on the order in which these operations are carried out and, therefore, the first operation should always take precedence in the expression used to represent these operations.

B. Symmetry Groups. A set of various operations by means of which a given figure can be transformed into self-coincidence forms a symmetry group. Thus, for example, the symmetry group of the figure shown in Fig. 2a comprises two different operations: identity (1) and reflection in a plane (m). The symmetry group of the figure in Fig. 2b also consists of two different operations: identity (1) and inversion (C).

The number of nonequivalent operations forming a symmetry group is called the order of the group. The order is equal to the maximum number of equal parts of a figure into which it can be divided. It follows, for example, that the order of the symmetry group of the figure shown in Fig. 2b is two and that shown in Fig. 3 is four, etc.

If the identity operation is the only possible symmetry transformation of a figure, such a figure is called asymmetric. The order of the symmetry group of such a figure is unity. When a symmetrical figure is divided into the maximum possible number of equivalent parts, each of these parts must be an asymmetric figure.

A set of different symmetry transformations of a figure which forms a group should satisfy the following postulates.

1. The product of any two operations M and N which are included in the symmetry group is equivalent to some operation P which is also included in that group:

$$MN = P.$$

2. The associative law applies to all symmetry operations:

$$(MN)P = M(NP).$$

3. The symmetry operations include an operation A such that

$$AM = MA = M$$

for any operation of the group. The operation A is called the identity or unit operation.

4. For each operation M there is an inverse operation which is also included in the symmetry group. It is denoted by the symbol M^{-1} and satisfies the relationship

$$MM^{-1} = M^{-1}M = A,$$

where A is the identity operation.

The concept of isomorphism is important in group theory. Two groups of the same order are called isomorphous if the elements of these groups have a one-to-one correspondence such that the product of any two elements in one of the groups corresponds to a product of two definite elements in the other group.

In crystallography and in crystal physics, we usually deal not with symmetry operations (elements of a group) but with elements of symmetry. According to Shubnikov's definition, a symmetry element is a group defined by one operation, i.e., a group containing all nonequivalent ranks of a given operation. For example, a fourfold axis is a group containing the following four operations: rotation to the left by 90°, rotation to the left by 180°, rotation to the left by 270°, and rotation to the left by 360° (identity). All other ranks of the operation and the inverse operations are equivalent to one of the four operations just listed. When this definition of a symmetry element is used we find that only simple rotation axes and rotation-reflection axes can be symmetry elements for finite figures.

The problem of possible combinations of symmetry elements forming a group is a special topic in the science of symmetry. Even a simple listing of symmetry elements shows that the total number of point symmetry groups is infinite. However, it is possible to classify groups by listing series of isotypic groups. One of these is the series of pyramid groups and another is the series of prism groups, etc. Although the total number of symmetry groups is infinite, it does not follow that all series of groups are also infinite. Thus, the series of symmetry groups of those polyhedra which have more than one symmetry axis of an order higher than two are finite and, in fact, very short. Here are some samples of series of groups:

$$1, \quad 2, \quad 3, \quad 4, \quad 5, \quad 6, \ldots, \quad \infty:$$
$$1 \cdot m, \quad 2 \cdot m, \quad 3 \cdot m, \quad 4 \cdot m, \ldots, \quad \infty \cdot m;$$
$$1:2, \quad 2:2, \quad 3:2, \quad 4:2, \ldots, \quad \infty:2.$$

The colon (:) between the axes and planes or between the axes indicates that they are mutually perpendicular, and the point (·) indicates that they are parallel. Symmetry groups are denoted using only the "generating" elements. For example, we can easily see that the "generating" elements of the symmetry groups $3 \cdot m$ are a set of symmetry elements consisting of a threefold axis and three symmetry planes passing through this axis but not intersecting it.

All possible series of symmetry groups are listed in Table 1. [An oblique (/) indicates that the symmetry axes form an angle other than 90°.] It is evident from Table 1 that all groups can be reduced to 19 series. The lowest row in Table 1 lists groups containing infinite-order axes (∞, ∞). Such groups are obtained by infinite extension of a series in the direction of increasing orders of the axis and are called the limiting groups. We note that the first terms of some series can be attributed to different limiting groups. This is due to the following equalities which apply to the group notation:

$$1 \cdot m = 1:m = m; \quad 2 = 1:2; \quad 2:m = \bar{2} \cdot m; \quad m \cdot 1:m = 2 \cdot m.$$

TABLE 1. Point

I	II	III	IV	V	VI	VII	VIII	IX	X	XI	XII
1	2	$\bar{2}$	$\bar{4}$	1 : 2	2 : 2	$1{\cdot}m$	$2{\cdot}m$	1 : m	2 : m	$\bar{2}{\cdot}m$	$\bar{4}{\cdot}m$
3	4	$\bar{6}$	$\bar{8}$	3 : 2	4 : 2	$3{\cdot}m$	$4{\cdot}m$	3 : m	4 : m	$\bar{6}{\cdot}m$	$\bar{8}{\cdot}m$
5	6	$\overline{10}$	$\overline{12}$	5 : 2	6 : 2	$5{\cdot}m$	$6{\cdot}m$	5 : m	6 : m	$\overline{10}{\cdot}m$	$\overline{12}{\cdot}m$
7	8	$\overline{14}$	$\overline{16}$	7 : 2	8 : 2	$7{\cdot}m$	$8{\cdot}m$	7 : m	8 : m	$\overline{14}{\cdot}m$	$\overline{16}{\cdot}m$
•	•	•	•	•	•	•	•	•	•	•	•
•	•	•	•	•	•	•	•	•	•	•	•
•	•	•	•	•	•	•	•	•	•	•	•
∞		$\bar{\infty}$		$\infty : 2$		$\infty{\cdot}m$		$\infty : m$		$\bar{\infty}{\cdot}m$	

Each pair of the first 14 series (such pairs are separated by double vertical lines) ends with the same limiting group. This division of the series of groups into pairs has the following meaning: groups belonging to two series of the same pair can describe crystals with different properties.

Three series −XV, XVII, XVIII − have only one crystallographic cubic group. However, even in the case of these groups, it is resonable to consider limiting groups. The symbols of these limiting groups stress the symmetry of the directions (for example, the symmetry of the polar vector ∞·m or of the axial vector ∞:m, etc.) forming a model of a given symmetry group (this point will be discussed later). Similar comments can be made with reference to the series XVI and XIX which contain only two groups each.

Let us consider the 12 limiting groups. Seven of these groups, namely, ∞, ∞:m, ∞·m; ∞:2, m·∞:m, ∞/∞:2, and ∞/m·∞, were introduced first by Pierre Curie. The simplest geometrical figures with infinite-order axes (Figs. 4l, 4h, 4i, 4j, 4f, 4d, and 4a, respectively) can be used to represent these limiting groups.

The representation of the remaining limiting groups is somewhat more complex. Thus, the group ∞·m can be represented by a cylinder in which all lines parallel to its axis are polar vectors, oriented so that half the vectors are directed upward and the other half downward (Fig. 4g). Such a cylinder, rotating about its axis, represents the limiting group $\bar{\infty}$ (Fig. 4k). A sphere whose diameters have the symmetry of the polar vector ∞·m represents the

Symmetry Groups

XIII	XIV	XV	XVI	XVII	XVIII	XIX
$m\cdot1:m$	$m\cdot2:m$	$3/2$	$3/4$	$3/\bar{4}$	$\bar{6}/2$	$\bar{6}/4$
$m\cdot3:m$	$m\cdot4:m$		$3/5$			$3/\bar{10}$
$m\cdot5:m$	$m\cdot6:m$					
$m\cdot7:m$	$m\cdot8:m$					
$\vdots$	$\vdots$					
$m\cdot\infty:m$		∞/∞	$\infty/\infty:2$	$\infty/\infty\cdot m$	$\infty/\infty:m$	$\infty/m\cdot\infty:m$

group $\infty/\infty\cdot$m (Fig. 4c), and a sphere whose diameters have the symmetry of the axial vector ∞:m represents the group ∞/∞:m (Fig. 4b). A sphere can represent the symmetry group ∞/∞ when its diameters have the symmetry ∞. Such symmetry is obtained when the diameters of a sphere are simultaneously polar and axial. A representation of the group ∞/∞ is shown in Fig. 4e.

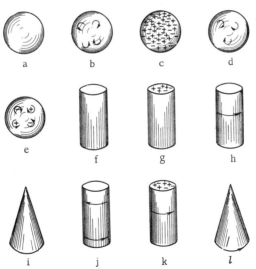

Fig. 4. Representations of limiting symmetry groups by three-dimensional figures. Figures a, d, f, h, i, j, l represent the limiting groups of Pierre Curie.

TABLE 2. Subordination of Limiting Groups

Subordinate (isotropic) groups	Original group	Subordinate groups	Subordinate (isotropic) groups	Original group	Subordinate groups
$\infty/\infty : m$ $\infty/\infty \cdot m$ $\infty/\infty : 2$ ∞/∞	$\leftarrow \infty/m \cdot \infty : m \rightarrow$	$m \cdot \infty : m$ $\overline{\infty} \cdot m$ $\infty : m$ $\infty \cdot m$ $\infty : 2$ $\overline{\infty}$ ∞		$m \cdot \infty : m \rightarrow$	$\overline{\infty} \cdot m$ $\infty : m$ $\infty \cdot m$ $\infty : 2$ $\overline{\infty}$ ∞
∞/∞	$\leftarrow \left\{ \begin{array}{c} \infty/\infty : m \\ \infty/\infty \cdot m \end{array} \right\} \rightarrow$	$m \cdot \infty : m$ $\overline{\infty} \cdot m$ $\infty : m$ $\infty \cdot m$ $\overline{\infty} : 2$ $\overline{\infty}$ ∞		$\overline{\infty} \cdot m \rightarrow$ $\infty : m \rightarrow$	$\infty \cdot m$ $\infty : 2$ $\overline{\infty}$ ∞ $\overline{\infty}$ ∞
∞/∞	$\leftarrow \infty/\infty : 2 \rightarrow$	$\infty : 2$ ∞		$\left. \begin{array}{c} \infty \cdot m \\ \infty : 2 \\ \overline{\infty} \end{array} \right\} \rightarrow$	∞
	$\infty/\infty \rightarrow$	∞			

The limiting groups are of great importance in crystal physics. Thus, for example, these groups can be used to select, in a simple manner, the symmetry groups of crystals having certain physical properties. In such a selection, we must know, in particular, the subordination of the limiting groups, given in Table 2 (a G_1 is subordinate to a group G_2, if G_1 is a subgroup of G_2). The selection rules for the subordinate groups, based on Table 2, will be given later in connection with a discussion of the properties of crystals.

C. Crystallographic Symmetry Groups. Systems, Divisions, and Classes. The symmetry groups considered in the preceding subsection describe the symmetry of a great variety of geometrical figures. (In particular, they can be used to describe the symmetry of atoms, molecules, etc.) However, in crystallography and in crystal physics, we are interested mainly in the crystallographic groups, which are the groups comprising only one-, two-, three-, four-, and sixfold simple (proper) rotation axes and rotation-reflection axes in any combination. Fivefold axes, as well as axes of orders higher than the sixth, are forbidden because the existence of such axes in a crystal is incompatible with the idea of a crystal lattice. The total number of the crystallographic groups is 32 [8].

All the crystals belonging to the same symmetry group con-
stitute a crystallographic class. In those cases, when we speak of
the symmetry, we can denote the crystal classes by symbols of the
corresponding symmetry groups.

Particles forming a crystal are distributed periodically in a
space lattice. For each type of lattice, we can select a unit parallelepiped whose edges are equal to the length of the shortest translations by means of which the lattice can be constructed. Any
three-dimensional lattice and its unit parallelepiped can be described by six parameters: three principal translations along the
a, b, and c axes, which are denoted by the same letters, and three
angles α, β, and γ, between the b and c, c and a, a and b axes, respectively. Consequently, all crystals can be described by one of
six different crystallographic systems of coordinates. One of these
systems (hexagonal) can be split into two divisions: hexagonal and
trigonal. This is based on the fact that hexagonal and trigonal crystals have different primitive Bravais lattices (this will be discussed
later). The division of crystals into classes, taking into account
the differences between the Bravais lattices, yields seven crystallographic systems. The crystal systems, parameters of the unit
cells, names of the classes, symmetry elements, and various symbols used for symmetry groups, are all given in Table 3. The symmetry element formulas give only the main symmetry elements of
the various classes. Thus, Table 3 does not give (except in the
crystal class 1) the symmetry element 1, which occurs in the symmetry groups of all the crystal classes. In those cases where a
higher-order axis is given, the subordinate lower-order axis (which
has the same direction) is omitted. The number of axes and planes
is indicated by parentheses in the symmetry formulas. The last
three columns give the symbols used in the present book (Shubnikov system), as well as the Schoenflies and International symbols.

§2. Microsymmetry of Crystals

A. Bravais Lattices. Unit parallelepipeds or unit cells
are not always primitive. This means that they may include sites
(apart from the cell vertices) located within the cell itself because
the shortest possible translations have been ignored in selecting
the cell axes. Once again we find that there are seven possibilities and thus there are 14 topologically different translation or

TABLE 3. Crystallographic Systems, Divisions, and Classes

Coordinate system and unit cell parameters	Crystallographic system	Class No.	Class	Symmetry elements	Point group symbols		
					Shubnikov	Schoen-flies	International
Triclinic $a \neq b \neq c$; $\alpha \neq \beta \neq \gamma$	Triclinic	1	Monohedral	1	1	C_1	1
		2	Pinacoidal	$\bar{2}$	$\bar{2}$	$C_i = S_2$	$\bar{1}$
Monoclinic $a \neq b \neq c$; $\alpha = \gamma = 90°$, $\beta \neq 90°$	Monoclinic	3	Dihedral axial	2	2	C_2	2
		4	Dihedral nonaxial	m	m	$C_{1h} = C_s$	m
		5	Prismatic	2, m, C	$2:m$	C_{2h}	$2/m$
Orthorhombic $a \neq b \neq c$; $\alpha = \beta = \gamma = 90°$	Orthorhombic	6	Rhombic tetrahedral	(3)2	$2:2$	$D_2 = V$	222
		7	Rhombic pyramidal	2, (2)m	$2·m$	C_{2v}	$mm\,2$
		8	Rhombic bipyramidal	(3)2, (3)m, C	$m·2:m$	$D_{2h} = V_h$	mmm
Tetragonal $a = b \neq c$; $\alpha = \beta = \gamma = 90°$	Tetragonal	9	Tetragonal pyramidal	4	4	C_4	4
		10	Tetragonal tetrahedral	$\bar{4}$	$\bar{4}$	S_4	$\bar{4}$
		11	Tetragonal trapezohedral	4, (4)2	$4:2$	D_4	422
		12	Ditetragonal pyramidal	4, (4)m	$4·m$	C_{4v}	$4\,mm$
		13	Tetragonal bipyramidal	4, m, C	$4:m$	C_{4h}	$4/m$
		14	Tetragonal scalenohedral	$\bar{4}$, (2)2, (2)m	$\bar{4}·m$	$D_{2d} = V_d$	$\bar{4}2\,m$
		15	Ditetragonal bipyramidal	4, (4)2, (5)m, C	$m·4:m$	D_{4h}	$4/mmm$

System	No.	Name				
Hexagonal $a=b\neq c;\ \alpha=\beta=90°;$ $\gamma=120°$ Trigonal	16	Trigonal pyramidal	3	3	C_3	3
	17	Rhombohedral	$\bar{6}$, C	$\bar{6}$	$C_{3i}=S_6$	$\bar{3}$
	18	Trigonal trapezohedral	3, (3) 2	3 : 2	D_3	32
	19	Ditrigonal pyramidal	3, (3) m	3·m	C_{3v}	3m
	20	Ditrigonal scalenohedral	$\bar{6}$, (3) 2, (3) m, C	$\bar{6}$·m	D_{3d}	$\bar{3}$m
Hexagonal	21	Hexagonal pyramidal	6	6	C_6	6
	22	Trigonal bipyramidal	3, m	3 : m	C_{3h}	$\bar{6}$
	23	Hexagonal trapezohedral	6, (6) 2	6 : 2	D_6	622
	24	Dihexagonal pyramidal	6, (6) m	6·m	C_{6v}	6mm
	25	Hexagonal bipyramidal	6, m, C	6 : m	C_{6h}	6/m
	26	Ditrigonal bipyramidal	3, (3) 2, (4) m	m·3 : m	D_{3h}	$\bar{6}$m2
	27	Dihexagonal bipyramidal	6, (6) 2, (7) m, C	m·6 : m	D_{6h}	6/mmm
Cubic $a=b=c;$ $\alpha=\beta=\gamma=90°$	28	Tritetrahedral	(3) 2, (4) 3	3/2	T	23
	29	Trioctahedral	(3) 4, (4) 3, (6) 2	3/4	O	432
	30	Hexatetrahedral	(3) $\bar{4}$, (4) 3, (6) m	3/$\bar{4}$	T_d	$\bar{4}$3m
	31	Didodecahedral	(3) 2, (4) $\bar{6}$, (3) m, C	$\bar{6}$/2	T_h	m3
	32	Hexaoctahedral	(3) 4, (4) $\bar{6}$, (6) 2, (9) m, C	$\bar{6}$/4	O_h	m3m

TABLE 4. Translation Lattices (shown in Fig. 5)

System	Lattice			
	primitive	base-centered	body-centered	face-centered
Triclinic	1	—	—	—
Monoclinic	2	3	—	—
Orthorhombic	4	5	6	7
Tetragonal	8	—	9	—
Rhombohedral	11	—	—	—
Hexagonal	10	—	—	—
Cubic	12	—	13	14

Bravais lattices [1]. All the translation lattices are shown in Fig. 5 and listed in Table 4.

These 14 translation lattices form the seven crystallographic systems referred to in the preceding section. Lattices belonging to the same system have the same point symmetry, which is highest for the system and is known as holohedry. The holohedral lattice symmetry is the highest symmetry among the classes of crystals belonging to the particular system considered. Hence, it follows that, if we replace the spheres at the sites of a translation lattice by figures of higher symmetry in the crystallographic system considered, we still obtain the same holohedral symmetry as for spheres. Translation lattices consisting of figures of lower symmetries at the lattice sites (having the symmetry of one of the groups in the given system) have the symmetry of these figures. Such a reduction of the symmetry within a given system is known as hemihedry.

B. Space Symmetry Groups. We have considered so far the symmetry of translation lattices and established the point symmetry of space lattices. However, the space symmetry of such lattices, described by space groups [3], is of greatest interest in the case of three-dimensional lattices.

In contrast to the symmetry of finite three-dimensional bodies, the symmetry of space lattices has an additional symmetry element which governs parallel translations in the lattice. The subgroup of parallel translations is not the only addition to the point symmetry of space lattices. Because of the possibility of parallel translations in a lattice (considered as an array of points in space), we can have other new symmetry elements. These elements (which occur only in the case of space lattices) are glide planes or glide reflection planes and screw axes.

We can study the nature of glide planes and screw axes by considering Fig. 6, which shows a set of two rows of points in a plane, which are assumed to be located at the sites of a simple (primitive) cubic lattice. All the points in this lattice can be obtained simply by translation from one point 1. In accordance with the symmetry of such a translation lattice, point 1 can be brought into self-coincidence with, for example, point 2' by using not only the rotation and reflection operations (point symmetry elements are not shown in Fig. 6) but also two new operations: screw

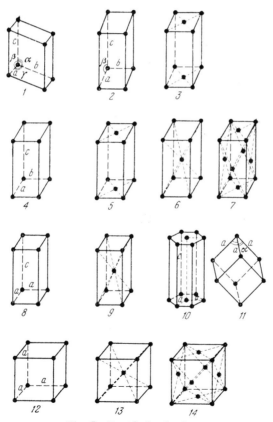

Fig. 5. Translation lattices.

Fig. 6. Symmetry operations corresponding to screw axes and glide planes.

rotation by 180° about an axis I-I or glide reflection in a plane perpendicular to the figure and intersecting it along the screw axis I-I (which lies in the glide plane). The superposition of points 1 and 2' by a twofold screw axis can be represented as a combination of two successive operations: rotation about the I-I axis (this transfers point 1 to point 1') and translation by a distance a parallel to the I-I axis. The superposition of the same two points using a glide reflection plane can be also represented as two consecutive operations: translation of point 1 by a distance a and reflection in the glide plane. Similar operations can be carried out to bring into self-coincidence the following points: point 2 with point 3', point 3 with point 4', etc. The sites of points 1, 2, 3, ... are then occupied by other points in the infinite lattice but the new state of the whole lattice after screw rotation of the glide reflection is identical with the original state. This explains the nature and operation of the I-I screw axis and of the I-I glide reflection plane. (We note that, in the case just discussed, the I-I axis is also a simple fourfold rotation axis 4, a simple twofold rotation axis 2, a twofold rotation-reflection axis $\bar{2}$, and fourfold rotation-reflection axis $\bar{4}$; the I-I plane is also a simple reflection plane.)

The combined effect of a screw axis and a glide plane can be understood easily by examining the operation of "multiplication" of a tetrahedron, shown in Figs. 7a and 7b.

Thus, space lattices can have screw axes and glide planes because their symmetry group includes the subgroup of parallel translations. These additional symmetry elements are a property not only of geometrical lattices but also of real crystals. The theory of space groups shows that a combination of certain symmetry elements of figures (having a symmetry lower than an array of spheres) located at lattice sites may also give rise to screw axes and glide planes (new elements of point symmetry can also appear but this is regarded as self-evident). Thus derivation of space groups consists of finding lattices of different symmetries (including screw axes and glide planes) whose sites (and other points, in

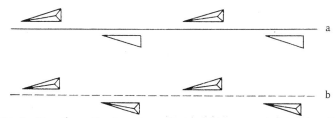

Fig. 7. Transformation by means of a twofold screw axis (a) and a glide reflection plane (b).

the case of nonprimitive lattices) are occupied by figures belonging to various point groups of the symmetry of the system to which a given lattice belongs. Each crystal class of point symmetry may correspond, in general, to several space groups. Combinations of symmetry elements in space groups are similar to combinations of symmetry elements in the corresponding point groups. Assuming that translations are equal to zero in a space group, i.e., drawing its symmetry elements through the origin of coordinates, we obtain one of the point groups of symmetry.

Let us consider some simple cases. There is only one triclinic Bravais lattice and it has only two point symmetry elements: identity and inversion in a point. In this case, allowance for the translation symmetry does not generate any new symmetry elements (such as screw axes and glide planes). Thus, there are only two space groups in the triclinic system: one corresponding to class 1 (group C_1), the other to class 2 (group C_i^1). The point group 2 of the monoclinic system includes the symmetry operations 1 and 2. The combination of a rotation axis 2 with a translation parallel to it gives rise to a screw axis 2. The combination of axes of type 2 with perpendicular translations generates two space groups $P2$ and $P2_1$ with primitive cells having only rotation or only screw axes, respectively. The combination of twofold symmetry axes with inclined translations produces another space group $C2$ with the cell centered on one pair of lateral faces and having axes 2 as well as axes 2_1.* The three groups $P2$, $P2_1$, and $C2$ are the space groups corresponding to class 2.

* The subscript indicates the presence of a screw axis, and its numerical value represents the order of that axis.

Examination of all the crystal classes shows that there are 230 space symmetry groups. (These groups were first derived by E. S. Fedorov in 1890.) These 230 groups include eleven isomorphous pairs, which differ only in the directions of rotation of their screw axes.

The international symbols used for space groups give the type of Bravais lattice and symmetry elements of the whole space symmetry group. In all crystallographic systems, the first place in the symbol is occupied by a capital letter indicating the type of Bravais lattice: P for primitive, F for face-centered, I for body-centered, and A, B, C for base-centered lattices of various configurations.

The triclinic and monoclinic classes with one symmetry element are represented by the Bravais lattice symbol followed by the symmetry element: $P1$, $C2$, Cm, etc. Classes of the monoclinic system having a center of inversion are represented as follows: the Bravais lattice symbol is followed by the axis symbol, then we have the oblique stroke indicating the orthogonality, and finally, the symbol for a plane which is perpendicular to the rotation axis (for example, $P2_1/m$). In the orthorhombic system, the Bravais lattice symbol is followed by the symmetry elements directed along the a, b, and c axes, respectively (for example, $Pmm2$, $P2_12_12$).

In the case of other systems, which have higher-order rotation axes, the designation of a space group consists of the lattice symbol followed by the symbol for the principal axis. If this principal axis has an orthogonal plane of symmetry, the symbol for the plane follows immediately the symbol for the axis and is separated from the latter by an oblique stroke. In the tetragonal system, the symbol for an axis is followed by the symbol for a plane (or an axis) which is parallel to the side of a unit square and then by the symbol for a diagonal of this square (for example, $P\bar{4}2m$, $I4_1cd$). In the hexagonal system, the order of symbols is the same, but the symbol representing the principal axis is followed by a letter indicating a plane passing through the long diagonal of a rhombus, and the last place is occupied by a symbol for a plane passing through the short diagonal.

In the cubic system, the number 3 symbolizes inclined three-fold axes. The numbers or letters standing in front of 3 represent axes or planes parallel to a face of the cube, which is the unit parallelepiped of this system. The symbol which follows 3 represents a plane (or an axis) parallel to the direction of diagonal translation. If there is no such symbol, the space beyond 3 is left unoccupied (for example, $P23$, $Fm3m$).

§3. Principle of the Superposition of Symmetries. Curie Principle

The principle of the superposition of symmetries of geometrical figures and physical phenomena can be briefly formulated as follows: a symmetry group of two (or more) objects considered as a whole is the highest common symmetry subgroup of these objects, determined taking into account the mutual orientations of their symmetry elements. This principle, which is fairly self-evident in the case of geometrical figures, was extended by Pierre Curie to physical phenomena and is therefore called the Curie symmetry principle. A clearer formulation of the principle of the superposition of symmetries in the case of geometrical figures has been given by A. V. Shubnikov and can be stated as follows: when two (or more) unequal symmetrical figures are joined to form one figure, the resultant figure retains only those symmetry elements which are common to all the original figures (for a given distribution of these figures in space).

Let us consider, for example, the symmetry of a figure consisting of a cube and a cylinder being attached to one of the faces of the cube (Fig. 8). We can easily see that such a figure has a fourfold symmetry axis and four planes passing through this axis (group 4·m). These symmetry elements are found in the symmetry groups of the cube and cylinder: they are subgroups of the cube group $\bar{6}/4$ and of the cylinder group m·∞:m.

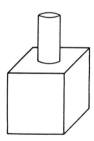

Fig. 8. Superposition of a cube and a cylinder. Symmetry group 4·m.

In spite of the apparent simplicity of the principle of superposition, some additional comments must be made. Thus, the
formulation of the principle draws our attention to the need to allow for the relative positions of the symmetry elements. In fact,
different relative positions of the symmetry elements of the same
two (or more) figures can give rise to different symmetry groups
of the composite figure. Let us consider again a combination of a
cube and a cylinder. We can easily show that the highest symmetry of the composite figure is m·4:m. This is obtained when
the centers of symmetry (inversion centers) of the cube and the
cylinder coincide and the axis of the cylinder is parallel to one of
the fourfold axes of the cube. Different results are obtained for
different relative positions of the figures. For example, when we
place a cylinder on one of the edges of a cube so that its axis coincides with a twofold axis of the cube, we find the symmetry group
of the combined figure is 2·m.

We can easily show that the composite figure cannot have a
symmetry group higher than the symmetry of that of the constituent figures which has the lowest symmetry. Thus, the highest
subgroup of the composite figure is the lowest symmetry subgroup
of the constituent figures.

We must stress that the principle of the superposition of symmetries is applicable only to nonequivalent figures. There is no
point in extending the principle to the case of equivalent figures
since this would simply mean the inclusion of everything that is
known about symmetry in general, including the cases of an increase in symmetry, i.e., those cases when the symmetry of a composite figure is higher than the symmetry of any of its constituent
figures. We must point out that symmetry may increase not only
when two equivalent figures are superimposed but also when one
of the constituent figures is a part of another symmetrical figure.
Thus, the superposition of a cube, one of whose vertices is cut off
obliquely (group 1), with the cut-off vertex itself (group 1) gives

Fig. 9. Increase in the symmetry when one of two superimposed
figures is a part of the other figure. 1, 2) Parts of a symmetrical figure.

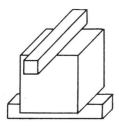

Fig. 10. Superposition of a cube and two parallelepipeds, each of which has a $\bar{4}$ axis.

rise to the group $\bar{6}/4$ (Fig. 9). Strictly speaking, we are consider-ing here not the superposition of symmetry elements but the re-establishment of the original symmetry.

All the symmetry elements of the constituent figures must be included rigorously when the superposition principle is used. Thus, for example, the fourfold cube axes, belonging to the group $\bar{6}/4$, are not only simple rotation axes but also rotation–reflection axes. This means that if a fourfold cube axis is made to coincide with a $\bar{4}$ axis of another figure, we find that the composite figure now has the $\bar{4}$ axis (Fig. 10); we are ignoring here the other symmetry ele-ments of this figure.

As pointed out at the beginning of the section, the principle of the superposition of symmetries can be applied not only to geo-metrical figures but also to physical phenomena. This is done by considering the superposition of the symmetry elements of sur-faces describing the relevant physical phenomena.

Our discussion of the principle of the superposition of sym-metries has been confined solely to the concepts of point symme-try. However, it is not difficult to extend the principle to space groups. This can be done by considering the superpositions of the sym-metry elements of various lattices. Since the lattices are infinite, they will interpenetrate. Once again we find that the combination of identical lattices can have, for certain orientations, a higher symmetry than the constituent lattices. Moreover, the addition of sites absent from a given lattice can also establish a high symmetry.

§4. Selected Topics in Crystallography and Crystal Chemistry

A. Rational Selection of a System of Coordi-nates in Crystals. Coordinate Systems. Indices of Faces. In general, we can use three edges of a crystal as the coordinate axes and call them the crystallographic axes a, b,

and c. In selecting the crystallographic axes, we must follow certain rules which minimize the indeterminacy involved in such a
selection. In order to select the crystallographic axes correctly,
we must know the coordinate system of a crystal. Table 5 gives
rules for the selection of the coordinate systems of crystals of all
crystal systems.

In addition to the crystallographic system of coordinates,
which need not be orthogonal, the physical properties of each class
of crystals are usually described by means of an orthogonal "physical" system of coordinates. The axes of this system are usually denoted by X, Y, Z. The rules for the selection of axes in the
crystal-physics systems of coordinates are also included in Table
5 [6].

Examination of Table 5 shows that four axes, a, b, u, and c
(the Bravais system), are used for hexagonal crystals. A different coordinate system (the Miller system) is used for trigonal
crystals. In this case, the a, b, c axes are taken along those three
edges of a rhombohedron (or a pyramid) which enclose a $\bar{6}$ axis
(or a 3 axis). In the crystal-physics system of axes, the $\bar{6}$ (or 3)
axis is taken to be the Z axis, one of the projections of the Miller
axes on the basal plane (i.e., on the plane perpendicular to the Z
axis) is assumed to be the X axis, and the Y axis is selected so
that the system is right-handed and orthogonal (Fig. 11).

We can impose arbitrary conditions on the selection of the positive directions of axes in crystals. Thus, in investigations of the

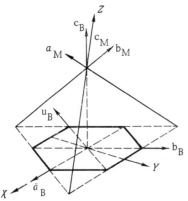

Fig. 11. Bravais and Miller coordinate
systems for hexagonal and trigonal crystals: a_B, b_B, u_B, c_B are the Bravais coordinate axes; a_M, b_M, c_M are the Miller coordinate axes; X, Y, Z are the crystal-physics axes.

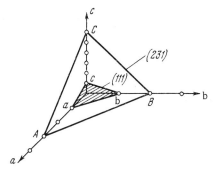

Fig. 12. Parametral plane (111) and a (231) plane in an orthorhombic crystal.

electrical properties of pyroelectric crystals, it is usual to assume that the positive end of a polar axis is that at which a positive electric charge appears during heating.

The selection of the crystallographic system of coordinates
determines also the parametral plane, which is a diagonal plane in
the unit parallelepiped of the lattice.

Important crystallographic quantities are the ratios of unit intercepts of the a, b, and c axes which define the parametral plane.
The position (orientation) of any plane of a crystal can be found by
considering the ratios of the unit intercepts a, b, and c and the intercepts A, B, C, cut-off along the axes by a given plane (Fig. 12):

$$\frac{a}{A} : \frac{b}{B} : \frac{c}{C}.$$

The numerators in these three ratios are equal to the unit intercepts along the crystallographic axes and the denominators
should be integers because any plane either cuts off an integral
number of unit intercepts along the coordinate axes or it can be
shifted parallel to itself to a position at which it passes through
three sites. Hence, it follows that a ratio of the type

$$\frac{a}{A} : \frac{b}{B} : \frac{c}{C}$$

can always be expressed as a ratio of the integers

$$\frac{a}{A} : \frac{b}{B} : \frac{c}{C} = h : k : l.$$

TABLE 5. Coordinate Axes of Crystals

Crystal system	Intercepts	Coordinate angles	Selection of crystallographic axes	Orientation of axes	
				crystallographic	physical
Cubic	$a = b = c$	$\alpha = \beta = \gamma = 90°$	Three mutually perpendicular four-fold (in classes $\bar{6}/4$ and $3/4$) or two-fold (in other classes) symmetry axes. Any one of them can be used as X, Y, or Z	c — vertical b — from left to right a — toward observer	c → Z b → Y a → X
Tetragonal	$a = b \neq c$	$\alpha = \beta = \gamma = 90°$	Principal axis (4 or $\bar{4}$) is taken as the c axis. Twofold axes are used as a and b. If there are no twofold axes, directions corresponding to these axes are selected	c — vertical b — from left to right a — toward observer	c → Z b → Y a → X
Hexagonal	$a = b \neq c$	$\alpha = \beta = 90°$ $\gamma = 120°$	Principal axes (6, 3, or $\bar{6}$) are used as the c axis; twofold axes are used as the a, b, and u axes. If there are no twofold axes, directions corresponding to these axes are selected	c — vertical a, u — toward observer, equally inclined b — from left to right	c → Z a → X b⊥X, Z from left to right
Orthorhombic	$a \neq b \neq c$	$\alpha = \beta = \gamma = 90°$	One of three twofold axes can be used as a, b, or c. In class 2·m, axis 2 is used as the c axis; normals to m are taken as the a and b axes	c — vertical b — from left to right a — toward observer	c → Z b → Y a → X

TABLE 5. (continued)

Crystal system	Intercepts	Coordinate angles	Selection of crystallographic axes	Orientation of axes	
				crystallographic	physical
Monoclinic	$a \neq b \neq c$	$\alpha = \gamma = 90°$ $\beta \neq 90°$	Twofold axis or normal to m (in class m) is used as the b axis. Directions of any two edges perpendicular to b are taken as the a and c axes	c – vertical b – from left to right a – toward observer, but inclined	$c \to X$ $b \to Z$ $a \to Y$
Triclinic	$a \neq b \neq c$	$\alpha \neq \beta \neq \gamma \neq 90°$	Directions of any three edges not lying in one plane are used as the a, b, and c axes	c – vertical b – from left to right a – toward observer	Selection of X, Y, Z axes arbitrary

The three integers h, k, l, thus determine the position of any plane or face of a crystal and they are usually called the Miller indices. The Miller indices of planes are enclosed in parentheses. For example, the indices of the parametral plane are always given in the form (111). The Miller indices can be positive or negative. If an index is negative, a bar is placed over it. It follows from the definition of the Miller indices that, if a plane in a crystal is parallel to any crystallographic axis, the Miller index along this axis is zero. Similarly, we can deduce the Miller indices for the directions in or edges of crystals. In this case, the indices are conventionally enclosed in square brackets: [h, k, l].

In the hexagonal (Bravais) system of coordinates, the sum of the indices (h + k + i), corresponding to the a, b, and u axes, is always equal to zero. In the Miller system the basal plane of trigonal crystals has the indices of the parametral plane (111). We shall now give the relationships between the Bravais and Miller indices for the same plane or face of a trigonal crystal:

$$h_B = (h_M - k_M); \quad i_B = (k_M - l_M); \quad k_B = (l_M - h_M);$$
$$l_B = (h_M + k_M + l_M).$$

Let us consider again the symmetry of crystals. A clear idea about the elements of symmetry and their mutual positions can be obtained by means of stereographic projections. Figure 13 shows, by way of example, stereographic projections of the symmetry elements of the tetragonal class $\overline{4}\cdot m$ and of the cubic class $3/\overline{4}$. As usual, the symmetry axes are represented by continuous lines

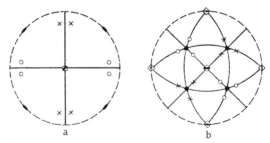

Fig. 13. Examples of stereographic projections of the symmetry elements of classes $\overline{4}\cdot m$ (a) and $3/\overline{4}$ (b).

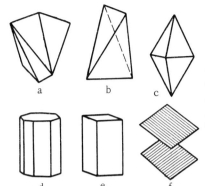

Fig. 14. Simple forms of crystal class 4·m: a) tetragonal scalenohedron (hk$l$); b) tetragonal tetrahedron (hh$l$); c) tetragonal bipyramid (h0l); d) ditetragonal prism (hk0); e) tetragonal prism (110) or (100); f) pinacoid (001).

and the reflection planes are shown dashed. Stereographic projection can be used to find easily all the simple forms of a given class of crystals, as well as the indices of simple forms.

A simple form is a figure which consists only of identical faces. The number of such faces determines the order of the symmetry group. All the faces of a simple figure can be deduced from a stereographic projection by specifying the direction of emergence of the normal to one face only (cross in Fig. 13a) and by subsequent "multiplication" of this face by using the symmetry elements (faces lying on the opposite sides of the sphere are denoted by circles). The general position of a face corresponds to the case when the normal to the face does not coincide with any of the symmetry axes and does not lie in any of the symmetry planes. The position of a face in Fig. 13a is selected in this way and a simple form (tetragonal scalenohedron) is obtained with a maximum (for this class) number of faces, which is eight. The indices of a general face are written in the form (hk$l$) and this stresses the fact that the intercepts cut off by this face along the coordinate axes are all different.

Figure 13b shows a face which is not in a general position but in one of the planes of symmetry (it does not coincide with any of the symmetry axes). The indices of this are (hh$l$). The symmetry elements of the class considered multiply the face and produce a simple form (hh$l$) which is a twelve-faced polyhedron, known as the tetragonal tritetrahedron. All the simple forms of the crystal classes $\bar{4}$·m and 3/$\bar{4}$ are shown in Figs. 14 and 15. The faces of a

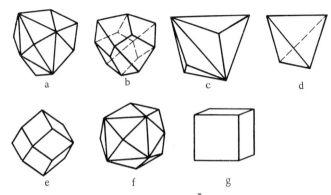

Fig. 15. Simple forms of crystal class 3/4: a) hexatetrahedron (hk$l$);
b) tetragonal tritetrahedron (hh$l$); c) trigonal tritetrahedron (hkk); d)
tetrahedron (111); e) rhombic dodecahedron (110); f) tetrahexahedron
(hk0); g) cube (hexahedron) (100).

real crystal are usually not simple forms but combinations of simple forms. Therefore, it is necessary to guard against common
mistakes such as regarding any face of a cubic crystal as the face
of a cube, etc.

B. Chemical Bonds in Dielectric Crystals. It
is known that the energy of chemical interaction of atoms in molecules and crystals is the principal factor which governs their electrical properties. The energy of chemical bonds is of the same
order of magnitude as the average binding energy of outer electrons in atoms, which shows that the chemical binding is due to
these outer electrons.

The ability of an atom to give up or capture valence electrons
in compounds is known as its electronegativity. If chemical elements are arranged as a series in accordance with their electronegativity, it is found that such a series begins with the least electronegative (i.e., electropositive) elements, which are alkali metals with a tendency to form positive ions, and it ends with the most
distributed halogen elements, which easily form negative ions.
When an electronegative atom is combined with an electropositive
atom (+ −), we obtain ionic (heteropolar) bonds. Homopolar covalent bonds are formed in compounds of two electronegative atoms
(− −) and homopolar metallic bonds are formed by two electropositive atoms (+ +).

These are the main types of bond. Different degrees of the electronegativity of atoms in specific compounds can give rise to structures with different degrees of covalence and ionicity.

Compounds consisting of atoms with filled shells or of molecules with saturated bonds are held by van der Waals forces. These forces are due to the presence of fairly strong short-lived dipoles. The energy of interaction of these forces is inversely proportional to the sixth power of the distance.

If molecules have permanent dipole moments (for example, water molecules) or if induced dipoles are generated because of the strong polarizability of molecules, an additional dipole interaction is observed between such molecules. The energy of this interactions is electrostatic and it also decreases in inverse proportion to the sixth power of the distance.

The hydrogen bond is worth considering separately. Bonds of hydrogen atoms with the most strongly negative atoms of F, O, and N are partly ionic. Therefore, HF, H_2O, and NH_3 molecules have permanent dipole moments. A strong dipole interaction is observed between such molecules and they form complexes. (If the temperature is sufficiently low, they form crystals.) Hydrogen atoms in such molecules form fairly strong covalent-ionic bonds of the following lengths: $F...H = 0.9$ Å, $O...H = 1.07$ Å, and $N...H = 1.09$ Å. Molecules are bound to other molecules also by hydrogen bonds, but the distances between molecules are large: $F...H = 1.6$ Å, $O...H = 1.8$ Å, $N...H = 1.9$ Å. The energy of hydrogen bonds is relatively low: ~ 5 kcal/mole (the energy of other chemical bonds is approximately 200 kcal/mole). Nevertheless, hydrogen bonds are responsible for the "unusual" behavior of several substances. In particular (see Chap. III), the hydrogen bond plays an important role in the appearance of spontaneous polarization in ferroelectrics.

Investigations of the electrical, optical, and mechanical properties of chemical compounds yield important information on chemical bonds and on the nature of chemical interactions. Molecular-structure investigations are particularly important: they yield information on configurations, valence angles, and interatomic distances. The configuration governs the coordination number k (the number of atoms bound directly to one another) and the symmetry of the distribution of the bonds, which is set by the valence angles.

Molecular-structure investigations can be carried out by diffraction methods (x-ray, electron, and neutron-diffraction techniques) as well as by spectroscopic, rf spectroscopic, nuclear magnetic resonance, and other methods.

Diffraction methods make it possible to determine the fine details of the electron-density redistribution which is governed by the difference between the electronegativities of atoms. Such a redistribution can alter the degree of polarity of bonds. Information on the polarity of bonds can be obtained also from paramagnetic electron resonance and, sometimes, from x-ray spectroscopy.

Apart from experimental investigations, many theoretical studies have been made of the spatial distribution of the valence-electron density. It is thus found that covalent compounds may have a noncentrosymmetric distribution of the valence-electron density. Such a distribution is observed, for example, for carbon atoms in aliphatic compounds. In these compounds, as in diamond, carbon has the tetrahedral symmetry. The presence of a noncentro-symmetric distribution of the electron density is of importance in the theory of the electrical properties of crystals, particularly in the case of the piezoelectric effect.

The most important difference between heteropolar and homopolar molecules is the appearance of dipole moments in the homopolar case. This is due to a redistribution of the electron density near one of the atoms. Such a redistribution gives rise to a molecular dipole moment. The absolute values of the dipole moments of such molecules as HF, HCl, HBr, and HI are of the order of 10^{-18} cgs esu.

Typical ionic compounds are alkali halides. This is confirmed, for example, by the fact that the calculated energies of formation of molecules (~ 100 kcal/mole), obtained on the assumption of ionic binding, are in good agreement with the energies of dissociation of alkali-halide molecules determined experimentally. The agreement between the calculated and experimental data is much poorer if it is assumed that alkali-halide molecules are held together by covalent bonds.

The ions of alkali metals and halogens have the electron configurations of inert gases and, therefore, they have closed spheri-

cally symmetrical electron shells. The interactions of such shells
are nondirectional and unsaturated. The unsaturation of ionic bonds
is manifested by the tendency of each ion to attract the largest possible number of oppositely charged ions, i.e., to form a structure
with the highest possible coordination number. The permissible
values of the coordination number are governed by the ratios of
ionic radii. The closer the value of the ratio of the cation radius
(r_c) to the anion radius (r_a) to unity, the higher is the coordination number. Structures with small cations, which can "tumble"
into an appropriate void or cavity, are unstable. This instability
leads to a change in the structure and a reduction of the coordination number. An increase in the cation radius can also alter
the structure and increase the coordination number.

C. Close Packing of Spheres. Let us consider the
packing of particles with nondirectional and unsaturated bonds,
which can be modeled by an array of identical spheres. The tendency of a given sphere to interact with the largest possible number of neighbors (this tendency gives rise to a minimum in the
potential energy of the interaction) produces structures with the
largest possible coordination number. The packing fraction, i.e.,
the ratio of the volume of spheres to the total volume (including
the voids between the spheres), is larger than for any other possible packing. The packing which satisfies these requirements is
known as the close packing of spheres. An example of a close
planar packing of spheres is shown in Fig. 16a. The coordination
number of such packing is six (each sphere in a plane is in contact
with six other spheres). A two-dimensional unit cell of this structure is a regular rhombus AAAA of side equal to 2R, where R is
the radius of these spheres. Two families of triangular cavities
B and C are formed between the spheres in such a layer (Fig. 16b).

A three-dimensional close packing of spheres is obtained by
constructing an array of close-packed planar layers. If the first
layer is horizontal, spheres in the next layer should be located in

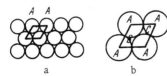

Fig. 16. Planar close packing (a) and
a unit cell in such packing (b).

a   b

one of the two families of triangular cavities. The two different positions in the second layer, corresponding to the two different families of voids, are equivalent. However, beginning from the third layer, the two methods of filling the voids give (if we consider three layers at a time) different types of packing in three dimensions. Any packing of spheres can be represented by symbols of the type ABAACABC ... in which each letter represents the positions of spheres relative to the axes A, B, and C. In the case of close packing, the combinations of two identical letters side by side are impossible. The number of letters in a period determines the layered structure of a given packing. It follows that there is an infinite number of three-dimensional close packings of spheres.

The most important crystallographic packings are those with few layers. Two-layer packing of the ...ABABAB... type is found in crystals of the hexagonal system and is sometimes called the hexagonal close packing. In this case, each sphere in the third layer lies directly above the corresponding sphere in the first layer. The hexagonal close packing cannot be generated simply by translation. Two particles are contained in each unit cell of a hexagonal close-packed structure. The space group of the hexagonal close packing is $D_{6h}^1 - C^6/mmc$.

A packing of the ...ABCABCABC... type is also of considerable interest. This is the only close packing of spheres which can be obtained in the cubic system. It has the structure of a face-centered cube. The space group of this packing is $O_h^5 - Fm3m$. In contrast to other packings, we have now not one but four equivalent families of close-packed planes parallel to the (111) faces of an octahedron. The cubic close packing is an example of a structure in which particle positions coincide with positions of the Bravais lattice sites and which models directly the symmetry subgroup of parallel translations.

A close packing of spheres can have octahedral or tetrahedral voids. The number of octahedral voids is equal to the number of spheres, and the number of tetrahedral voids is double the number of spheres.

In some compounds these voids are filled with atoms of a different kind. Atomic structures of such compounds can be conveniently described by the close-packing configurations.

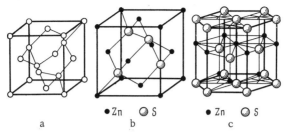

• Zn ◎ S   • Zn ◎ S
a   b   c

Fig. 17. Structures of diamond and diamond-like compounds:
a) diamond; b) α-ZnS (sphalerite); β-ZnS (wurtzite).

Spheres in the hexagonal and cubic close packings have different symmetries (taking into account the environment). In the hexagonal packing, we have the m·3:m point symmetry but in the cubic
packing this symmetry is 6̄/4. The packing fraction for all close-
packing configurations is the same and equal to 74%. Thus, voids
occupy about one-quarter of the total volume. This should be compared with the fact that in the simple (primitive) cubic structure
voids occupy nearly half the total volume. The carbon atoms in
diamond occupy only about one-third of the total volume.

All close-packed configurations have the coordination number 12. The cubic body-centered structure has the coordination number 8, the simple cubic structure 6, and the cubic diamond 4.

Many crystalline substances have the close-packed structure.
Metals frequently crystallize in the cubic or hexagonal close packing. Other examples, typical of dielectric crystals, will be considered in the next subsection.

D. Structures of Some Dielectrics [5]. A sim-
ple example of the structure of a dielectric crystal is diamond,*
which crystallizes in the centrosymmetric cubic structure with
the point symmetry group 6̄/4 and the space group $Fd3m - O_h^7$.
The unit-cell parameter of diamond at room temperature is $a =$
3.56 Å. The distribution of the carbon atoms in diamond is shown
in Fig. 17a. The structure of diamond can be described as follows:
the unit cell can be divided figuratively into eight octants by three
mutually perpendicular planes which pass through the center of the

_____

*The other modification of carbon — graphite — belongs to the hexagonal system (space
symmetry group $D_{6h}^4 - P6/mmc$, point group m·6:m), is not a dielectric, and will not
be considered in the present book.

cell and are parallel to the faces. Each unit cell of diamond contains eight atoms: four of them occupy sites in a face-centered
cubic cell, and the other four are located at the centers of four of
the octants. The "filled" octants alternate regularly with the
"empty" octants along each coordinate. All the carbon atoms are
located at the points of one regular system and, therefore, they
are crystallochemically identical. The structure of diamond is
typically homopolar (covalent) with four carbon bonds directed at
tetrahedral angles. The length of the C＝C bond is 1.54 Å.

Some other crystals of simple dielectrics crystallize in structures similar to that of diamond. The interaction of binary components in such structures produces tetrahedral bonds if the components have similar values for the electronegativity. The simplest structures with tetrahedral bonds are two modifications of
zinc blende: cubic sphalerite (α-ZnS) and hexagonal wurtzite (β-
ZnS), shown in Figs. 17b and 17c. The structure of sphalerite
transforms to that of diamond if both atoms are identical. When
the difference between the electronegativities of the components
is increased, the bonds become primarily ionic, and ionic structures are observed.

In binary (AB) compounds, the coordination number for atoms
of both components is the same. For cubic structures of the CsCl-
type (Fig. 18a), the coordination number is 8. The structures of
some inorganic compounds can be regarded as close packings
formed by the largest particles (usually anions), with the voids
between these particles filled by cations in accordance with a law
characteristic of a given type of structure. Thus, the chlorine
ions in the lattice of NaCl (Fig. 18b) form the cubic close packing
in which all the octahedral voids are occupied by sodium ions. The
coordination number of this compound is 6. The structure of α-

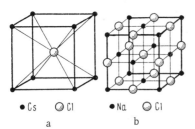

Fig. 18. Structures of ionic binary
(AB) crystals: a) CsCl; b) NaCl.

• Cs   ◔ Cl   • Na   ◔ Cl

       a   b

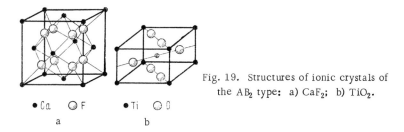

Fig. 19. Structures of ionic crystals of the AB$_2$ type: a) CaF$_2$; b) TiO$_2$.

• Ca   ○ F   • Ti   ○ O

a   b

ZnS and β-ZnS are formed in accordance with a similar principle: the sulfur atoms form the cubic and hexagonal close packings, and the zinc atoms occupy half the available tetrahedral voids; the coordination number is 4.

The calcium ions in the cubic structure of fluorite, CaF$_2$ (Fig. 19a), form the cubic close packing in which all the tetrahedral voids are occupied by the fluorine ions. The coordination number for calcium is 8 and that for fluorine is 4. In the tetragonal structure of titanium dioxide, known as rutile (Fig. 19b), the titanium ions form a body-centered structure and these ions are surrounded

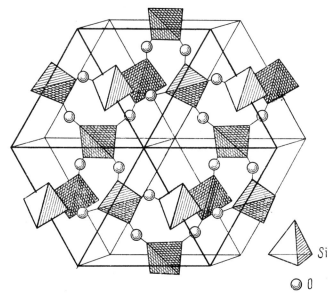

○ Si

◎ O

Fig. 20. Structure of β-quartz.

octahedrally by oxygen ions. Oxygen ions are located at the centers of equilateral triangles, formed by the titanium ions.

The various modifications of silicon dioxide (SiO_2) are based on combinations of silicon−oxygen tetrahedra. The low−temperature modification of SiO_2 (which exists below 573°C) is known as β-quartz (Fig. 20) and belongs to the trigonal system (point symmetry group 3:2, space group $D_3^4 - C3_121$ or $D_3^6 - C3_221$). The unit cell parameters are a = 4.90 and c = 5.39 Å at room temperature, and each cell contains three "molecules" of SiO_2. The structure motif is formed by [SiO_4] tetrahedra, which are joined at their vertices. Oxygen atoms are located at the vertices of the tetrahedra and silicon atoms are at the centers of the tetrahedra. These tetrahedra are slightly distorted: the two Si−O bonds are 1.61 Å long and the other two bonds are 1.62 Å. The helices of linked [SiO_4] tetrahedra form a screw-like motif along the c axis with voids at the centers of triple hexagonal unit cells.

Near 573°C, quartz undergoes a phase transition and becomes hexagonal above this temperature (the point symmetry group is 6:2, the space group $D_6^5 - P6_122$ or $D_6^4 - P6_222$. This modification, usually called α-quartz, is stable in the temperature range 573–870°C. A third modification of SiO_2, tridymite, is stable in the temperature range 870–1470°C. The most symmetrical is the fourth (cubic) modification of SiO_2, known as cristobalite. In this modification, the atoms of silicon, considered separately from those of oxygen, form a diamond−type structure. Cristobalite is stable in the temperature range 1470–1710°C. SiO_2 metals at 1710°C.

These structures of monatomic and diatomic dielectrics are relatively simple and usually highly symmetrical. However, the majority of dielectrics, particularly pyroelectric and piezoelectric crystals, have fairly complex structures and are of low symmetry. We shall consider briefly the structure of tourmaline, lithium sulfate, and saccharose [2]. These crystals are pyroelectric (polar) and exhibit both pyroelectric and piezoelectric properties.

The structures of sphalerite and of α- and β-quartz, described in the preceding paragraphs, are examples of piezoelectric crystals which do not exhibit pyroelectric properties (they are called "polar-neutral" crystals, and will be discussed again later).

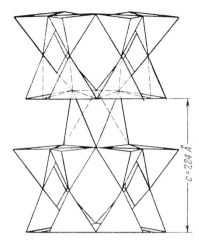

Fig. 21. Principal motif in the structure of tourmaline; c is the unit-cell parameter in the hexagonal system of coordinates.

The trigonally structured tourmaline or dimetaalumoborosilicate, $NaMg_6[Al_3B_3Si_6(O, OH)_{30}]$, has the unit cell parameters $a = 9.52$ Å, $\alpha = 113°49'$, and one molecule per unit cell. Its point symmetry group is $3 \cdot m$ and its space group is $C_{3v}^5 - R3m$. The principal motif of the tourmaline structure, shown in Fig. 21, consists of two-layer six-member polar rings of tetrahedra. Whereas the upper layer of a ring consists of $[SiO_4]$ groups, the lower layer consists of tetrahedra containing both Al and B atoms. The Na and Mg atoms are surrounded octahedrally by oxygen atoms and, whereas an octahedron enclosing an Na atom is located between the six-member rings, the octahedra with Mg atoms are located around the screw axes and are linked into a common structure whose voids contain the two-layer six-member rings referred to earlier. The calculated interatomic spacings in tourmaline are as follows: $Si-O = 1.57-1.78$ Å, $(Al, B)-O = 1.58-1.76$ Å, $Mg-O = 1.97-2.27$ Å.

Lithium sulfate monohydrate ($Li_2SO_4 \cdot H_2O$) belongs to the monoclinic system. Its point symmetry group is 2, the space group is $P2_1$, and the unit cell parameters are: $a = 5.430 \pm 0.010$ Å, $b = 4.836 \pm 0.010$ Å, $c = 8.140 \pm 0.015$ Å, $\beta = 107°14' \pm 5'$. The structure is a packing of $[SO_4]^{2-}$ regular tetrahedra; the distance between the sulfur and oxygen atoms is 1.50 ± 0.02 Å and the distance between two oxygen atoms is 2.45 ± 0.03 Å. Hydrogen bonds

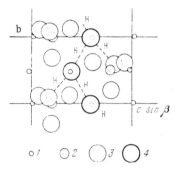

Fig. 22. Projection of the structure of
lithium sulfate $Li_2SO_4 \cdot H_2O$ onto a (100)
plane: 1) lithium atoms; 2) sulfur
atoms; 3) oxygen atoms of the $[SO_4]^{2-}$
group; 4) oxygen atoms of the H_2O
molecule; the dashed lines show hydrogen bonds.

are formed between the molecules of the water of crystallization.
The length of these bonds is 2.87 Å and they are in the form of
zigzag chains along the b axis. The $[SO_4]^{2-}$ tetrahedra are attached by hydrogen bonds to such a chain, as shown in Fig. 22.

Saccharose, $C_{12}H_{22}O_{11}$, crystallizes in the dihedral axial class
of the monoclinic system (class 2), and has the space group $P2_1$ and
the following unit parameters: a = 10.89 Å, b = 8.69 Å, c = 7.77 Å,

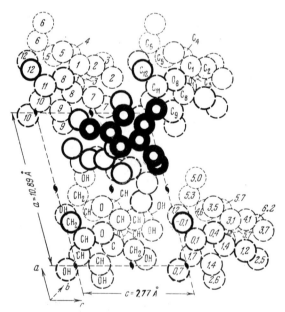

Fig. 23. Projection of the structure of saccharose onto a (010)
plane.

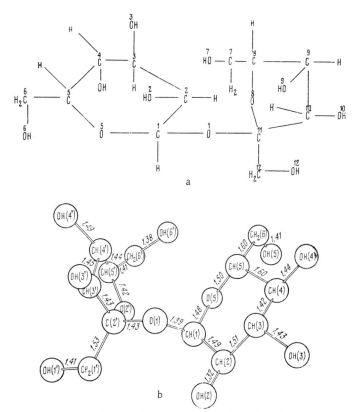

Fig. 24. Structure formula (a) and configuration (b) of the saccharose molecule. The distances between atoms and atomic complexes are shown in Å.

$\beta = 103°$. Two $C_{12}H_{22}O_{11}$ molecules are contained in each unit cell. The structure is a complex packing of saccharose molecules. The projection of the structure onto a (010) plane is shown in Fig. 23. The numbering of atoms in the molecule shown in the top left-hand corner in Fig. 23 is the same as the numbering of atoms or atom complexes in the structure formula given in Fig. 24a. The numbers which are used to label atoms in the molecule shown in the lower right-hand corner (Fig. 23) give the heights of these atoms along the b axis. It is evident from the structure formula (Fig. 24a) that the saccharose molecule consists of a six-member pyranose ring and a five-member furanose ring (Fig. 24b). The substituents at C(1) and C(2) in the six-member pyranose ring are in the cis position relative to one another so that the fructose radical has the β configuration. The pyranose ring itself has the chair (trans) configuration. The C = C bond length in the pyranose ranges from 1.42 to 1.60 Å (the average value is 1.50 ± 0.05 Å). The valence angles in this ring (108 ± 4°) differ little from the angles in the tetrahedral configuration. The trans configuration allows all the atoms in the ring and the substituent groups [except O(1)] to be located close to one common plane, while retaining the tetrahedral valence angles. The four atoms in the furanose ring [C(2'), C(3'), C(5'), and O(2')] are located in one plane and the fifth atom C(4') projects by about 0.5 Å from this plane. However, since the ring is not coplanar, the substituents OH(3'), OH(4'), and CH_2(6') are located in practically the same plane as the first four atoms of the furanose ring. Thus, as in the case of pyranose, all the atoms in the furanose ring and the substituents tend to be located very close to one common plane. However, in the furanose ring this tendency is so strong that it disturbs the coplanarity of the ring and gives rise to a considerable deviation of the valence angles from the tetrahedral value [the average value of the valence angle in the ring is 104° and the angles formed by bonds of the OH(3') and OH(4') groups with nearby ring bonds are 115, 118, 116, and 113°]. The average C = C bond length in the furanose ring is 1.44 ± 0.01 Å. The average value of the C = O bond length over the whole molecule is 1.42 ± 0.04 Å.

The dielectrics whose structures we have considered so far are all linear. The electric polarization in such dielectrics depends linearly on the field. The structure of nonlinear dielectrics (ferroelectrics and antiferroelectrics) is considered in Chaps. II and III.

E. Ionic Radii. If we consider a compound as purely ionic, we cannot assume that the interionic distances are equal to the sum of the atomic radii, because $d_{AB} \neq r_A + r_B$ but $d_{AB} = (r_{A^+}) + (r_{B^-})$. To determine the ionic radii in a compound, we must know the value of the ionic radius of at least one component of the compound or the ratio of the ionic radii. The ionic radii can be determined from measurements of polar ionic refraction or by calculations using formulas which yield electron orbits. The screening constant, required in such calculations, can be found from x-ray terms or molar refraction. In those cases when direct contact between anions can be assumed, the values of the radii can be found directly from the unit-cell dimensions. The value of the ionic radius of oxygen is of special importance in crystal chemistry. Depending on the method of determination, this radius is within the range 1.32–1.40 Å. The fullest information on the ionic radii of various elements (with all types of bond) are given by Bokii [2]. The tables in Bokii's book include corrections for the coordination number, the multiplicity of covalent bonds, etc. Knowledge of the ionic radii in ionic crystals makes it possible to estimate various physical constants and, in particular, to determine the coordination of a structure, the range of temperatures of morphotropic transformations (transformations of the structure accompanied by a change of the coordination number), etc.

An analysis of crystallochemical data shows that the structure of crystals is governed by the number, shape, size, and polarization properties of constituent atoms, ions or their groups, as well as by the conditions under which crystals are formed. This is the basic law of crystal chemistry.

§5. Selected Topics in Physical Crystallography

A. Symmetry of Physical Properties. Neumann's Principle. Each real crystal has its own specific physical properties. Some crystals can be polarized in an electric field, their plane of polarization of light can be rotated by an electric field, they can conduct an electric current, etc. The symmetry of a property of a crystal is the symmetry of the tensor which describes this property. Thus, the electric conductivity of cubic crystals is described by a degenerate second-rank tensor which has the symmetry of a scalar.

The concept of the symmetry of a property can be extended by defining it as the symmetry of the tensor surface which describes this property.

Having defined the symmetry of properties as the symmetry of the tensors describing them, we imply that the medium whose properties are being investigated is continuous and uniform because the tensor description ignores the lattice structure of crystals. If we consider the symmetry of symmetrical polar tensors, which are used to describe many physical properties (polarization, electrical conductivity, birefringence, etc.), we find that all crystals can be classified into three groups of symmetry of their tensors [4]: the symmetry of any physical property described by a symmetrical polar tensor of the second rank is either $\infty/m \cdot \infty : m$, or $m \cdot \infty : m$, or $m \cdot 2 : m$.

The symmetry of the properties of a crystal defined in this way is always higher than or equal to the symmetry of the crystal itself. When crystal properties are described by symmetrical second-rank tensors, the symmetry of the properties is identical with the symmetry of the crystal only for class $m \cdot 2 : m$. In all other cases, the symmetry of the properties is higher than the symmetry of the crystal. For example, we have mentioned that symmetry of a sphere $\infty/m \cdot \infty : m$, which describes the symmetry of the electrical conductivity of cubic crystals, is higher than the symmetry of any cubic crystal.

This means that all the symmetry elements of a crystal are included in the symmetry elements of a physical property; the symmetry of a crystal cannot be higher than the symmetry of any of its physical properties. This is Neumann's principle, which is widely used in crystal physics to find crystal classes which can exhibit a particular property or set of properties. This determination is based on the following rule (which is another way of expressing Neumann's principle): the symmetry groups of crystals which can exhibit a certain physical property can only be subgroups of the symmetry group of this property, or they can have the symmetry group of the property.

In addition to the symmetry of properties, we can consider the symmetry of states of crystals. Thus, under the action of electric and magnetic fields, crystals can be polarized and magnetized. (Such polarization and magnetization can also appear in the absence of external fields, as discussed in the next subsection.) In agreement with the principle of superposition of symmetries (§3 in the present chapter), the symmetry of such polarized or magnetized states can be determined by considering the superposition of symmetry elements of the applied field and of the crystal symmetry. Examination of the possible symmetry groups of crystals which are in a given state shows that these groups are either identical with the symmetry groups of a given property or they are its subgroups. This means that the symmetry elements of a crystal are included in the symmetry elements of the field causing a given state to arise. From this point of view, Neumann's principle can be regarded as a consequence of the principle of superposition of symmetries (Curie principle). However, the use of Neumann's principle often simplifies the determination of the symmetry groups of crystals exhibiting specified properties or existing in a specified state. We shall now consider some applications of the principle.

B. Electrical Properties of Crystals Which Follow from Their Symmetry and Which Are Not Due to External Effects. The electrical properties of crystals are closely connected with their symmetry. The symmetry of a crystal determines the distribution of the electric charge within it. We can identify three types of electric charge distribution in dielectrics. In the first type, the distribution of positive or negative charges is centrosymmetric, with the centers of gravity of the charges of each sign coinciding with each other. Such a coincidence within one unit cell means that these centers of gravity coincide with the center of the cell. Crystals with such a charge distribution have no polar directions and are called nonpolar. Since, in the final analysis, the distribution of the charges determines the symmetry of a crystal, we can give a symmetry criterion by which nonpolar crystals can be recognized: they have a center of symmetry (inversion center). This requirement is satisfied by crystals belonging to 11 symmetry groups: $\bar{6}/4$, $\bar{6}/2$, m·6:m, m·4:m, m·2:m, $\bar{6}$·m, 6:m, 4:m, 2:m, $\bar{6}$ and $\bar{2}$.

The distribution of charges in dielectrics of the second type is characterized by the noncoincidence of the centers of gravity of charges of opposite sign within one unit cell, and by the resultant parallel orientation of the electric dipoles in all the neighboring domains. Such unit cells give rise to the macroscopic polarization of a crystal in the absence of an external field (spontaneous polarization). Crystals with this type of charge distribution are called polar. A symmetry criterion of polar crystals is the presence of preferential polar orientations.

The state of spontaneous polarization of a crystal can be regarded as a result of the action of an internal electric field of charges whose symmetry should, in this case, be described by the

∞·m group. According to Neumann's principle, all those crystals whose symmetry groups are subgroups of the ∞·m group should be (more exactly, may be) spontaneously polarized. These crystals belong to the symmetry groups: 6·m, 4·m, 3·m, 2·m, m, 6, 4, 3, 2, 1; they are known as pyroelectric crystals.

The third type of charge distribution in dielectrics is that in which the centers of gravity of positive and negative charges coincide but the systems of positive and negative charges are not centrosymmetric. Under these conditions, a unit cell may have an array of dipole moments which does not give rise to a single preferential polarization direction because the geometrical sum of all the dipole moments is equal to zero (the centers of gravity of charges of opposite sign coincide).

Thus, in this case, the absence of centrosymmetry in the distribution of charges of each sign makes it possible for polar directions to appear, but the crystal as a whole does not have a preferential polar direction. Crystals with such a charge distribution will be called polar-neutral. The symmetry criterion of such crystals is the absence of centrosymmetry and of preferential polar directions. These crystals have elementary polar directions but no unique polar directions. These requirements are satisfied by the remaining 11 crystal classes: $3/\bar{4}$, $3/4$, $3/2$, m·3:m, 6:2, 3:m, 3:2, $\bar{4}$·m, 4:2, $\bar{4}$, 2:2.

The ordering of the dipoles in the polar crystals just discussed may be called linear. It is obvious that in polar-neutral crystals the ordering of dipoles may be two- or three-dimensional. Examples of such ordering for some crystals are given in Fig. 25.

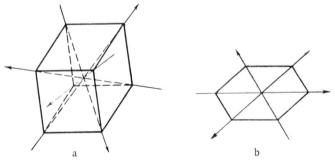

Fig. 25. Three- (a) and two-dimensional (b) ordering of electric dipoles in polar-neutral structures: a) group $3/\bar{4}$; b) group m·3:m.

Fig. 26. Ordering of dipoles in which a linear configuration is combined with a two-dimensional arrangement (group 3·m).

It should be mentioned that a different type of ordering of dipoles, which is a combination of linear ordering with a two- or three-dimensional configuration, may be encountered. Possible symmetry groups which permit the simultaneous existence of these two types of ordering can be found by analyzing the superposition of the symmetry elements of the 11 groups of polar-neutral crystals and of the ∞·m group, which describes the linear ordering of dipoles. Such combinations may give rise to groups 6, 4, 3, 2, 1, 3·m, 2·m, m. Thus, these eight groups can be considered as those in which the polar ordering of dipoles may coexist with the polar-neutral order. An example of such a coexistence is given in Fig. 26. The linear type of ordering can exist on its own only in crystals of two polar groups: 6·m and 4·m.

The electrical properties governed by external agencies are discussed in Chaps. V and VII-X.

References

1. N. V. Belov, Structural Crystallography [in Russian], Izd. AN SSSR, Moscow (1951).
2. G. B. Bokii, Introduction to Crystal Chemistry [in Russian], Izd. MGU, Moscow (1954).
3. B. N. Delone, N. Padurov, and A. Aleksandrov, Mathematical Fundamentals of Crystal Structure Analysis and X-ray Determination of Unit Cells [in Russian], GTTI, Moscow-Leningrad (1934).
4. I. S. Zheludev, Kristallografiya, 2(6):728 (1957).
5. G. S. Zhdanov, Crystal Physics, Oliver and Boyd, Edinburgh-London (1965).
6. E. E. Flint, Practical Handbook on Geometrical Crystallography, 3rd ed. [in Russian], Nedra, Moscow (1956).
7. A. V. Shubnikov, Symmetry and Antisymmetry of Finite Figures [in Russian], Izd. AN SSSR, Moscow (1951).
8. A. V. Shubnikov, E. E. Flint, and G. B. Bokii, Principles of Crystallography [in Russian], Izd. AN SSSR, Moscow (1940).

Chapter II

Structure and Crystal Chemistry
of Oxygen-Octahedral Ferroelectrics
and Antiferroelectrics

Introduction

Experimental investigations of pyroelectric materials (polar crystals) have demonstrated that they can be divided into linear and nonlinear dielectrics in accordance with their behavior in electric fields. The electric polarization P of linear dielectrics depends linearly on the electric field E, while the electric polarization of nonlinear dielectrics is a nonlinear function of the electric field. The most important materials among nonlinear solid dielectrics are ferroelectric crystals, which can exhibit (in a limited range of temperatures) a spontaneous polarization P_s in the absence of an external electric field and which can split into spontaneously polarized regions known as domains.* Thus, ferroelectrics can be considered formally as a subclass of polar crystals (pyroelectric materials): we can say that ferroelectrics are those pyroelectric materials which split into domains. In fact, pyroelectric crystals (we shall use this term to denote only those polar crystals which do not split into domains) differ considerably from ferroelectrics and these differences will be discussed in both volumes of this book.

---

*We shall use the term "ferroelectrics" to denote not only ferroelectrics but also antiferroelectrics and ferrielectrics (these substances will be discussed later). The definition of ferroelectrics given here applies to all three types of crystal.

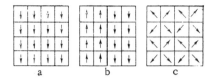

Fig. 27. Schematic representations of the orientations of unit-cell dipoles in pyroelectric (a), ferroelectric (b), and antiferroelectric (c) materials.

It is convenient to consider the spontaneous polarization of individual unit cells rather than that of the whole crystal. In ordinary pyroelectric crystals, all the unit cells exhibit a spontaneous polarization P_s, whose direction is the same for all cells in a given crystal (Fig. 27a). In ferroelectrics, the directions of P_s are the same within one domain but differ from one domain to another (Fig. 27b). In antiferroelectrics, even neighboring unit cells can have different orientations of P_s. Consequently, in an antiferroelectric, a group of unit cells (subcells), which has existed before a phase transition and which has suffered small distortions as a result of this transition, forms a multiple (superstructure) unit cell. A multiple unit cell, considered as an entity, does not have a preferred direction (particularly a polar direction) and, therefore, it is not spontaneously polarized (Fig. 27c).

It is generally assumed that ferrielectrics are similar in their structure to antiferroelectrics but there are as yet no reliable experimental data confirming this assumption. Ferrielectrics are considered as a separate group because they exhibit ferroelectric properties along some directions, and behave as antiferroelectrics along other directions. Ferrielectrics are sometimes called "cone ferroelectrics" to distinguish them from ordinary "line ferroelectrics." They are also called weak ferroelectrics because of the low value of the ferroelectric polarization of these materials.

About 20 years ago, only a few ferroelectric crystals were known (Rochelle salt, potassium dihydrogen phosphate, and some compounds isomorphous with these two materials) and the ferroelectric properties exhibited by these crystals (an anomalously high permittivity, dielectric hysteresis, etc.) were regarded as a rare curiosity. But the investigations carried out in the last two decades led to the discovery of a large number of compounds with ferroelectric properties. At present, more than 100 pure compounds of this type are known. There are so many solid solutions exhibiting ferroelectric properties that it is difficult to estimate their number.

Various attempts to classify ferroelectrics were made as more and more of these materials were discovered. Thus, it was initially suggested that ferroelectric properties were solely due to hydrogen bonds; later, ferroelectrics with hydrogen bonding were separated into a special group. The discovery of ferroelectric properties in many compounds with the structure of perovskite ($CaTiO_3$) resulted in the separation of these compounds into a perovskite group. However, it was later found that the ferroelectric properties were observed also in compounds with the structure of pyrochlore, lead metaniobate, pseudo-ilmenite, etc., whose structures had several oxygen octahedra. This made it possible to assign such ferroelectrics (together with perovskite ferroelectric materials) to a group known as oxygen-octahedral ferroelectrics.

The division of all ferroelectrics into two groups, one of which contains ferroelectrics with hydrogen bonds and the other oxygen-octahedral materials, is based on the following considerations. Ferroelectrics belonging to the same group have similar properties (for example, all the oxygen-octahedral ferroelectrics are insoluble in water, have a considerable mechanical strength, are easily synthesized in the polycrystalline form by the ceramic techniques, etc.), whereas ferroelectrics belonging to different groups differ appreciably in their properties (for example, the spontaneous polarization of the oxygen-octahedral ferroelectrics is usually an order of magnitude higher than the polarization of hydrogen-bond ferroelectrics, etc.). However, this division cannot be regarded as fully satisfactory because recent years have brought the discovery of several new compounds [ammonium sulfate $(NH_4)_2SO_4$, dicalcium-strontium propionate $Ca_2Sr(CH_3CH_2COOH)_6$, sodium nitrite $NaNO_2$, and others] whose structures and properties make it difficult to assign them satisfactorily to either of the aforementioned two groups. Moreover, the division is also unsatisfactory from the formal point of view because assignments to one group are based on the chemical binding and those to the other group are based on the type of structure.

Unfortunately, the nature of the ferroelectric properties cannot yet be regarded as fully determined and this makes it impossible to provide a satisfactory classification of ferroelectrics.

Nevertheless, investigations show that a fairly clear division of ferroelectrics (and antiferroelectrics) can be made on the basis of the mechanism of the appearance of spontaneous polarization. There are two mechanisms. One of them is typical of ferroelectrics with the oxygen-octahedral type of structure: in this case, a rearrangement of the structure produces spontaneous polarization, because of the displacements of certain ions, and the direction of the polarization coincides with the direction of the displacements. The polarization of such ferroelectrics (and antiferroelectrics) is usually associated with the displacement of a cation (Ti, Nb, Ta, and other ions) from the center of the surrounding oxygen octahedron. Depending on the geometry of the structure (the dimensions of the ions, their mutual positions, the dimensions of voids, etc.), the nature of the binding, and the electronic configuration of the atoms, the resulting dipole moments are oriented either parallel or antiparallel in a given structure. Oxygen ions play the most important role in these orientation processes.

All other ferroelectrics and antiferroelectrics (i.e., all ferroelectrics which are not of the oxygen-octahedral type) exhibit a transition to the polarized state which is associated with the ordering of certain structure elements which are disordered before the transition. In such crystals, the transition is often (but not always) associated with the ordering of protons in hydrogen bonds (for example, this happens in sulfites, fluoroberyllates, and cyanides). In other cases, the radicals are ordered because of hindered rotation (sodium nitrite, dicalcium-strontium propionate, and other compounds). The polarization process in "orderable" ferroelectrics (antiferroelectrics) can be considered to take place in two stages: the appearance of dipoles, due to the deformation of atomic groups of the $(SO_4)^{2-}$, $(SeO_4)^{2-}$, $(PO_4)^{2-}$ type, and the alignment (to produce a parallel or antiparallel orientation) of dipole moments due to the ordering of structure elements (particularly due to the ordering of hydrogen bonds). The ordering mechanism acts as a "trigger."

A fairly large change in the entropy at the ferroelectric transition (~ 1 cal·mole^{-1}·deg^{-1}), typical of ordering processes, is observed for the majority of ferroelectrics in which the spontaneous polarization is due to ordering. On the other hand, the change in the entropy at the phase transitions in the oxygen-octahedral structures is small.

We shall use these two mechanisms of the appearance of polarization in ferroelectrics and antiferroelectrics in discussions of the atomic structure and its changes at the phase transitions.

Knowledge of the atomic structure and its change at a phase-transition point is essential for the understanding of the causes and nature of the appearance of spontaneous polarization as well as for the understanding of other atomic processes which give rise to ferroelectric or antiferroelectric properties of crystals [see, for example, H. D. Megaw, Ferroelectricity in Crystals, Methuen, London (1957)].

Table 6 gives information on all known ferroelectrics of the oxygen-octahedral type. However, our discussion of these materials in Chap. II will be limited to the most typical and most thoroughly investigated materials.*

§1. Changes in the Point Symmetry of Crystals

at Ferroelectric Phase Transitions

The structure of many dielectric crystals changes with temperature, i.e., they undergo a phase transition.†

A phase transition is caused by uniform heating, which has scalar properties. The symmetry of a crystal changes at a phase transition point. However, in spite of a change in the internal symmetry of a crystal, its macrosymmetry is unaffected because of its splitting into regions oriented in different ways. In other words, a scalar effect causing a phase transition does not alter the symmetry of a crystal as a whole, in agreement with the principle of superposition of symmetries.

In the final analysis, all phase transitions in crystals are due to a change in the forces of interaction between the particles in a crystal. This change can give rise to various new properties in crystals. We shall consider only those phase transitions which

---

*This discussion will be preceded by §§ 1 and 2, which deal with general problems of changes in the symmetry of crystals at the ferroelectric phase-transition points.

†We shall consider only the changes in the crystal structure under constant pressure. Transitions occurring due to the variation of pressure at constant temperature will not be discussed.

TABLE 6. Principal Properties of Oxygen–Octahedral Ferroelectrics and Antiferroelectrics

Compound		Symmetry in paraelec. phase		Direction of spont. polarization P_s	Temperature of phase transition, °C	Symmetry in polar phase		Type of phase transition	P_s, μC/cm²	References (adjoining list)
formula	name	space	point			space	point			
BaTiO₃	Barium titanate	$Pm3m$	$\bar{6}/4$	[100] [110] [111]¹	120 5 −80	$P4mm$ Amm $R3m$	4·m 2·m 3·m	1	26	1, 2
CdTiO₃	Cadmium titanate[2]	$Pm3m$	$\bar{6}/4$				2·m			3, 4
CaTiO₃	Calcium titanate[3] (perovskite)				1260	$Pcmn$	m·2:m			5
SrTiO₃	Strontium titanate[4]	$Pm3m$	$\bar{6}/4$							6, 7
PbTiO₃	Lead titanate	$Pm3m$	$\bar{6}/4$	[100]	~500	$P4mm$	4·m			4, 8
KTaO₃	Potassium tantalate				−260					4, 9
NaTaO₃	Sodium tantalate[5]				475 450	Orthorhombic	3·m			10, 11
LiTaO₃	Lithium tantalate				245				23	2, 12
RbTaO₃	Rubidium tantalate	$Pm3m$	$\bar{6}/4$							13
KNbO₃	Potassium niobate			[100] [110] [111]	410 210 −40	$P4mm$ Amm $R3m$	4·m 2·m 3·m		26	11, 14, 15
NaNbO₃	Sodium niobate	Pseudo-ilmenite Cubic $Pm3m$	$\bar{6}/4$		640 518 470 360	Tetragonal				11, 14, 15
LiNbO₃	Lithium niobate				450	$P2_12_1$ $R3c$ $Pbam$	2:2 3·m 3·m			2, 12
PbZrO₃	Lead zirconate	Cubic	$\bar{6}/4$		230	Tetragonal $Pbam$				6, 16, 17
PbHfO₃	Lead hafnate				215	Tetragonal	m·2:m			
LaGaO₃	Lanthanum gallate[6]	Cubic			163 100					18
NaVO₃	Sodium vanadate[7]				170 280					10 19
WO₃	Tungsten trioxide				900 740	$P4/nmm$ $P2_1/a$ Tetragonal Trigonal	m·4:m 2:m			11, 20, 21
Cd₂Nb₂O₇	Cadmium niobate	$Fd3m$	$\bar{6}/4$		−178				6	11, 22
Pb₂Nb₂O₇	Lead niobate[8]	$Fd3m$	$\bar{6}/4$		−258					11, 22

					$2:m$ or $2 \cdot m$	23 2, 4, 24
$Sr_2Ta_2O_7$ $Pb_2Nb_2O_6$	Strontium tantalate Lead metaniobate	Tetragonal $m \cdot 4:m$	Monoclinic or orthorhombic	10 570		
$PbTa_2O_6$	Lead metatantalate	Ortho-rhombic	Orthorhombic	265		25, 26
$BiFeO_3$	Bismuth ferrite[9]	Cubic				40, 41

[1] Direction of polarization is in dispute. It is shown in [37] that the $BaTiO_3$ modification which exists below $-80°C$ has, most probably, the space symmetry group Cm (point group m) and the spontaneous polarization is directed along [hkk].

[2] The ferroelectric properties of $CdTiO_3$ have not yet been confirmed.

[3] According to electrical measurements, $CaTiO_3$ has neither ferroelectric nor antiferroelectric properties.

[4] Ferroelectric properties of $SrTiO_3$ are observed only in strong electric fields.

[5,6,7,8] The ferroelectric (antiferroelectric) properties of $NaTaO_3$, $LaGaO_3$, $NaVO_3$, and $Pb_2Nb_2O_7$ have not yet been confirmed.

[9] Bismuth ferrite is both antiferroelectric and antiferromagnetic.

Notes:

A. Relatively recently G. A. Smolenskii et al. [27-36] found several new types of oxygen-octahedral ferroelectric of complex compositions: a) Pb_2FeNbO_6, Pb_2FeTaO_6, Pb_2SeNbO_6, and Pb_2SeTaO_6 which have the perovskite structure and undergo phase transitions at temperatures from -30 to $+100°C$ and whose spontaneous polarization is 3-5 $\mu C/cm^2$; b) $Pb_3MgNb_2O_9$, $Pb_3MgTa_2O_9$, $Pb_3NiNb_2O_9$, $Pb_3NiTa_2O_9$, $Pb_3CoNb_2O_9$, $Pb_3CoTa_2O_9$, $Pb_3ZnNb_2O_9$, and $Pb_3Fe_2WO_9$ which also have the perovskite structure and undergo phase transitions at temperatures from -150 to $+130°C$; c) $Pb_2Bi_2Nb_2O_9$, $CaBi_2Nb_2O_9$ and $CaBi_2Ta_2O_9$ whose Curie temperatures lie close to 600-700°C and which are all tetragonal in the paraelectric phase (group $m \cdot 4:m$) and become orthorhombic after the ferroelectric transition (group $2 \cdot m$). The compounds listed under a), b), and c) are not included in the above table because little is known about them.

B. The above table does not give information on ferroelectric (antiferroelectric) solid solutions. Information on such solid solutions can be found in [2, 11, 12, 38-39].

References in Table 6

1. B. M. Vul and I. M. Gol'dman, Dokl. Akad. Nauk SSSR, 46:139 (1945); 49:177 (1945).

2. W. Känzig, "Ferroelectrics and antiferroelectrics", Solid State Phys., 4:1 (1957).

3. G. A. Smolenskii, Dokl. Akad. Nauk SSSR, 70:405 (1950); Zh. Tekh. Fiz., 20:137 (1950).

4. G. A. Smolenskii, Usp. Fiz. Nauk, 62:41 (1957).

5. H. F. Kay and P. C. Bailey, Acta Cryst., 10:219 (1957).

6. G. A. Smolenskii, Dokl. Akad. Nauk SSSR, 70:405 (1950); Zh. Tekh. Fiz., 20:137 (1950); Zh. Tekh. Fiz., 21:1045 (1951).

7. H. Gränicher, Helv. Phys. Acta, 29:211 (1956).

8. G. H. Jonker and J. H. van Santen, Chemisch Weekblad, 43:672 (1947).

9. See Ref. 10.

10. B. T. Matthias, Phys. Rev., 75:1771 (1949).

11. H. D. Megaw, Ferroelectricity in Crystals, Methuen, London (1957).

12. B. T. Matthias and J. P. Remeika, Phys. Rev., 76:1886 (1949).

13. G. A. Smolenskii and N. V. Kozhevnikova, Dokl. Akad. Nauk SSSR, 76:519 (1951).

14. B. T. Matthias and J. P. Remeika, Phys. Rev., 82:727 (1951).

15. B. T. Matthias, E. A. Wood, and A. N. Holden, Bull. Am. Phys. Soc., Ser. 1, 24(4):21 (1949).

16. S. J. Roberts, J. Am. Ceram. Soc., 33:63 (1950).

17. G. A. Smolenskii, Izv. Akad. Nauk SSSR, Ser. Fiz., 21:233 (1957).

18. G. Shirane and R. Pepinsky, Phys. Rev., 91:812 (1953).

19. S. Sawada and S. Nomura, J. Phys. Soc. Japan, 6:192 (1951).

20. B. T. Matthias, Phys. Rev., 76:430 (1949).

21. S. Tanisaki, J. Phys. Soc. Japan, 15:566 (1960).

22. W. R. Cook, Jr. and H. Jaffe, Phys. Rev., 88:1426 (1952).

23. G. A. Smolenskii, V. A. Isupov, and A. I. Agranovskaya, Dokl. Akad. Nauk SSSR, 108:232 (1956).

24. G. Goodman, J. Am. Ceram. Soc., 36:368 (1953).

25. G. A. Smolenskii and A. I. Agranovskaya, Dokl. Akad. Nauk SSSR, 97:237 (1954).

26. E. C. Subbarao, G. Shirane, and F. Jona, Acta Cryst., 13:226 (1960).

27. G. A. Smolenskii, A. I. Agranovskaya, S. N. Popov, and V. A. Isupov, Zh. Tekh. Fiz., 28:2152 (1958).

28. V. A. Isupov, A. I. Agranovskaya, and N. P. Khuchua, Izv. Akad. Nauk SSSR, Ser. Fiz., 24:1271 (1960).

29. G. A. Smolenskii, A. I. Agranovskaya, and V. A. Isupov, Fiz. Tverd. Tela, 1:990 (1959).

30. G. A. Smolenskii, V. A. Isupov, and A. I. Agranovskaya, Fiz. Tverd. Tela, 1:169 (1959).

31. G. A. Smolenskii, A. I. Agranovskaya, V. A. Isupov, and S. N. Popov, in: Physics of Dielectrics (Proc. Second All-Union Conf., Moscow, 1958) [in Russian], Izd. AN SSSR, Moscow (1960).

32. G. A. Smolenskii, V. A. Isupov, A. I. Agranovskaya, and N. N. Krainik, Fiz. Tverd. Tela, 2:2982 (1960).

33. G. A. Smolenskii and A. I. Agranovskaya, Zh. Tekh. Fiz., 28:1491 (1958).
34. V. A. Isupov and I. E. Myl'nikova, Fiz. Tverd. Tela, 2:2728 (1960).
35. G. A. Smolenskii and A. I. Agranovskaya, Fiz. Tverd. Tela, 1:1562 (1959).
36. G. A. Smolenskii, V. A. Isupov, and A. I. Agranovskaya, Abstracts of Papers presented at Third Conf. on Ferroelectricity [in Russian], Moscow (1960).
37. F. Jona and R. Pepinsky, Phys. Rev., 105:861 (1957).
38. T. N. Verbitskaya, Varikonds (BaTiO$_3$–SnO$_2$ Solid Solutions) [in Russian], Gosénergoizdat, Moscow (1958).
39. A. V. Shubnikov, I. S. Zheludev, V. P. Konstantinova, and I. M. Sil'vestrova, Investigation of Piezoelectric Textures [in Russian], Izd. AN SSSR (1955).
40. S. V. Kiselev, R. P. Ozerov, and G. S. Zhdanov, Dokl. Akad. Nauk SSSR, 145:1255 (1962).
41. Yu. Ya. Tomashpol'skii and Yu. N. Venevtsev, Kristallografiya, 12:24 (1967).

produce or alter the spontaneous polarization P_s. We shall call these the ferroelectric phase transitions.

Generally speaking, a ferroelectric phase transition may consist of a sudden change in the unit-cell parameters without a change in its symmetry. This case occurs only in polar crystals in which the spontaneous polarization P_s suddenly changes its magnitude but retains its direction. A sudden change in the direction of the spontaneous polarization (whether accompanied by a change in its magnitude or not) may also take place without a corresponding change in the symmetry of a crystal. However, these two types of ferroelectric phase transition are of no great interest from the crystallographic symmetry point of view and we shall restrict ourselves simply to mentioning the possibility of their existence (such ferroelectric phase transitions have not yet been observed experimentally).

The greatest interest lies in ferroelectric phase transitions accompanied by a change in the symmetry of a crystal.* The simplest case is the appearance of the spontaneous polarization P_s at a phase transition. The polarization, which appears at a given temperature, may have any direction. However, we shall consider only crystallographically different directions, i.e., the directions with different types of crystallographic index.

---

* We note that a general tendency at phase transitions is for the symmetry to become lower when the temperature of a crystal is reduced. This property is observed in the majority of ferroelectric crystals in which the spontaneous polarization exists at moderately low temperatures (this may not apply at very low temperatures).

In order to determine a change in the symmetry which may accompany the appearance of the spontaneous polarization, we must consider, in accordance with the principle of superposition of symmetries, the symmetry of a crystal before a phase transition and the symmetry of a polar vector which describes the resultant polarization P_s.* There are other methods of finding changes in the symmetry, such as studies of the piezoelectric effect and electrostriction of a crystal, but we shall not consider them because the information given by these methods is less definite.

The results of an analysis of the appearance of the polarization in all classes of crystals† for the spontaneous polarization vectors oriented along all possible crystallographic directions [2a, 2b] are given in Tables 7-11. Here, the symbols representing the new groups of symmetry are followed (in parentheses) by the number of directions which are crystallographically identical with the direction considered (for example, in crystals of the $\bar{6}/4$ symmetry group there are six crystallographically identical directions of the type [100], [001], [010], [$\bar{1}$00], [0$\bar{1}$0], and [00$\bar{1}$]).

We shall now consider phase transitions accompanied by a change in the direction (and, in general, a change in the magnitude) of the spontaneous polarization, as well as by a change of the symmetry of a crystal. We shall consider specifically the ten polar classes of crystals. It is more difficult to find the symmetry after such a phase transition than after a phase transition which gives rise to spontaneous polarization. In fact, the existence of spontaneous polarization in a crystal can be regarded as evidence that this crystal has already undergone a ferroelectric transition. This means that in order to determine the new symmetry of a polar crystal after a change of the direction of its spontaneous polarization P_s, we must find first the symmetry group of a crystal before the first phase transition and then find its symmetry (as considered in the preceding paragraphs) after the second phase transition, i.e., after a change in the direction and magnitude of P_s.

---

*In agreement with Neumann's principle, the groups obtained by superposition should be subgroups of the ∞·m group, i.e., groups which describe the symmetry of polar classes.

† The spontaneous polarization can appear only in nonpolar and polar-neutral crystals (22 classes) and it is impossible (by definition) in polar crystals (10 classes).

TABLE 7. Changes in the Symmetry of Cubic Crystals Due to the Appearance of Spontaneous Polarization

Direction of P_s	Possible ferroelectric phases for the following initial phases				
	$\bar{6}/4$	$3/4$	$3/\bar{4}$	$\bar{6}/2$	$3/2$
$\langle 100\rangle$	$4\cdot m$ (6)	4 (6)	$2\cdot m$ (6)	$2\cdot m$ (6)	2 (6)
$\langle 111\rangle$	$3\cdot m$ (8)	3 (8)	$3\cdot m$ (4)	3 (8)	3 (4)
$\langle 110\rangle$	$2\cdot m$ (12)	2 (12)	m (12)	m (12)	
$\langle hk0\rangle$			1 (24)		1 (12)
$\langle hkk\rangle$	m (24)	1 (24)	m (12)	1 (24)	
$\langle hhk\rangle$					
$\langle hkl\rangle$	1 (48)		1 (24)		

TABLE 8. Changes in the Symmetry of Hexagonal Crystals Due to the Appearance of Spontaneous Polarization

Direction of P_s	Possible ferroelectric phases for the following initial phases				
	$m\cdot6:m$	$6:m$	$6:2$	$m\cdot3:m$	$3:m$
$\langle 0001\rangle$	$6\cdot m$ (2)	6 (2)	6 (2)	$3\cdot m$ (2)	3 (2)
$\langle 11\bar{2}0\rangle$	$2\cdot m$ (6)	m (6)	2 (6)	$2\cdot m$ (2)	m (3)
$\langle 10\bar{1}0\rangle$					
$\langle hki0\rangle$				m (6)	
$\langle h\bar{h}2hl\rangle$	m (12)	1 (12)	1 (12)		1 (12)
$\langle h0\bar{h}l\rangle$					
$\langle hkil\rangle$	1 (24)			1 (12)	

*Symbols in Tables 8 and 9 are given for the Bravais lattices.

TABLE 9. Changes in the Symmetry of Trigonal Crystals due to the Appearance of Spontaneous Polarization

Directions of P_s	Possible ferroelectric phases for the following initial phases		
	$\bar{6}:m$	$\bar{6}$	$3:2$
$\langle 0001\rangle$	$3\cdot m$ (2)	3 (2)	3 (2)
$\langle 11\bar{2}0\rangle$	2 (6)		2 (3)
$\langle 10\bar{1}0\rangle$	m (6)		
$\langle hki0\rangle$	1 (12)	1 (6)	
$\langle h\bar{h}2hl\rangle$			1 (6)
$\langle h0\bar{h}l\rangle$	m (6)		
$\langle hkil\rangle$	1 (12)		

TABLE 10. Changes in the Symmetry of Tetragonal Crystals Due
to the Appearance of Spontaneous Polarization

Directions of P_s	Possible ferroelectric phases for the following initial phases				
	$m \cdot 4 : m$	$4 : m$	$4 : 2$	$\bar{4} : m$	$\bar{4}$
$\langle 001 \rangle$ $\langle 100 \rangle$ $\langle 110 \rangle$ $\langle hk0 \rangle$ $\langle h0l \rangle$ $\langle hhl \rangle$ $\langle hkl \rangle$	$4 \cdot m\ (2)$ $2 \cdot m\ (4)$ $m\ (8)$ $1\ (16)$	$4\ (2)$ $m\ (4)$ $1\ (8)$	$4\ (2)$ $2\ (4)$ $1\ (8)$	$2 \cdot m\ (2)$ $2\ (4)$ $m\ (4)$ $1\ (8)$ $m\ (4)$ $1\ (8)$	$2\ (2)$ $1\ (4)$

In other words, a change in the direction (and magnitude) of
the spontaneous polarization can be regarded as taking place in
two stages: the disappearance of the polarization along the original direction and the appearance of the polarization along a new
direction. In the first stage, we must first solve the problem which
is the inverse of that considered earlier in the present section: we
must find the symmetry of a crystal before the appearance of spontaneous polarization. Table 12 shows the solution of this problem, obtained using Tables 7-11 and considering the problem in
the "reverse" order: given a polar group, we seek all groups from
which this group could originate. In the second stage, the solution

TABLE 11. Changes in the Symmetry
of Orthorhombic, Monoclinic, and Triclinic Crystals
Due to the Appearance of Spontaneous Polarization

Directions of P_s	Possible ferroelectric phases for the following initial phases			
	$m \cdot 2 : m$	$2 : 2$	$2 : m$	$\bar{2}$
$\langle 001 \rangle$ $\langle 010 \rangle$ $\langle 100 \rangle$ $\langle hk0 \rangle$ $\langle h0l \rangle$ $\langle 0kl \rangle$ $\langle hkl \rangle$	$2 \cdot m\ (2)$ $m\ (4)$ $1\ (8)$	$2\ (2)$ $1\ (4)$	$2\ (2)$ $m\ (2)$ $1\ (4)$	$1\ (2)$

TABLE 12. Symmetry Groups of Polar Crystals before the First Phase Transition

Symmetry group	6·m	4·m	3·m	2·m	6	4	3	2	m	1
Groups which a crystal can have before the appearance of P_S	m·6:m	$\bar{6}$/4, m·4:m	$\bar{6}$/4; 3/4; 6·m, m·3:m	6/4; 3/4̄; 6/2; m·6:m m·4:m; 4̄·m; m·3:m, m·2:m	6:m; 6:2	3/4 4:2 4:m	3/4; 6/2; 3/2; 3:m; $\bar{6}$; 3:2	3/4; 3/2; 6:2; $\bar{6}$·m; 3:2; 4:2; 4̄·m; 4̄; 2:2	Any group which has a symmetry plane	Any symmetry group

is similar to that discussed earlier in the present section and can be obtained using Tables 7-11 in the original order.

We shall now consider a specific example. Let us assume that the point symmetry group of a polar crystal is 4·m. The question is how the symmetry of this crystal changes when the direction (and magnitude) of its spontaneous polarization change as a result of a phase transition. We find from Table 12 that, before the phase transition, such a crystal could have belonged to the group $\bar{6}$/4 or m·4:m. It is evident from Table 7 that different changes in the direction of P_s can alter the symmetry group $\bar{6}$/4 into groups 4·m, 3·m, 2·m, m, and 1. Similarly, for the class m·4:m we obtain from Table 10 m·4:m → 4·m, 2·m, m, 1. The final solution of this problem can be written in the form 4·m → 3·m, 2·m, m, 1.

We shall now make some general comments about Tables 7-12. First, we must stress that the tabulated relationships governing changes in the symmetry of crystals at phase-transition points are obeyed only if these crystals undergo ferroelectric phase transitions, i.e., transitions associated either with the appearance of or a change in the spontaneous polarization P_S. Generally speaking, crystals need not undergo any phase transitions when the temperature is varied and they need not undergo ferroelectric transitions. It follows from Tables 7-12 that a given crystal may acquire different symmetries at ferroelectric phase transitions but Tables 7-12 do not (and cannot) give the sequence in which a crystal acquires a particular symmetry.

Finally, we must mention that ferroelectric phase transitions are reversible and can take place in both directions: if a crystal having a particular symmetry acquires a spontaneous polarization and changes its symmety when it is cooled, we find that when the crystal is heated the polarization disappears at the same temperature at which it appeared originally and the initial symmetry of the crystal is re-established.

§ 2. Changes in the Space Symmetry of Crystals at Ferroelectric Phase Transitions

A discussion of changes in the crystal symmetry, which accompany ferroelectric phase transitions (see preceding section), can be based also on changes in the space symmetry. After undergoing a ferroelectric phase transition, a crystal belongs to one of the ten polar classes and, therefore, its space symmetry in the ferroelectric state can only belong to one of 68 space groups corresponding to the ten polar (pyroelectric) classes. These 68 space groups should therefore be called the polar groups.

Knowing the space symmetry of a crystal before a phase transition and the space symmetry of the field of the spontaneous polarization vectors, and using the principle of superposition of symmetries, we can obtain the space symmetry group of a crystal after the phase transition. The field of the spontaneous polarization vectors is a result of the action, on the vector P_s, of a lattice translation operation T. We shall denote the resultant space symmetry of the P_s vector field by the symbol $(\infty \cdot m)$ T. The results of the superposition of various space symmetry groups and of the $(\infty \cdot m)$ T group are given in Tables 13–17 [4] for various (relative to the lattice) orientations of the vectors P_s of all initially nonpolar crystals. Changes in the space symmetry of those crystals which already exhibit spontaneous polarization (i.e., the crystals undergoing a second phase transition) can also be found employing Tables 13–17. We must use these tables first in the reverse order (as in the case of Table 12 in the preceding section) and then in the original order. Using the tables in the reverse order, we find the space symmetry group of a crystal before the first phase transition; and then using them in the original order, we find the new space-symmetry group corresponding to the new direction of the spontaneous polarization.

TABLE 13. Changes in the Space Symmetry of Cubic Crystals Due to Appearance of Spontaneous Polarization

| Original groups | | Ferroelectric space groups for following directions of P_s | | | | | | |
point	space	⟨100⟩	⟨111⟩	⟨110⟩	⟨hk0⟩	⟨hkk⟩	⟨hhk⟩	⟨hkl⟩
	$Ia3d$	$I4cd$	$R3c$	Fdd	Cc	Pc	Pc	
	$Im3m$	$I4mm$	$R3m$	Fmm	Cm	Cm	Cm	
	$Fd3c$	$I4cd$	$R3c$	Iba	Pc	Cc	Cc	
	$Fd3m$	$I4md$	$R3m$	Ima	Pc	Cm	Cm	
$\bar6/4 - O_h$	$Fm3c$	$I4cm$	$R3c$	Ima	Cm	Cc	Cc	$P1$
	$Fm3m$	$I4mm$	$R3m$	Imm	Cm	Cm	Cm	
	$Pn3m$	$P4nm$	$R3m$	Abm	Pc	Cm	Cm	
	$Pm3n$	$P4mc$	$R3c$	Ama	Pm	Cc	Cc	
	$Pn3n$	$P4nc$	$R3c$	Aba	Pc	Cc	Cc	
	$Pm3m$	$P4mm$	$R3m$	Amm	Pm	Cm	Cm	
	$I4_13$	$I4_1$						
	$I43$	$I4$						
	$F4_13$	$I4_1$						
$3/4 - O$	$F43$	$I4$	$R3$	$C2$	$P1$	$P1$	$P1$	$P1$
	$P4_23$	$I4_2$						
	$P4_13$	$P4_1$						
	$P4_33$	$P4_3$						
	$P43$	$P4$						
	$I\bar43d$	Fdd	$R3c$	Pc		Pc	Pc	
	$I\bar43m$	Fmm	$R3m$	Cm		Cm	Cm	
$3/\bar4 - T_d$	$F\bar43c$	Iba	$R3c$	Cc	$P1$	Cc	Cc	$P1$
	$P\bar43m$	Imm	$R3m$	Cm		Cm	Cm	
	$P\bar43n$	Ccc	$R3c$	Cc		Cc	Cc	
	$P\bar43m$	Cmm	$R3m$	Cm		Cm	Cm	
	$Ia3$	Iba		Cc	Cc			
	$Im3$	Imm		Cm	Cm			
	$Fd3$	Fdd		Pc	Pc			
$\bar6/2 - T_h$	$Fm3$	Fmm	$R3$	Cm	Cm	$P1$	$P1$	$P1$
	$Pa3$	Pca		Pc	Pc			
	$Pn3$	Pnn		Pc	Pc			
	$Pm3$	Pmm		Pm	Pm			
	$I2_13$							
	$I23$	$C2$						
$3/2 - T$	$F23$		$R3$	$P1$	$P1$	$P1$	$P1$	$P1$
	$P2_13$	$P2_1$						
	$P23$	$P2$						

TABLE 14. Changes in the Space Symmetry of Hexagonal Crystals Due to the Appearance of Spontaneous Polarization

Original groups		Ferroelectric space groups for following directions of P_s						
point	space	$\langle 0001\rangle$	$\langle 11\bar{2}0\rangle$	$\langle 10\bar{1}0\rangle$	$\langle h\bar{k}i0\rangle$	$\langle h\bar{h}2hl\rangle$	$\langle h0\bar{h}l\rangle$	$\langle hkil\rangle$
$m\cdot 3{:}m - D_{3h}$	$H\bar{6}c2$	$H3c$	Ama	Cc		Cc	Cc	
	$H\bar{6}m2$	$H3m$	Amm	Cm	Pm	Cm	Cm	$P1$
	$C\bar{6}c2$	$C3c$	Ama	Cc		Cc	Cc	
	$C\bar{6}m2$	$C3m$	Amm	Cm		Cm	Cm	
$3{:}m - C_{3h}$	$C\bar{6}$	$C3$	Pm	Pm	Pm	$P1$	$P1$	$P1$
$m\cdot 6{:}m - D_{6h}$	$C6/mmc$	$C6mc$	Ama	Amm		Cc	Cm	
	$C6/mcm$	$C6cm$	Amm	Ama	Pm	Cm	Cc	$P1$
	$C6/mcc$	$C6/cc$	Ama			Cc		
	$C6/mmm$	$C6mm$	Amm	Amm		Cm	Cm	
$6{:}2 - D_6$	$C6_32$	$C6_3$						
	$C6_42$	$C6_4$						
	$C6_22$	$C6_2$	$C2$	$C2$	$P1$	$P1$	$P1$	$P1$
	$C6_52$	$C6_5$						
	$C6_12$	$C6_1$						
	$C62$	$C6$						
$6{:}m - C_{6h}$	$C6_3/m$	$C6_3$	Pm	Pm	Pm	$P1$	$P1$	$P1$
	$C6/m$	$C6$						

Considering Tables 13–17, we can make the same comments as those made in connection with Tables 7–12: a crystal need not undergo a phase transition in general or a ferroelectric transition in particular; transitions can take place due to some other (not electrical) singularities, such as those connected with the magnetic, optical, or other properties. Tables 13–17 do not give the order in which changes in the symmetry appear when the temperature is varied, and so on.

§3. Structure of Ferroelectrics

A. Barium Titanate ($BaTiO_3$) and Other Perovskite Ferroelectrics. Ferroelectrics with the general formula ABO_3 ($BaTiO_3$, $PbTiO_3$, $KNbO_3$, etc.) have the ideal cubic perovskite structure (Fig. 28) in the paraelectric high-temperature phase. The point group of the paraelectric phase of the perovskite ferroelectrics is $\bar{6}/4$ and the space group of these crystals is $Pm3m$. The cube edge in the unit cell is about 4 Å; each cell contains one formula unit. All the atoms are at special positions. If the origin of coordinates is assumed to lie at the B atom, the

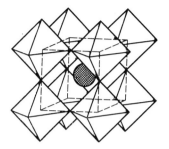

Fig. 28. Ideal structure of an ABO_3 perovskite. The B atoms are located at the centers of octahedra; the oxygen atoms are at the vertices of the octahedra; the A atom is shown shaded.

atomic coordinates of the structure can be written in the following form: 000 (vertices of the cube) for the B atoms; 1/2 1/2 1/2 (center of the cube) for the A atom; 1/2 0 0, 0 1/2 0, 0 0 1/2 (midpoints of the cube edges) for the O atoms. Each B ion is surrounded by six atoms of oxygen located at the vertices of a regular octahedron. The octahedra are linked by their vertices and form a space structure in which large cavities are occupied by the A atoms. Each A atom is surrounded by 12 equidistant oxygen atoms; each oxygen atom has two B-type and four A-type nearest neighbors.

TABLE 15. Changes in the Space Symmetry of Trigonal Crystals Due to the Appearance of Spontaneous Polarization

Original groups		Ferroelectric space groups for following directions of P_s						
point	space	$\langle 0001\rangle$	$\langle 11\bar{2}0\rangle$	$\langle 10\bar{1}0\rangle$	$\langle hki0\rangle$	$\langle h\bar{h}2hl\rangle$	$\langle h0\bar{h}l\rangle$	$\langle hkil\rangle$
$\bar{6}\cdot m - D_{3d}$	$R\bar{3}c$	$R3c$					Cc	
	$R\bar{3}m$	$R3m$					Cm	
	$H\bar{3}c$	$H3c$	$C2$	$C2$	$P1$	$P1$	Cc	$P1$
	$H\bar{3}m$	$H3m$					Cm	
	$C\bar{3}c$	$C3c$					Cc	
	$C\bar{3}m$	$C3m$					Cm	
$\bar{6} - C_{3i}$	$R\bar{3}$	$R3$	$P1$	$P1$	$P1$	$P1$	$P1$	$P1$
	$C\bar{3}$	$C3$						
$3:2 - D_3$	$R32$	$R3$						
	$H3_22$	$C3_2$						
	$H3_12$	$C3_1$						
	$H32$	$C3$	$C2$	$P1$	$P1$	$P1$	$P1$	$P1$
	$C3_22$	$C3_2$						
	$C3_12$	$C3_1$						
	$C32$	$C3$						

TABLE 16. Changes in the Space Symmetry of Tetragonal Crystals Due to the Appearance of Spontaneous Polarization

| Original groups | | Ferroelectric space groups for following directions of $\mathbf{P}_s$ | | | | | | |
point	space	$\langle 001 \rangle$	$\langle 100 \rangle$	$\langle 110 \rangle$	$\langle hk0 \rangle$	$\langle h0l \rangle$	$\langle hhl \rangle$	$\langle hkl \rangle$
$m \cdot 4 : m - D_{4h}$	$I4/amd$	$I4md$	Ima	Fdd	Cc	Cm	Pc	$P1$
	$I4/acd$	$I4cd$	Iba	Fdd	Cc	Cc	Pc	$P1$
	$I4/mcm$	$I4cm$	Ima	Fmm	Cm	Cc	Cm	$P1$
	$I4/mmm$	$I4mm$	Imm	Fmm	Cm	Cm	Cm	$P1$
	$P4/nmc$	$P4mc$	Pmn	Aba	Pc	Pm	Cc	$P1$
	$P4/mbc$	$P4bc$	Pmc	Ama	Pm	Pc	Cc	$P1$
	$P4/ncm$	$P4cm$	Pna	Abm	Pc	Pc	Cm	$P1$
	$P4/mnm$	$P4nm$	Pmn	Amm	Pm	Pc	Cm	$P1$
	$P4/nbc$	$P4bc$	Pnc	Aba	Pc	Pc	Cc	$P1$
	$P4/nnm$	$P4nm$	Pnn	Abm	Pc	Pc	Cm	$P1$
	$P4/mcm$	$P4cm$	Pma	Amm	Pm	Pc	Cm	$P1$
	$P4/mmc$	$P4mc$	Pmm	Ama	Pm	Pm	Cc	$P1$
	$P4/ncc$	$P4cc$	Pna	Aba	Pc	Pc	Cc	$P1$
	$P4/mnc$	$P4nc$	Pmn	Ama	Pm	Pc	Cc	$P1$
	$P4/nmm$	$P4mm$	Pmn	Abm	Pc	Pm	Cm	$P1$
	$P4/mbm$	$P4bm$	Pmc	Amm	Pm	Pc	Cm	$P1$
	$P4/nnc$	$P4nc$	Pnn	Aba	Pc	Pc	Cc	$P1$
	$P4/nbm$	$P4bm$	Pnc	Abm	Pc	Pc	Cm	$P1$
	$P4/mcc$	$P4cc$	Pma	Ama	Pm	Pc	Cc	$P1$
	$P4\,mmm$	$P4mm$	Pmm	Amm	Pm	Pm	Cm	$P1$
$\bar{4} \cdot m - D_{2d}$	$I\bar{4}2d$	Fdd	$C2$	Pc	$P1$	$P1$	Pc	$P1$
	$I\bar{4}2m$	Fmm	$C2$	Cm	$P1$	$P1$	Cm	$P1$
	$F\bar{4}2c$	Iba	$C2$	Cc	$P1$	$P1$	Cc	$P1$
	$F\bar{4}2m$	Imm	$C2$	Cm	$P1$	$P1$	Cm	$P1$
	$C\bar{4}2n$	Pnn	$C2$	Pc	$P1$	$P1$	Pc	$P1$
	$C\bar{4}2b$	Pba	$C2$	Pc	$P1$	$P1$	Pc	$P1$
	$C\bar{4}2c$	Pcc	$C2$	Pc	$P1$	$P1$	Pc	$P1$
	$C\bar{4}2m$	Pmm	$C2$	Pm	$P1$	$P1$	Pm	$P1$
	$P\bar{4}2_1c$	Ccc	$P2_1$	Cc	$P1$	$P1$	Cc	$P1$
	$P\bar{4}2_1m$	Cmm	$P2_1$	Cm	$P1$	$P1$	Cm	$P1$
	$P\bar{4}2c$	Ccc	$P2$	Cc	$P1$	$P1$	Cc	$P1$
	$P\bar{4}2m$	Cmm	$P2$	Cm	$P1$	$P1$	Cm	$P1$
$4 : 2 - D_4$	$I4_12$	$I4_1$	$C2$	$C2$	$P1$	$P1$	$P1$	$P1$
	$I42$	$I4$	$C2$	$C2$	$P1$	$P1$	$P1$	$P1$
	$P4_22_1$	$P4_2$	$P2_1$	$C2$	$P1$	$P1$	$P1$	$P1$
	$P4_32_1$	$P4_3$	$P2_1$	$C2$	$P1$	$P1$	$P1$	$P1$
	$P4_12_1$	$P4_1$	$P2_1$	$C2$	$P1$	$P1$	$P1$	$P1$
	$P4_22$	$P4_2$	$P2$	$C2$	$P1$	$P1$	$P1$	$P1$
	$P4_32$	$P4_3$	$P2$	$C2$	$P1$	$P1$	$P1$	$P1$
	$P4_12$	$P4_1$	$P2$	$C2$	$P1$	$P1$	$P1$	$P1$
	$P42_1$	$P4$	$P2_1$	$C2$	$P1$	$P1$	$P1$	$P1$
	$P42$	$P4$	$P2$	$C2$	$P1$	$P1$	$P1$	$P1$

TABLE 16 (continued)

Original groups		Ferroelectric space groups for following directions of P_s						
point	space	⟨001⟩	⟨100⟩	⟨110⟩	⟨hk0⟩	⟨h0l⟩	⟨hhl⟩	⟨hkl⟩
	$I4_1/c$	$I4_1$	Cc	Cc	Cc			
	$I4/m$	$I4$	Cm	Cm	Cm			
	$P4_2/n$	$\}\,P4_2$	Pc	Pc	Pc			
$4:m - C_{4h}$	$P4_2/m$		Pm	Pm	Pm	$P1$	$P1$	$P1$
	$P4/n$	$\}\,P4$	Pc	Pc	Pc			
	$P4/m$		Pm	Pm	Pm			
$\bar{4} - S_4$	$I\bar{4}$	$C2$	$P1$	$P1$	$P1$	$P1$	$P1$	$P1$
	$P\bar{4}$	$C2$						

Barium titanate ($BaTiO_3$) is the most typical perovskite ferroelectric. Its structure is cubic above 120°C. When it is cooled, barium titanate passes through a phase-transition point and becomes tetragonal below this temperature. The temperature of 120°C is the Curie point of $BaTiO_3$, because below this temperature it is ferroelectric.

The point symmetry group of the tetragonal symmetry of $BaTiO_3$ is 4·m and the space group is $P4mm$; a unit cell of barium titanate contains only one formula unit. The ratio of the crystallographic axes a/c is about 1.01. The atoms in the original ideal cubic cell are displaced by an amount δc along a fourfold axis, which is the polar axis. The most accurate available neutron-diffraction data for the positions of atoms in the tetragonal structure are given in Table 18. Table 19 gives information on the bond lengths and angles for the tetragonal phase of $BaTiO_3$. The notation used for various oxygen atoms and the reference system employed in Tables 18 and 19 are given in Fig. 29.

It is evident from Tables 18 and 19 that the oxygen octahedra in tetragonal $BaTiO_3$ are distorted only slightly. The displacement of the O_I oxygen atoms relative to the O_{II} oxygens is small. The titanium atoms are displaced by 0.13 Å relative to the centers of the corresponding octahedra and therefore the two $O_{II} - Ti$ bonds form an angle which is not equal to 180° (this angle is, in fact, 171°28').

The change in the point and space symmetries which occur at the 120°C phase transition in $BaTiO_3$ can be found using the Curie symmetry principle (Table 7) and the experimental observation that the spontaneous polarization P_s appears at this temperature along the fourfold axis of the original cubic crystal (see also Fig. 30A).

TABLE 17. Changes in the Space Symmetry of Crystals of Lower-Symmetry Systems Due to the Appearance of Spontaneous Polarization

Original groups		Ferroelectric space groups for following directions of P_s						
point	space	<001>	<010>	<100>	<hk0>	<h0l>	<0kl>	<hkl>
$m\cdot2:m-D_{2h}$	Ibca	Iba	Iba	Iba	Cc	Cc	Cc	P1
	Imma	Imm	Ima	Ima	Cc	Cm	Cm	P1
	Ibam	Iba	Ima	Ima	Cm	Cc	Cc	P1
	Immm	Imm	Imm	Imm	Cm	Cm	Cm	P1
	Fddd	Fdd	Fdd	Fdd	Pc	Pc	Pc	P1
	Fmmm	Fmm	Fmm	Fmm	Cm	Pc	Cm	P1
	Cmca	Cmc	Abm	Aba	Pc	Cc	Cc	Cm
	Cmcm	Cmc	Amm	Ama	Pm	Cc	Cc	Cm
	Ccca	Ccc	Aba	Aba	Pc	Cm	Cc	Cc
	Cmma	Cmm	Abm	Abm	Pc	Cc	Cc	Cc
	Cccm	Ccc	Ama	Ama	Pm	Cm	Cm	Cm
	Cmmm	Cmm	Amm	Amm	Pm	Pc	Cm	Cm
	Pbca	Pca	Pca	Pca	Pc	Pm	Pm	P1
	Pnma	Pmn	Pna	Pmc	Pc	Pc	Pc	P1
	Pccn	Pcc	Pna	Pna	Pc	Pc	Pc	P1
	Pbcn	Pca	Pnc	Pna	Pc	Pc	Pc	P1
	Pnnm	Pnn	Pmn	Pmn	Pm	Pm	Pm	P1
	Pmmn	Pmm	Pmn	Pmn	Pc	Pc	Pc	P1
	Pbcm	Pca	Pmc	Pma	Pm	Pm	Pm	P1
	Pbam	Pba	Pmc	Pmc	Pm	Pc	Pc	P1
	Pnna	Pnn	Pna	Pnc	Pc	Pc	Pc	P1
	Pcca	Pcc	Pnn	Pca	Pc	Pc	Pc	P1
	Pmna	Pmn	Pma	Pnc	Pc	Pm	Pm	P1
	Pmma	Pmm	Pma	Pmc	Pc	Pc	Pc	P1
	Pnnn	Pnn	Pnn	Pnn	Pc	Pc	Pc	P1
	Pban	Pba	Pnc	Pnc	Pc	Pc	Pc	P1
	Pccm	Pcc	Pma	Pma	Pm	Pm	Pm	P1
	Pmmm	Pmm	Pmm	Pmm	Pm	Pm	Pm	P1
$2:2-D_2$	$I2_12_12_1$	C2	C2	C2	P1	P1	P1	P1
	$I222$	C2	C2	C2	P1	P1	P1	P1
	$F222$	C2	C2	C2	P1	P1	P1	P1
	$C222_1$	$P2_1$	C2	C2	P1	P1	P1	P1
	$C222$	P2	C2	C2	P1	P1	P1	P1
	$P2_12_12_1$	$P2_1$	$P2_1$	$P2_1$	P1	P1	P1	P1
	$P2_12_12$	P2	$P2_1$	$P2_1$	P1	P1	P1	P1
	$P222_1$	$P2_1$	P2	P2	P1	P1	P1	P1
	$P222$	P2	P2	P2	P1	P1	P1	P1
$2:m-C_{2h}$	$C2/c$	Cc	C2	Cc	P1	Cc	P1	P1
	$C2/m$	Cm	C2	Cm	P1	Cm	P1	P1
	$P2_1/c$	Pc	$P2_1$	Pc	P1	Pc	P1	P1
	$P2_1/m$	Pm	$P2_1$	Pm	P1	Pm	P1	P1
	$P2/c$	Pc	P2	Pc	P1	Pc	P1	P1
	$P2/m$	Pm	P2	Pm	P1	Pm	P1	P1
$\bar{2}-C_i$	$P\bar{1}$	P1	P1	P1	P1	P1	P1	P1

TABLE 18. Positions of the Atoms in Tetragonal $BaTiO_3$ [8] (Cell parameters at 20°C [19]: a = 3.992, c = 4.032 Å)

Atom	Atomic coordinates	Value of δc
Ti	0, 0, 0	0
Ba	1/2, 1/2, 1/2 $+ \delta c_{Ba}$	−0.014
O_I	0, 0, 1/2 $+ \delta c_{oI}$	−0.037
O_{II}	$\begin{cases} 1/2,\ 0,\ \delta c_{oII} \\ 0,\ 1/2,\ \delta c_{oII} \end{cases}$	−0.028

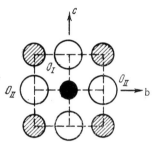

Fig. 29. Designations of the oxygen atoms and the coordinate system in $BaTiO_3$. The structure is shown projected on the (bc) plane.

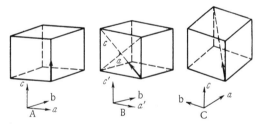

Fig. 30. Unit cells of three ferroelectric modifications of $BaTiO_3$: A) tetragonal; B) orthorhombic; C) trigonal. The heavy arrows indicate the direction of P_s.

TABLE 19. Bond Lengths (Å) and Angles in Tetragonal $BaTiO_3$

Ti—O_I	$\begin{cases} 1.869 \\ 2.167 \end{cases}$
Ti—O_{II}	1.999
Ba—O_I	2.824
Ba—O_{II}	2.800
	2.886
Ti—O_2—Ti	171°28′

TABLE 20. Positions of the Atoms in Orthorhombic
BaTiO$_3$

Cell parameters at 4°C [19]:* "a" = "c" = 4.017 Å;
"β" = 90°12'; a = 5.656 Å; b = 3.986 Å; c = 5.675 Å

Atom	Atomic coordinates
Ti	0, 0, 0; 1/2, 0, 1/2
Ba	1/2, 1/2, δc_{Ba}; 0,1/2, 1/2 + δc_{Ba}
O$_I$	1/4 + δa_{O_I}, 0, 1/4 + δc_{O_I};
	1/4 − δa_{O_I},0, 3/4 + δc_{O_I}; 3/4 − δa_{O_I}, 0, 1/4 + δc_{O_I};
	3/4 + δa_{O_I}, 0, 3/4 + δc_{O_I}
O$_{II}$	0, 1/2, $\delta c_{O_{II}}$; 1/2, 1/2, δc_{O_I}

*Here and later the cell parameters shown in quotes refer to the
axes of the original paraelectric cube.

When tetragonal BaTiO$_3$ is cooled still further, it undergoes a
second phase transition at 0°C and becomes orthorhombic. The
orthorhombic structure can be regarded as a slightly distorted
cubic structure, obtained by stretching it along one face diagonal
and compressing it along the other diagonal. These two diagonals
become the new orthorhombic axes (Fig.30B). The third axis (b)
retains its original direction but its relative length changes slightly. The point symmetry group of the orthorhombic modification
of BaTiO$_3$ is 2·m and the space group is *Bmm2*. The new cell is
face-centered and a twofold axis coincides with the c axis. The cell
now contains two formula units. All the atoms in the cell are displaced parallel to one another along the c axis. However, structure investigations do not tell us whether the atoms are displaced
(relative to their initial positions in the cubic cell) along the long
or short face diagonal of the orthorhombic cell. By analogy with
the tetragonal structure of BaTiO$_3$ (in which atoms are displaced
along the direction of expansion of the cell), we may assume that
the atoms in the orthorhombic phase of BaTiO$_3$ are displaced along
the long diagonal. The positions of the atoms in orthorhombic
BaTiO$_3$ are given in Table 20.

Assuming that the direction of the spontaneous polarization P$_s$
in orthorhombic barium titanate lies along the [110] axis (along a
face diagonal of the original cube), we find that the space symmetry
group of the orthorhombic phase is 2·m and the space group is
Bmm2 (see Tables 7 and 13).

Barium titanate undergoes a third phase transition in the temperature range between -70 and $-90°C$ and becomes trigonal.* In this case, the unit cell is a rhombohedron formed by stretching the original cube along one of its body diagonals (Fig. 30C). The point group of rhombohedral $BaTiO_3$ is $3 \cdot m$ and the space group is $R3m$. A unit cell of this phase contains only one formula unit. The angle between the trigonal axes differs by 8' from 90°. By analogy with the tetragonal distortion, this angle is assumed to be acute, i.e., it is assumed that the atoms are displaced along the body diagonal of the cube, which has become longer.

This change of symmetry to the trigonal (rhombohedral) form $(\bar{6}/4 \rightarrow 3 \cdot m,\ Pm3m \rightarrow R3m)$ can be deduced using Tables 7 and 13 by assuming that the direction of the spontaneous polarization is oriented along the [111] body diagonal of the original cube.

The positions of the atoms in trigonal $BaTiO_3$, referred to hexagonal axes, are given in Table 21.

TABLE 21. Positions of the Atoms in Trigonal $BaTiO_3$

Cell parameters [14]: $a_{trig} = 3.998$ Å; $\alpha = 89°52$; $c_{hex} = 6.942$ Å; $a_{hex} = 5.649$ Å

Atom	Coordinates referred to hexagonal axes
Ti	0, 0, 0; 2/3, 1/3, 1/3; 1/3, 2/3, 2/3;
Ba	0, 0, $1/2 + \delta c_{Ba}$; 2/3, 1/3, $5/6 + \delta c_{Ba}$; 1/3, 2/3, $1/6 + \delta c_{Ba}$;
O	$1/3 + 2\delta a_O$, $1/6 + \delta a_O$, $1/6 + \delta c_O$;
	$5/6 - \delta a_O$, $1/6 + \delta a_O$, $1/6 + \delta c_O$;
	$5/6 - \delta a_O$, $2/3 - 2\delta a_O$, $1/6 + \delta c_O$;
	$1/2 - \delta a_O$, $-2\delta a_O$, $1/2 + \delta c_O$;
	$2\delta a_O$, $1/2 + \delta a_O$, $1/2 + \delta c_O$;
	$1/2 - \delta a_O$, $1/2 + \delta a_O$, $1/2 + \delta c_O$;
	$1/6 - \delta a_O$, $1/3 - 2\delta a_O$, $5/6 + \delta c_O$;
	$1/6 - \delta a_O$, $5/6 + \delta a_O$, $5/6 + \delta c_O$;
	$2/3 + 2\delta a_O$, $5/6 + \delta a_O$, $5/6 + \delta c_O$.

*Unjustified objections have been raised against the attribution of the trigonal structure to this phase.

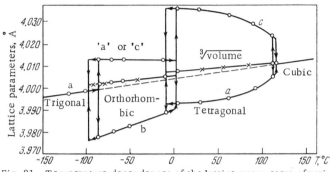

Fig. 31. Temperature dependences of the lattice parameters of various BaTiO₃ modifications [14].

The temperature dependences of the cell parameters and the volumes of all the BaTiO₃ modifications are given in Fig. 31. It is evident from this figure that, at the phase transition points, the cell parameters and volumes change suddenly. Thermal hysteresis, i.e., different transition temperatures during cooling and heating, is observed at all the phase-transition points.

We shall now give the main results of the investigations of the structure of BaTiO₃ by nondiffraction methods. A study of the infrared absorption spectrum of cubic BaTiO₃ has indicated the presence, in the 12.5–25 μ wavelength range, of lines corresponding to stretching-compression deformations, and to the bending of the TiO₆ octahedron. These lines have practically the same frequency and intensity in the tetrahedral modification, i.e., below the Curie point. A change in the symmetry of the crystal and the presence of the spontaneous polarization split these lines somewhat [17].

A slight anisotropy of the absorption of light waves is observed at room temperature for the tetragonal modification of BaTiO₃; this anisotropy is found when the direction of the electric vector of the wave is rotated from the tetragonal c axis to a direction normal to this axis [5, 15].

The fundamental absorption band edge of BaTiO₃ is located approximately at 4000 Å. The temperature dependence of the edge wavelength shows no anomalies at the transition point of the tetragonal modification. The results of investigations of the infrared absorption spectra of perovskite ferroelectrics (including BaTiO₃) are given and discussed in §4 of Chap. VI.

TABLE 22. Positions of the Atoms in Tetragonal
PbTiO$_3$ [27]

Atom	Coordinates	Value of δc_i
Ti	0, 0, 0	0
Pb	1/2, 1/2, 1/2 + δc	− 0.041
O$_I$	0, 0, δc_{O_I}	+ 0.069
O$_{II}$	1/2, 0, $\delta c_{O_{II}}$	+ 0.069
	0, 1/2, $\delta c_{O_{II}}$	

BaTiO$_3$ does not contain paramagnetic ions but some features of its structure can be investigated by the EPR method when iron impurity ions are introduced into this compound. Ferric ions (Fe^{3+}), located at the titanium sites in the tetragonal modification, give (at room temperature) five strong resolved lines corresponding to a spin of 5/2. The cubic modification has only three such lines: a central one and two satellites, each of which consists of two unresolved lines [9a, 9b, 16].

At room temperature, lead titanate (PbTiO$_3$) has the tetragonal symmetry and is isomorphous with tetragonal BaTiO$_3$. The cell dimensions are a = 3.904 Å and c = 4.150 Å. The space symmetry group is $P4mm$; a unit cell contains only one formula unit. The axial ratio c/a = 1.063 is considerably larger than that for BaTiO$_3$. Atomic parameters, found by the neutron-diffraction method, are listed in Table 22.

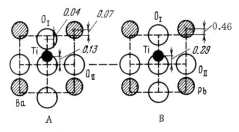

Fig. 32. Schematic representation of the displacements (in Å) of the ions in the tetragonal modifications of BaTiO$_3$ (A) and PbTiO$_3$ (B). The dimensions of the ions are relative [24].

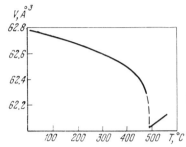

Fig. 33. Temperature dependence of the
unit-cell volume of PbTiO$_3$ [23].

Comparison of Tables 22 and 18 shows that the lead atoms in
PbTiO$_3$ are shifted relatively strongly (Fig. 32). The oxygen sublattice in PbTiO$_3$ remains undistorted because the two kinds of oxygen atom, O$_I$ and O$_{II}$, do not interchange their positions. The Pb
and Ti atoms shift, respectively, by 0.46 and 0.29 Å in the same
direction relative to the oxygen framework; in the case of BaTiO$_3$,
the Ba and Ti atoms shift only by 0.07 and 0.13 Å, respectively.
When the temperature is raised above room temperature, the c
parameter of the PbTiO$_3$ cell decreases and the parameter a increases so that the ratio c/a reaches 1.02 near 490°C. At this
temperature, PbTiO$_3$ undergoes a phase transition and becomes
cubic. Figure 33 shows the temperature dependence of the unit
cell volume of lead titanate. It is worth noting a sudden change in
the volume at the phase transition point and the negative expansion
coefficient just below the transition temperature. Slow cooling of
PbTiO$_3$ induces a phase transition at −100°C, which produced a
multiple-cell structure (a' = 4a, c' = 2c). It is most likely that
the multiple-cell modification of PbTiO$_3$ is an antiferroelectric,
but no detailed investigations of the structure and properties of
this phase have yet been carried out.

Potassium niobate (KNbO$_3$) is isomorphous with BaTiO$_3$ in all
its modifications. The temperatures of the ferroelectric phase transitions are approximately 410°C (transition from the cubic to the
tetragonal modification at the Curie temperature), 210°C (transition from the tetragonal to the orthorhombic modification), and
−40°C (transition from the orthorhombic to the trigonal modification). The dimensions of the unit cells of the various modifications
of KNbO$_3$ are listed in Table 23.

At room temperature, KNbO$_3$ is orthorhombic. The temperatures of the transitions in KNbO$_3$ are higher than the temperatures

TABLE 23. Unit Cell Parameters of $KNbO_3$ [22, 25]

Temperature, °C	Symmetry	Cell parameters, Å
425	Cubic	$a = 4.0214$
220	Tetragonal	$a = 3.9972$
		$c = 1.0166$
25	Orthorhombic*	$a = 5.6974$
		$b = 3.9711$
		$c = 5.7222$
		$"a" = "c" = 4.075$
		$\beta = 90°15'$
—140	Trigonal	$a = 4.016$
		$\alpha = 89°50'$

*The directions a and c are selected in the same way as for $BaTiO_3$ (Table 20).

of the corresponding transitions in $BaTiO_3$. The ratio of the a/b axes of the orthorhombic modification is 1.017 at room temperature and 1.013 immediately after the transition to the orthorhombic phase. The ratio c/a of the tetragonal modification lies within the range 1.012-1.017 (the corresponding values of the ratio c/a of $BaTiO_3$ are smaller). These and other data on the phase transitions in $KNbO_3$ indicate that the distortion of the structure is greater than that in barium titanate.

The quadrupole splitting of the nuclear magnetic resonance lines and the simple quadrupole resonance of Nb^{93} were investigated in $KNbO_3$ [7]. These investigations show that all three transitions in potassium niobate are sudden but two phases coexist near each transition point. Considerable changes in the electric field gradient occur near the Nb nuclei at the transition points. This gradient vanishes when potassium niobate becomes cubic. In the polar phases, the electric field gradient is so high that it cannot be explained by a simple ionic model, but we must assume at least partial covalent binding of the Nb and O ions.

B. Ferroelectrics with the Pseudo-Ilmenite Structure. The room-temperature structure of lithium niobate ($LiNbO_3$) is similar to the structure of ilmenite ($FeTiO_3$). The space group of lithium niobate is $R3c$; it has a trigonal cell in which a = 5.4920 Å and α = 55°53' [6]. This cell contains two formula units. When the cell parameters are referred to the hexagonal axes, it is found that a_{hex} = 5.147 Å and c_{hex} = 13.856 Å. In this case, the cell contains six formula units.

This structure can be represented most simply in the form of a hexagonal close-packed array of oxygen atoms. These atoms form a simple lattice and their coordinates are (x, $\frac{1}{2}-x-\varepsilon$, $\frac{1}{4}+\varepsilon$), where x = 0.628 and ε is very close to zero. Cations lie on threefold axes at two points whose coordinates are (u, u, u) and ($\frac{1}{2}+u$, $\frac{1}{2}+u$, $\frac{1}{2}+u$). For Li we have $u_1 = 0.18$ and for Nb $|u_2| = 0.02$.* The coordinates x of the oxygen atoms (0.628 Å) differs slightly from the value which would give perfect close packing (7/12 or 0.583). Consequently, the oxygen atoms are shifted slightly in the plane perpendicular to the c axis. Neither the Li nor Nb atoms are located at the centers of their oxygen octahedra.

Although the structure of $LiNbO_3$ is similar to that of ilmenite ($FeTiO_3$), the sequence of occupation of the octahedral sites in the hexagonal close-packed structure of $LiNbO_3$ is: Nb, Li, empty octahedral vacancy, Nb, Li, empty octahedral vacancy, Nb,..., while in $FeTiO_3$ the sequence is: empty octahedral vacancy, Fe, Ti, empty octahedral vacancy, Ti, Fe, empty octahedral vacancy, Fe,....

The structure of $LiNbO_3$ can be regarded as a strongly distorted perovskite lattice. We can easily show that the continuous displacement of the atoms in lithium niobate by an increase in the coordinate of the oxygen to 0.75 produces the perovskite structure. However, it is difficult to see how such relatively large displacements (the Li should shift by 1 Å along a threefold axis and the oxygen should shift by 0.6 Å) could be achieved in practice. Regarded as a distorted perovskite, $LiNbO_3$ is somewhat similar to the trigonal form of $BaTiO_3$. In this approach, a subcell of $LiNbO_3$ can be regarded as trigonal with the parameters a = 3.762 Å and $\alpha = 93°40'$. The subcell is in the form of a cube compressed along a body diagonal, while $BaTiO_3$ is a cube stretched along this diagonal.

Trigonal $LiNbO_3$ is ferroelectric. There is no published information on the other modifications of lithium niobate, although, if we consider $LiNbO_3$ to be a strongly distorted perovskite, we should expect the compound to assume an ideal perovskite structure at high temperatures. However, if it is assumed that the trigonal structure of $LiNbO_3$ ($R3c$) is solely due to the spontaneous polarization along the [111] axis, it follows from Table 7 that the

---

*The sign of u_2, relative to the sign of u_1, is not known.

TABLE 24. Coordinates of the Atoms in the
Pyrochlore Structure
Space group Fb3m, Z = 8. General formula
$A_2B_2O_6X$, where A is a large cation, B is a small
cation, X is either oxygen O, or OH, or F. Origin
of coordinates at the center of symmetry

Atom or or group of atoms	Number of atoms	Positions of atoms	Atomic coordinates†
A	16	d	1/2, 1/2, 1/2; 1/2, 1/4, 1/4; 1/4, 1/2, 1/4; 1/4, 1/4, 1/2
B	16	c	0, 0, 0; 0, 1/4, 1,2; 1/4, 0, 1/4; 1/4, 1/4, 0
X	8	b	3/8, 3/8, 3/8; 5/8, 5/8, 5/8
O	48	f	± (u, 1/8, 1/8; 1/8, u, 1/8; 1/8, 1/8, u; 1/4 − u, 1,8, 1,8; 1/8, 1/4, 1/8; 1/8, 1/8; 1/4 − u)

*The designations of the positions follow the International Tables.
† Coordinates of other atoms can be deduced from those given using the lattice translation operations: 0, 0, 0; 0, 1/2, 1/2; 1/2,
0, 1/2; 1/2, 1/2, 0. For a regular tetrahedron, we have u = 5/16.

high-temperature cubic structure of $LiNbO_3$ cannot be of the perovskite type.

Lithium tantalate ($LiTaO_3$) is isomorphous with $LiNbO_3$. The
unit cell parameters are a = 5.4703 Å, a = 56°10' (in the hexagonal
axes a_{hex} = 5.150 Å and c_{hex} = 13.744 Å). This modification of
$LiTaO_3$ is ferroelectric.

C. Ferroelectrics with the Pyrochlore Struc-
ture. Cadmium niobate ($Cd_2Nb_2O_7$) is a typical ferroelectric with
the pyrochlore-type structure. This compound has cubic symmetry at room temperature, and belongs to the space group $Fd3m$; its
unit cell parameter is a = 10.372 Å. The cell contains eight formula units. The coordinates of the atoms in the pyrochlore structure are given in Table 24.

The structure of cadmium niobate is a framework of almost
regular NbO_3 octahedra which have common vertices. The cadmium ions and the remaining oxygen ions occupy the voids between
these octahedra (Fig. 34). Each Cd atom has eight neighbors, six

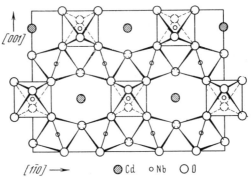

$[001]$

$[1\bar{1}0]$ →   ⊘ Cd   ∘ Nb   ◯ 0

Fig. 34. Projections of the NbO_6 octahedra in
$Cd_2Nb_2O_7$ onto the (110) plane [11].

of which are oxygen atoms located at the vertices of an octahedron
and the other two of which are nearby cadmium atoms.

The structure of pyrochlore resembles the perovskite structure. The pyrochlore lattice also consists of octahedra in which
the larger voids are occupied by atoms which are weakly bound to
the octahedra. However, the pyrochlore structure differs considerably from the perovskite lattice because the oxygen atoms in
pyrochlore are surrounded by four cadmium atoms and are not
bound to any niobium atoms. Consequently, the formula $Cd_2Nb_2O_7$
should be written in the form $Cd_2Nb_2O_6 \cdot O$ (the true structure of
pyrochlore is written in the form $CaNaNb_2O_6 \cdot F$). Moreover, the
pyrochlore structure is geometrically more complex since it contains eight formula units per unit cell (instead of one in the perovskite structure). Moreover, although the niobium atoms are located at the centers of the oxygen octahedra in the structure of
$Cd_2Nb_2O_7$, they do not lie on fourfold or twofold axes. Consequently, the symmetry axes of the octahedra are not the symmetry axes
of the structure as a whole. Therefore, we should not expect analo-
gies between the low-temperature transitions in $Cd_2Nb_2O_7$ and in
perovskites.

At −88°C, $Cd_2Nb_2O_7$ undergoes a phase transition and becomes
a ferroelectric. The structure of the low-temperature phase has
not yet been investigated in detail, but the available data indicate
that is it not cubic and there are grounds for assuming that this
phase is tetragonal (for a pure crystal, the tetragonality should be
very slight: $c/a = 1.0005$). The available data indicate that at

this transition point the Nb ions shift relative to the Cd ions and the oxygen framework remains practically undistorted. Moreover, we may also assume that the Nb ions are shifted from the centers of their oxygen octahedra along the [001] or [111] directions. In the second case, the ferroelectric phase should be trigonal. If the transition of $Cd_2Nb_2O_7$ at −88°C produces a trigonal phase, the Curie temperature of this transition is close to the temperature of the transition of $KNbO_3$ (−40°C) to the same phase. The transition of $KNbO_3$ and of other perovskite ferroelectrics to the trigonal phase is associated with the displacement of Nb from its oxygen octahedron. Suggestions have been made that the transition of $Cd_2Nb_2O_7$ to the trigonal phase takes place directly from the cubic modification, bypassing the tetrahedral and orthorhombic forms, as observed in perovskites, particularly in $KNbO_3$.

The temperature dependence of the permittivity of $Cd_2Nb_2O_7$ indicates that this ferroelectric has an additional phase transition close to 85°K. However, no structure investigations have yet been carried out at these low temperatures.

A maximum of the permittivity of $Pb_2Nb_2O_7$, which differs from $Cd_2Nb_2O_7$ by the replacement of Cd with Pb, is found near 15.4°K. However, this lead compound exhibits no ferroelectric properties. Structure investigations of $Pb_2Nb_2O_7$ show that it belongs to the pyrochlore group, but at room temperature its structure is orthorhombic. The cell parameters are a = 10.675 Å, α = 88°50'.

§4. Structure of Antiferroelectrics

A. Calcium Titanate ($CaTiO_3$). The principal elements of the structure of calcium titanate ($CaTiO_3$) resemble the structure of antiferroelectrics, although antiferroelectric properties have not yet been found for this compound. In fact, the physical properties of $CaTiO_3$ have not yet been investigated sufficiently thoroughly. This gives some justification for considering the structure of calcium titanate in the section on antiferroelectrics.

At room temperature, $CaTiO_3$ is orthorhombic and its lattice parameters are: a = 5.370 Å, b = 3.815 Å, c = 5.432 Å [13]. The space group of calcium titanate crystal is $PCmn$. Its unit cell contains four molecules. The angle between the [101] and [10$\bar{1}$] directions is 90°40'.

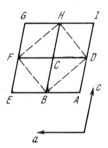

Fig. 35. Comparison of a cubic
distorted subcell and a multiple
cell of orthorhombic $CaTiO_3$.
The dashed lines indicate the correct selection of orthorhombic
cell.

Figure 35 shows the relationship between the original distorted cubic cell and the cell of $CaTiO_3$. Here, ABCD is the base
of the subcell, formed by distorting a square into a rhombus with
the obtuse angle 90°40'. The atoms in neighboring subcells are
shifted by different amounts, although they are oriented symmetrically with respect to the displacement in the ABCD subcell. Along
the b direction (perpendicular to the plane of the figure), the structure is repeated after every two subcells. The CFGH subcell is
identical with the ABCD subcell and this means that the structure,
referred to the original axes, is b-face-centered. The large cell
has two sites and these contain eight molecules. The dashed out-
line in Fig. 35 shows the correct selection of coordinates for the
orthorhombic multiple cell.

The distortion of the subcell in $CaTiO_3$ is similar to the orthorhombic distortion of the $BaTiO_3$ cell, for which a similar
change is assumed in the selected axes (see § 2 in this chapter).
However, the orthorhombic cell of $BaTiO_3$ is face-centered and
the small subcell of this compound reflects the symmetry of the
whole structure, which is obtained by the simple translation of this
cell. The orthorhombic cell of calcium titanate is primitive and
the multiple cell contains eight small subcells.

The titanium atoms in $CaTiO_3$ are located at inversion centers, while the calcium atoms and one-third of the oxygen atoms
lie on reflection planes located halfway between the titanium planes.
The positions of the calcium atoms and of one-third of the oxygen
atoms on the reflection planes are arbitrary. Each titanium atom
is at the center of an oxygen octahedron. These octahedra are
centrosymmetric but are not perfectly regular. All these octahedra are identical but neighboring octahedra are oriented in different ways. Each calcium ion is surrounded by twelve oxygen

atoms and there are grounds for assuming (on the basis of the ionic radii of Ca and O) that six of these atoms are closer to the calcium ion than the other oxygen atoms.

The naturally occurring perovskite $CaTiO_3$ is always twinned. This is regarded by mineralogists as evidence that this compound is cubic at high temperatures. This is supported also by the observation that the angle between the (101) and (10$\bar{1}$) planes decreases from 90°54' to 90°18' when the temperature is increased from 150 to 700°C. Moreover, an anomaly of the specific heat is observed at 1260°C, which may be associated with the transition of $CaTiO_3$ to the cubic form.

B. Sodium Niobate ($NaNbO_3$). Difficulties have been encountered in the structure of sodium niobate because it exists in several modifications in a relatively narrow range of temperatures. At room temperature, $NaNbO_3$ is orthorhombic with a multiple cell having the following parameters: a = 5.568 Å $\approx \sqrt{2}a_0$, b = 15.518 Å $\approx 4a_0$, c = 5.505 Å $\approx \sqrt{2}a_0$, where a_0 is the edge of a small cubic subcell [29]. The correct selection of the cell is made in the same way as in the case of $CaTiO_3$ (Fig. 35). However, in this case, the a axis is taken along the longer diagonal of the rhombic (originally cubic) subcell. The structure of $NaNbO_3$ differs considerably from that of $CaTiO_3$. Thus, for example, the unit cell of $NaNbO_3$ contains eight molecules; the angle between the directions [101] and [10$\bar{1}$] is 90°40' and the space group of sodium niobate is $P22_12$.

The structure of $NaNbO_3$ can be described best by considering layers of atoms parallel to the (010) plane. There are four such nearly planar and very similar layers, containing Nb and O_{II} ions, as well as four other layers, located between the first four and containing Na and O_I ions (Fig. 36). In this figure, the arrows indicate the directions of the displacements of the atoms during a phase transition. We note that, although according to the symmetry considerations the central atom need not shift by the same distance as the atoms located at corners, the actually observed shift is the same for all the atoms. Moreover, the displacements of the atoms in the layers shown in Figs. 36B and 36D are also equal. The displacements of the Nb atoms in the layers shown in Figs. 36C and 36E should also be equal. The positions of the O_{II} ions are not known accurately and, therefore, they are not shown in Fig. 36.

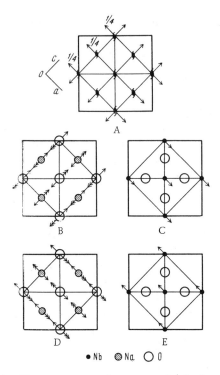

Fig. 36. Symmetry and structure of orthorhombic $NaNbO_3$ (at room temperature): A) symmetry elements of the space group; B) sections
at b = 0 (single arrows) and 1 / 2 (double arrows);
C) sections at b = 1 / 8 and 3 / 8; D) sections at
b = 1 / 4 (single arrows) and 3 / 4 (double arrows);
E) sections at b = 5 / 8 and 7 / 8.

The displacements of all the atoms from their ideal positions
(with reference to the symmetry axes) are fairly large and they
are oriented in the (010) plane. Thus, the Nb atoms are displaced
by 0.11 Å in this plane, the Na atoms by 0.15 Å, and the O atoms by
0.2 Å. The displacements of all the atoms at right angles to the
(010) plane are less than 0.05 Å.

The distortion of the structure from the original cubic shape
is fairly strong. Thus, the ratio of the axes in the distorted structure is a/b = 1.009, which indicates a stronger distortion than that
in orthorhombic $BaTiO_3$, although the shear angle of 40' is comparable with 12' in the case of barium titanate. The displacements of
individual atoms in $NaNbO_3$ are also greater than those in $BaTiO_3$.

Investigations of the structure of NaNbO$_3$ show (Fig. 37)* that it undergoes a phase transition at 360°C (± 15°C) which does not alter the symmetry or the structure, but c/a becomes 1.0023, so that the cell approaches the pseudotetragonal form. The value of this ratio increases when the temperature is increased (above 375°C).

At temperatures over 430°C, the x-ray diffraction data indicate that NaNbO$_3$ has the ideal cubic lattice. However, optical investigations show that additional phase transitions occur at temperatures of 450–470, 518, and 640°C. All the observations indicate that NaNbO$_3$ is definitely cubic above 640°C. Optical data show that sodium niobate is tetragonal (or very close to tetragonal) in the temperature range 640–518°C. In this temperature range, the optical (refraction) indicatrix is close to an ellipsoid of revolution. The short axis of the indicatrix coincides with the pseudotetragonal axis. At 518°C the direction of the pseudotetragonal axis changes: below 518°C it coincides with the c axis of the unit cell but above 518°C it coincides with the a axis.

The optical properties of the orthorhombic modification of NaNbO$_3$ are similar to those of the orthorhombic form of BaTiO$_3$.

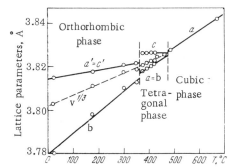

Fig. 37. Temperature dependences of the lattice parameters of NaNbO$_3$ and of the unit-cell volume. The starting point is the original cubic cell (the data are taken from [25]).

_____

*The data on the structure of NaNbO$_3$ given in Fig. 37 are not in full agreement with other information reported in the present book. The extensive data on this structure and certain contradictions between the results deduced from the structure and optical investigations make it difficult to draw final conclusions about the structure of sodium niobate.

Both crystals are optically negative. The short axis of the indicatrix lies along the long diagonal of the rhombus and the long axis is perpendicular to the rhombus. At 0°C, the birefringence of $NaNbO_3$ is somewhat higher than that of $BaTiO_3$. The short axis of the indicatrix of $NaNbO_3$, $BaTiO_3$, and $PbZrO_3$ (discussed in the next subsection) is oriented along the direction of the displacement of the small cations, although there is no definite correlation between the magnitude of this displacement and the birefringence of crystals.

The crystal structure and the optical investigations suggest that the displacement of the Nb ions, relative to the oxygen lattice, disappears in a transition near 450-470°C. Below this temperature, these displacements are possible. If this conclusion is correct, it follows that the NbO_6 octahedra are centrosymmetric above 470°C, but that they may be inclined with respect to one another in the (100) and (010) planes. Consequently, the transitions at 518 and 640°C can be regarded as transitions which destroy these inclinations in two steps.

Structure investigations show that during cooling a phase transition also occurs in $NaNbO_3$ at −200°C. This transition shows a very strong thermal hysteresis: during heating, the same transition occurs at −10°C. The low-temperature modification is monoclinic and the cell parameters (measured at −160°C during a heating cycle) are: a = 5.564 Å, b = 5.548 Å, c = 2 × 3.906 Å, β = 91°09'. In this connection, it is worth mentioning that the usual dielectric hysteresis loops, indicating ferroelectric properties, are observed in strong electric fields applied along the b axis at low temperatures (between −120 and −55°C). These loops may be observed also in weak fields, but the temperature must be lowered.

C. Lead Zirconate and Hafnate ($PbZrO_3$ and $PbHfO_3$). Powder x-ray diffraction patterns suggest that, at room temperature, $PbZrO_3$ is tetragonal and has a multiple cell with the subcell dimensions: a = 4.150 Å, c = 4.099 Å, c/a = 0.988. However, the results obtained for single crystals show that $PbZrO_3$ is orthorhombic, the cell parameters are approximately $\sqrt{2}a_0$, 2 × $\sqrt{2}a_0$, and $2a_0$ (where a_0 is the edge of the original cubic cell), and has the space symmetry group *Pbam* [21]. The multiple cell contains eight molecules (formula units). An antiparallel displacement of the atoms along the a axis (which is assumed to be parallel to the face diagonal of the subcell), amounting to about 0.2 Å, is observed in this structure.

More detailed x-ray and neutron diffraction investigations [10] show that although the Pb and Zr ions are displaced only in the (ab) plane, the oxygen ions are displaced also along the c axis. These displacements are not compensated and, consequently, the space group of the crystal is of the polar type $Pba2$ (point group 2·m). According to a discussion of the structure of ferroelectrics given in §1 of the present chapter, $PbZrO_3$ should be ferroelectric because it has a polar symmetry group. We must add that piezo-electric properties have been found experimentally in lead zirconate along the c axis.

Optical investigations of $PbZrO_3$ show that it is optically negative at room temperature. The shortest axis of the optical (refraction) indicatrix coincides with the a axis of the cell and the longest axis coincides with the b axis. The birefringence of $PbZrO_3$ is much weaker than that of $NaNbO_3$ or of the orthorhombic form of $BaTiO_3$. The largest value of the refractive index is about 2.2.

$PbZrO_3$ undergoes a phase transition at about 230°C and above this temperature it becomes cubic. The temperature dependences of the subcell parameters are shown in Fig. 38.

Lead hafnate ($PbHfO_3$) is isomorphous with lead zirconate. However, its unit cell is somewhat smaller than that of $PbZrO_3$ because hafnium ions are smaller than zirconium ions. The subcell has the following parameters: a = 4.136 Å, c = 4.099 Å, c/a =

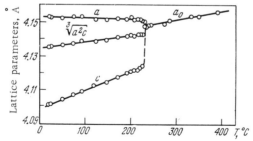

Fig. 38. Temperature dependences of the unit-cell parameters of $PbZrO_3$. The starting point is the original cubic cell (the data are taken from [20]).

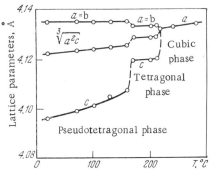

Fig. 39. Temperature dependences of the unit-cell parameters of PbHfO₃. The starting point is the original cubic lattice (the data are taken from [26]).

0.991. The multiple-cell structure lines in the x-ray diffraction patterns are of similar intensities as the analogous lines in the diffraction patterns of $PbZrO_3$.

$PbHfO_3$ undergoes two phase transitions at 163 and 215°C. Above 215°C, it has the perovskite structure and its unit cell is ideal cubic. The intermediate modification (which exists between 163 and 215°C) has a multiple cell and is tetragonal; the subcell axial ratio c/a is 0.997, and the positions of the multiple-cell structure lines in the x-ray diffraction patterns are different from the room-temperature positions. The temperature dependences of the lattice parameters are given in Fig. 39.

D. Tungsten Trioxide (WO_3). At room temperature, tungsten trioxide (WO_3) has a pseudo-orthorhombic unit multiple cell whose dimensions are approximately $2a_0$, $2a_0$, and a_0 (a_0 is the edge of a cubic subcell). Early investigators assumed that the structure of WO_3 was triclinic, but it was later regarded as monoclinic with the cell parameters: $a = 7.274$ Å, $b = 7.501$ Å, $c = 3.824$ Å, $\beta = 89°56'$ [28]. Each unit cell contains four molecules and the space group is $P2_1/a$.

The structure has an inversion center, which can be used as a reference point in the measurement of atomic displacements. The displacements of the tungsten ions are antiparallel with respect to the center of inversion: they lie almost exactly in the (010) plane and are directed along the two face diagonals of the subcell. The displacements are 0.2-0.3 Å, i.e., they are considerably larger than the displacements of the Ti ions in $BaTiO_3$ and comparable with the displacements of the Nb ions in $NaNbO_3$. The oxy-

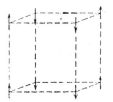

Fig. 40. Schematic representation of the displacements of W ions in the tetragonal (700-900°C) modification of WO_3 [12].

gen octahedra are distorted: the W—O distances along the +c and −c axes are substantially different (2.11 and 1.71 Å, respectively), but they differ less along the a and b axes (1.83 and 1.87 Å, respectively). Crystals of tungsten trioxide are usually twinned along the (110) plane.

Above 740°C, tungsten trioxide is tetragonal and the lattice parameters are: a = $\sqrt{2}a_0$ = 5.272 Å, c ≈ 3.920 Å. The space group is $P4/nmm$, and each unit cell contains two molecules. All the atoms are located at special positions along fourfold or twofold axes. The tungsten ions are displaced along the c axis from the symmetrical positions which they would occupy in a perfect lattice. The displacements are of the same magnitude as in $PbTiO_3$ and it may be assumed that they are antiparallel, as shown in Fig. 40 [12].

Studies of the thermal expansion have indicated phase transition of WO_3 at 900°C, which takes place without any change in the structure. A transition at −50°C results in an increase in the symmetry compared with that at room temperature. This low-temperature modification is ferroelectric.

§5. Dipole Arrays, Mechanism of Structure Changes, and Chemical Bonding in Oxygen-Octahedral Ferroelectrics and Antiferroelectrics

The most typical common properties of the ferroelectrics and antiferroelectrics described in §§ 3 and 4 of the present chapter are, first, an oxygen octahedron enclosing a small-radius ion, which is the basic element of the crystal structure; and, secondly, a high-temperature cubic structure of all these materials (practically without exception) as well as phase transitions at low temperatures. The second property allows us to regard the structure changes in these ferroelectrics and antiferroelectrics as processes involving small distortions of the cubic structure. Thus, the general theory of changes in the structure at ferroelectric phase transitions (§ 1 of the present chapter) can be easily applied to these ferroelectric and antiferroelectric materials because the symmetry of the high-temperature phase is almost always known.

A. Changes in the Point and Space Symmetries of Ferroelectrics. First of all, we note that ferroelectric phase transitions in oxygen-octahedral materials are associated with small distortions of the original cell (there is reliable evidence that, in most cases, the original cell is cubic). Moreover, the same cubic cell is the basis of the new cell after distortion. The essence of this distortion is that it changes the symmetry from nonpolar to polar, i.e., a spontaneous polarization P_s can appear in the distorted structure. An array of parallel cells forms a spontaneous polarization region known as a domain. Thus, after undergoing a ferroelectric phase transition, a crystal of this type consists of domains oriented along various directions. The dipole arrays in ferroelectric domains, which are chains of parallel dipoles directed in the same way, are very simple (Fig. 27). It is not difficult to determine the dipole arrays of unit cells in ferroelectrics, but it is not easy to determine the actual orientation of the domains (§ 1 in the present chapter and Chap. IV).

Possible changes of the structure in ferroelectrics can be determined and predicted quite easily. These changes are governed solely by the symmetry of the high-temperature phase and by the direction of the resultant spontaneous polarization (Tables 7-11). Moreover, we can easily analyze the transitions from one ferroelectric phase to another. Such transitions are considered simply as transitions involving the "return" of a crystal to the high-temperature structure and the subsequent appearance of the polarization along a new direction (Table 13 and § 1 in the present chapter).

All known changes in the symmetry which occur at phase transitions in $BaTiO_3$ and $KNbO_3$ ($\bar{6}/4 \rightarrow 4 \cdot m$, $2 \cdot m$, $3 \cdot m$), and at a phase transition in $PbTiO_3$ ($\bar{6}/4 \rightarrow 4 \cdot m$) follow from Tables 7-11. Changes in the space symmetry of these crystals ($Pm3m \rightarrow P4mm$, Amm, $R3m$) follow from Table 13.

Tables 7-17 can be useful also in further studies of these ferroelectric structures. Thus, only the space group of the tri-

gonal modification $R3c$ is known for the pseudo-ilmenite ferroelectrics ($LiNbO_3$, $LiTaO_3$). Using Table 13 we can easily show
that, if this modification is obtained by the distortion of the cubic
cell solely because of the appearance of the spontaneous polarization, the space groups of the high-temperature cubic cell can
be $Pm3n$, $Pn3n$, $Fm3c$, $Fd3c$, $Ia3d$, $I\bar{4}3d$, $F\bar{4}3c$ and $P\bar{4}3n$. It is interesting to note that this list does not include the perovskite group
($Pm3m$). This makes it unlikely that the pseudo-ilmenite structure
of $LiNbO_3$ can be regarded as a distorted perovskite (this has been
suggested in §3 of the present chapter on the basis of structure investigations).

Cadmium niobate ($Cd_2Nb_3O_7$) has the pyrochlore structure;
its space-symmetry group at room temperature is $Fd3m$. It is evident from Table 13 that if the transition of $Cd_2Nb_2O_7$ at $-88°C$ is
due to the appearance of the spontaneous polarization along the
[100] direction of the original cubic lattice, the space group of the
resultant tetragonal modification is $I4md$; however, if this transition is due to the appearance of the spontaneous polarization along
the [111] direction, the space group of the resultant trigonal modification is $R3m$ (the trigonal group of $BaTiO_3$).

B. Changes in the Symmetry and Dipole Arrays in Antiferroelectrics. Changes in the symmetry and
structure of antiferroelectrics are somewhat more complex. We have
mentioned at the beginning of the present chapter that the principal
indication of the antiferroelectric ordering is the presence of multiple-cell structure in a crystal. Each subcell (formerly a unit
cell of the high-temperature — usually cubic — paraelectric phase)
of a new multiple-cell antiferroelectric cell is spontaneously polarized. An assembly of polarized subcells forms a nonpolar multiple cell. We shall describe the dipole arrays of multiple cells
of some antiferroelectrics of the oxygen-octahedral type.

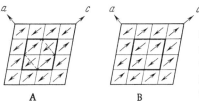

Fig. 41. Dipole array in the structure of orthorhombic $CaTiO_3$: A) first layer; B) second layer. The heavy lines show the multiple cell and the dashed lines indicate the
correct selection of the orthorhombic cell.

Figure 41 shows the dipole array in the multiple cell of $CaTiO_3$, which satisfies the experimentally established structure and symmetry of this compound (§4A) in the orthorhombic modification. It is evident from Fig. 41 that the multiple cell consists of subcells (which have become polar after the transition), having only two antiparallel directions of dipoles out of 12 possible equivalent directions in the original cubic cell. A layer of cells lying below the layer shown in Fig. 41A (along the b direction) consists of cells in which the direction of polarization is opposite to the direction in the cells of the upper layer (Fig. 41B). The multiple cell consists of eight subcells, each of which has the symmetry 2·m. The symmetry of $CaTiO_3$ in the antiferroelectric modification is m·2:m. The multiple cell does not have all the equivalent orientations of P_S in the subcells and is therefore not the general but a special unit cell of trigonal $CaTiO_3$, corresponding to one type of domain in this compound (the domains in antiferroelectrics are discussed in Chap. IV). Figure 41 shows also the correct selection of the new orthorhombic cell containing four molecules of $CaTiO_3$.

It is evident from Fig. 41 that orthorhombic $CaTiO_3$ can be represented by an array of polar subcells, in full agreement with the experimentally determined structure and symmetry of this compound. Hence, we may conclude that the subcells in orthorhombic $CaTiO_3$ are polarized although the Ti ions are not displaced from the centers of the oxygen octahedra (this has been discussed in §4A). On the other hand, this provides an additional reason why $CaTiO_3$ should be classified as an antiferroelectric and why a search should be made for antiferroelectric properties.

Figure 42 shows the dipole array of the multiple cell of $NaNbO_3$, which is also in agreement with the experimentally established symmetry and structure of the orthorhombic modification of this compound. The multiple cell of orthorhombic $NaNbO_3$ consists of 16 subcells. The point symmetry group of the antiferroelectric modification is 2:2. The correctly selected orthorhombic cell consists of eight molecules.

The dipole array of sodium niobate is a four-layer structure and consists of subcells of symmetry 2. Each layer contains only left-handed or right-handed modifications of the cell. Thus, if the first and third layers are right-handed, the second and fourth layers should be left-handed. A left-handed layer, with the opposite

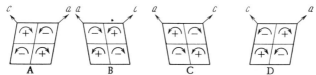

Fig. 42. Dipole array in the orthorhombic multiple cell of NaNbO₃:
A-D) successive layers of cells along the b axis.

orientation of dipoles, lies below a right-handed layer. This, together with the antiparallel orientation of the dipoles, gives rise
to four different layers (and cells) lying above one another along
the b axis. The directions of the unit dipoles in Fig. 42 are denoted by + or − and the sign of the enantiomorphism is given by
the direction of the semicircular arrows. To determine the sign
of enantiomorphism, it is necessary to establish, for all subcells,
the directions of rotation of these semicircular arrows by viewing them from the same (for example, positive) end of a dipole.

   Figure 42 shows the orientation of dipoles in one of the domains of the orthorhombic modification. The direction of polarization in any other domain is described by indices of the [100] type.

   We have mentioned, in connection with the description of the
room-temperature orthorhombic structure of NaNbO₃, that the principal displacements of ions at a phase transition take place in the
ac plane. Experiments show that the displacements of ions along
the b axis are less than 0.05 Å. However, the present discussion
shows that these are the displacements which are responsible for
the spontaneous polarization of the subcells. It is evident that the
spontaneous polarization of the subcells produces an orthorhombic distortion which causes the displacement of ions in the (010)
plane.

   We know that a strong field, applied along the b axis of orthorhombic NaNbO₃, may polarize this compound at low temperatures
and give rise to the ferroelectric rather than the antiferroelectric
state. The model shown in Fig. 42 does not contradict this observation.

   The b axis is the preferred direction along which the spontaneous polarization is oriented. If the energies corresponding
to the orientation of dipoles shown in Fig. 42 and the orientation
of all the dipoles along the same direction are not very different,

we find that the dipoles oriented by a strong field along the same
direction still behave in the same way as the dipoles in ferroelectric domains. We note that the reorientation of the dipoles in
the subcells does not alter the sign of the enantiomorphism.

Assuming that the orthorhombic subcell has the symmetry 2
and the new orthorhombic cell has the symmetry 2:2, we can draw
some conclusions about the structure and symmetry of $NaNbO_3$
above the phase transition at 360°C, where $NaNbO_3$ still remains
orthorhombic. (According to some investigators the structure is
close to tetragonal.) It can be easily seen from Table 11 that,
when the spontaneous polarization appears in an orthorhombic
crystal, group 2 can be obtained only if the crystal has the symmetry group 2:2 before the transition. This group should be exhibited by a nearly cubic subcell. The full structure should contain both right- and left-handed cells whose symmetry is 2:2, while
the multiple cell above 360°C may have a higher symmetry, for
example, m·2:m. The room-temperature orthorhombic modification of $NaNbO_3$ may then have a structure consisting of one pair
of three possible (but not equivalent) antiparallel orientations of
the P_s vectors. We must point out that at room temperature other
orientations are impossible.

The occurrence of several phase transitions in $NaNbO_3$ above
360°C can be used to draw other conclusions. We may assume that
one of the high-temperature forms (it need not exist in the temperature range immediately above 360°C) has small cells with the
symmetry 2:2. A series of transitions (not only the transition
at 360°C) can then be regarded as transitions caused by the appearance of the spontaneous polarization along each pair of the
equivalent directions coinciding with different twofold axes. Transitions at higher temperatures (518 and 640°C) in $NaNbO_3$ are evidently not associated with the appearance (or change of the direction) of the spontaneous polarization but they represent a gradual
increase of the symmetry of this compound right up to the cubic
form.

Figure 43 shows the dipole array of the multiple cell of orthorhombic $PbZrO_3$, which is in agreement with the *Pbam* space symmetry group of this compound. Figure 43 shows the orientation
of dipoles in a layer perpendicular to the c axis. In contrast to
$CaTiO_3$ (Fig. 41), the antiparallel orientation of the dipoles along

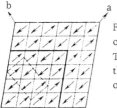

Fig. 43. Dipole array in the multiple cell of orthorhombic PbZrO₃ (point group m·2:m). The heavy lines show the multiple cell and the dashed lines indicate the correct selection of the new orthorhombic cell.

the a and b directions of the original cubic subcell of PbZrO₃ is not exhibited by neighboring cells but by neighboring pairs of cells. It is evident from Fig. 43 that the multiple cell consists of 32 sub-cells, and the new orthorhombic cell contains eight molecules of PbZrO₃. The point-symmetry group of the crystal after the transition is m·2:m.

In §4 of the present chapter, we have pointed out that ortho-rhombic PbZrO₃ can also have the space group *Pba*. The point group corresponding to this space group is 2·m. If PbZrO₃ can be described by this symmetry group, it follows that its multiple cell should consist of uncompensated dipoles, i.e., it should be ferro-electric. The piezoelectric effect, which has been found by some investigators, can occur in this structure.

The structure of WO₃ is relatively simple and has been in-vestigated quite thoroughly. Figure 44A shows the dipole array of orthorhombic tungsten trioxide (at room temperature), correspond-ing to the experimentally established structure and symmetry of

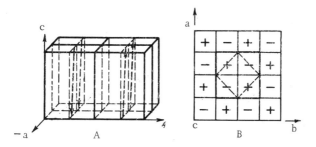

Fig. 44. Dipole array in the multiple cells of the orthorhombic (A) and tetragonal (B) modifications of WO₃. The multiple cell of the orthorhombic modification is identical with the unit cell. The unit cell of the tetragonal modification is shown dashed and heavy lines are used for the multiple cell.

this compound. The multiple cell consists of four subcells, each
of which is of symmetry m. The same multiple cell is the unit
cell of the orthorhombic modification. The symmetry of the antiferroelectric modification is 2:m. In this case, the dipole moments
lie in the ac plane and the direction of polarization in the subcells
lies in a symmetry plane but does not coincide with any of the symmetry axes of the high-temperature cubic phase that exists above
900°C.

The WO_3 has the tetragonal structure at temperatures above
740°C. The dipole array of this modification is shown in Fig. 44B.
The multiple cell consists of four subcells and the correctly selected tetragonal cell consists of two subcells. The simplicity of
the orientation of dipoles in this modification does not require
further comment.

We must point out that the two multiple-cell modifications of
WO_3 can be regarded as a result of the successive appearance of
the polarization in the cubic sublattice of symmetry $\bar{6}/4$ – first
along the [100] axis and then along the [h0l] direction, which is an
arbitrarily oriented direction in a plane perpendicular to the b axis.

C. Relationship between Structure Distortions
and the Polarization of Ferroelectrics and Antiferroelectrics. The formal relationship between the structure distortions and the polarization of ferroelectrics of all types
(perovskite, pseudo-ilmenite, and pyrochlore) can be established
relatively easily. All these structures become polar at the ferroelectric phase transition. The polarity appears because of the noncentrosymmetric displacement of the ions* which gives rise to
electric dipole moments, i.e., it produces a spontaneous polarization P_s. The direction of the resultant polarization of ferroelectrics coincides with the direction of the displacements of the ions.

The relative simplicity of the structures allows us to consider a large number of cases of displacements of various atoms and
to relate these displacements to the nature of the resultant polarization. Before we consider this point, we must point out that, in
general, all the atoms in a given structure are responsible for the
polarization since (strictly speaking) they are all displaced at a

---

*All the compounds discussed in the present chapter can be regarded as at least partly
ionic (this point is discussed later in the present section).

phase transition: the dipole moment is the result of the summation of the electric moments of all the charges (Chap. VII). Nevertheless, in some structures, we may find that the displacement of a given type of atom is stronger. This allows us to say that the polarization is due to that particular atom. In this connection, we must mention that the first qualitative explanation of the polarization of $BaTiO_3$, whose ferroelectricity is attributed to the displacement of a small titanium ion from the center of the large octahedron formed by the surrounding six oxygen ions, is still attractive because of its simplicity and clarity.

In an analysis of the displacements of the ions in a structure, we must pay special attention to the packing of these ions. In the perovskite ferroelectrics and antiferroelectrics, the packing is described by the parameter t:

$$t = \frac{r_A - r_B}{\sqrt{2}(r_B + r_0)} ,$$

where r_A, r_B, r_O are the radii of the A, B, and O ions in the structure of ABO_3. The parameter t determines the contacts of A and B ions with O ions: $t = 1$ corresponds to the close packing of the ions; $t > 1$ corresponds to the loose packing of the B cations, and $t < 1$ corresponds to the loose packing of the A cations. An analysis of the crystal structure by means of this formula shows that, in the perovskite compounds, the values $t > 1$ and $t \approx 1$ correspond to ferroelectric structures and the value $t < 1$ corresponds to antiferroelectric configurations. Venevtsev and Zhdanov [1] used this analysis as the basis of their crystallochemical classification of perovskites undergoing ferroelectric transitions (Table 25). According to the theory of Venevtsev and Zhdanov, the ferroelectric polarization is due to the fact that the A or B cations are loosely packed in the structure, while the antiferroelectric polarization is due to the fact that the A cations are loosely packed. Even if this is correct, it is difficult to see the origin of the relationship between the nature of the packing of cations and the type of polarization; and it does not follow at all that if a given cation is loosely packed ("free") it must undergo a displacement and give rise to the ferroelectric polarization. Moreover, the relationship is not unique: a loose packing of the A and B cations gives rise to ferroelectricity.

TABLE 25. Crystallochemical Classification of Perovskite
Compounds Exhibiting Ferroelectric Transitions [1]

ABO_3 crystal	t	Most displaced cation	Type of polarization
$BaTiO_3$	1.0_3	} B	
$KNbO_3$	1.0_5		
$KTaO_3$	1.0_0	} A	} ferroelectric
$PbTiO_3$	0.9_8		
$SrTiO_3$ *	0.9_6		
$PbHfO_3$	0.9_2	} A	} antiferroelectric
$PbZrO_3$	0.9_0		
$CaTiO_3$	0.8_9		
$CdTiO_3$ **	0.8_7		
$NaNbO_3$	0.8_6		
$NaTaO_3$	0.8_6		

* Induced ferroelectric in an electric field.
† According to other workers, this compound is ferroelectric.

The nature of the distortions (but not the type of polarization)
in the case of loose packing of a given cation can sometimes be
understood quite easily. We must point out that the ferroelectrics
and antiferroelectrics considered in the present chapter have basic
structure elements in the form of oxygen octahedra which form the
framework of the structure. If a cation of type A is "free," we
find that the oxygen octahedra can easily rotate (even without suf-
fering distortion) so that the oxygen atoms make contact with the
A cations (crumpled structures, Fig. 45). Such a rotation can give

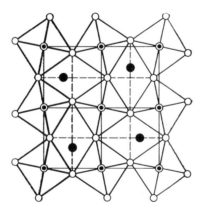

Fig. 45. Projection of an imaginary
structure showing the displacements of
the A ions (black dots) and the tilts of
the BO_6 octahedra in one plane [18].

rise to electric moments in unit cells but the rotation can also easily produce a multiple cell which compensates the dipoles. It is this sort of structure that occurs in antiferroelectrics. However, the crumpling of the structure does not necessarily follow from the "freedom" of the A cations: a change in the structure may be such that it gives rise to the parallel polarization of neighboring cells. An example of such a change is $PbTiO_3$, in which the Pb cations are "free" but the compound is ferroelectric. All that we can say is that if a structure can suffer crumpling, then multiple-cell dipole arrays may be formed in it.

If only the B cations are "free," the nature of the distortion occurring when these cations are displaced from the centers of the octahedra can be understood easily: they are deformations of the octahedra without rotation. In $BaTiO_3$ and $KNbO_3$ such displacements give rise to ferroelectric structures (Fig. 46a), whereas in WO_3 the displacement of W in the tetragonal modification (Figs. 40 and 46b) gives rise to an antiferroelectric structure. The following sequence of modifications is usually observed in ferroelectrics when the temperature is lowered: cubic, tetragonal, orthorhombic, and trigonal. This is due to an increase in the stability of the structure when a small cation, located in an oxygen octahedron, "sticks" successively to one, two, and three oxygen ions.

Comparison of the displacements of ions with the directions of polarization in antiferroelectrics is not as simple as in the ferroelectric case. Firstly, it is not self-evident that an oxygen octahedron forms a dipole moment in conjunction with a central cation. Moreever, in some antiferroelectrics ($CaTiO_3$ and $PbZrO_3$) the central ion is not displaced from the center of the octahedron when the compound undergoes a phase transition to the antiferroelectric modification. It appears that the rotation of oxygen octahedra

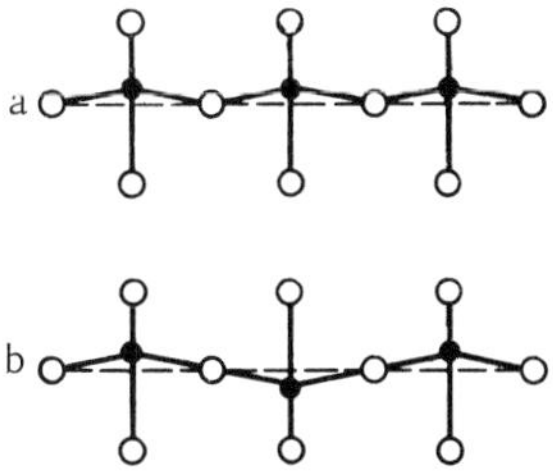

Fig. 46. Section through lines of octahedra with parallel (a) and antiparallel (b) displacements of the central atom.

("crumpling"), so that they come in contact with small A ions, is
the most important mechanism of structure deformation in antiferroelectrics. The displacement of the centers of gravity of the A
and B cations with respect to the centers of gravity of the oxygen
octahedra gives rise to an overall dipole moment. This provides
some justification for the conclusion that the state of polarization
in antiferroelectric structures is governed by the mobility (freedom) of the A cations.

Comparing the dipole arrays of antiferroelectrics (Figs. 41-
44) with the displacements of ions, we find that the principal displacements usually coincide with the directions of the dipoles.
Thus, the orientation of the dipoles in $PbZrO_3$ coincides with the
displacements of the Pb ions, and the orientation of the dipoles in
tetragonal tungsten trioxide coincides with the direction of displacement of the W ions. This relationship is far less clear in
other structures. Thus, it is reported that the Ca ions and one-
third of the O ions in $CaTiO_3$ are displaced in the (010) plane but
that the directions of these displacements are arbitrary, while the
orientation of the dipoles can have only one direction along the c
axis (Fig. 41). It has been mentioned that the orientation of the
dipoles in $NaNbO_3$ coincides with the direction of the smallest displacements of ions. In the monoclinic modification of WO_3, the
largest displacements are observed along the c axis, while the
electric dipoles lie in a plane perpendicular to this axis, and so on.
These observations stress that the polarization is influenced by all
ions in the structure and only a precise knowledge of the displacements of all the ions can give a reliable relationship between the
displacement and the polarization.

D. Some Problems of Chemical Bonding. So far,
we have regarded all the ferroelectrics and antiferroelectrics described in the present chapter as ionic compounds. Detailed studies
of the structure and properties of these compounds show that they
are indeed (at least in some modifications) either wholly or mainly ionic. Nevertheless, purely ionic bonds are not directional and,
therefore, we cannot explain the directed displacements of the
atoms at ferroelectric and antiferroelectric phase transitions in
ionic crystals. In view of this, some authors (H. D. Megaw, I. N.
Belyaev, G. A. Smolenskii) have suggested that covalent bonds play
an important role in these compounds. Moreover, in some cases,
covalent-type bonding is observed not only in the polar forms but

also in the high-temperature cubic modifications of the oxygen-octahedral ferroelectrics and antiferroelectrics. The phase transition to the polar state in such substances is then treated as a change of the degree of covalence.

No objection can be raised against the self-evident importance of covalent bonds in the polar modifications of ferroelectrics and antiferroelectrics. However, even simple considerations of the symmetry show that dipole moments cannot exist (in a unit cell, in general, and in an oxygen octahedron containing a cation, in particular) in at least two cubic centrosymmetric classes: $\bar{6}/4$ and $\bar{6}/2$. Nevertheless, the high-temperature structures of the majority (if not all) of the oxygen-octahedral ferroelectrics and antiferroelectrics belong to the $\bar{6}/4$ cubic class. Thus, covalent bonds cannot exist in the cubic modifications of these compounds.

The fact that covalent bonds cannot exist in the cubic modification does not mean that these compounds are purely ionic. In fact, these compounds can easily exhibit a centrosymmetric redistribution of the density of valence electron clouds, which gives rise to some degree of ionicity. On this basis, a transition to the polarized state should be regarded as the result of a basic change in chemical bonding representing the appearance of some degree of covalence. Calculations of the internal electric fields show that the new modification is not fully covalent and that it retains some measure of ionicity.

Experimental confirmation of these conclusions is provided by the quadrupole splitting of the nuclear magnetic resonance and simple quadrupole resonance lines of Nb^{93} in $KNbO_3$ crystals (§3).

The angle of the oxygen−central cation−oxygen bond is of importance in discussions of covalent bonds in the oxygen-octahedral ferroelectrics. In purely covalent oxygen compounds this angle should be 109°. Thus, a departure from the 180° angle is likely to enhance rather than reduce the stability of an oxide. Distortions involving a departure from the 180° bond angle, which is typical of ionic compounds, are observed in all ferroelectrics (Fig. 46a). In tetragonal WO_3 (Fig. 46b), this angle remains 180° and the structure is antiferroelectric. Following Megaw, we may assume that the general relationship between the energies governing the freedom of rotation of the oxygen octahedra (packing distortion), on the one hand, and the possibility that the angle of the oxygen−central cation—oxygen bond is not equal to 180°, on the other, determines the ferroelectric or antiferroelectric polarization of each specific structure.

In stressing the importance of covalent bonds, we must point out that a noncentrosymmetric position of the central ion in the oxygen octahedron is typical of Nb^{5+} and Ta^{5+} ($KNbO_3$, $NaNbO_3$, $Cd_2Nb_2O_7$, $NaTaO_3$, and $LiTaO_3$). These examples show that the nature of the central ion governs many properties of the structures of various compounds. Thus, for example, the temperatures of the cubic—tetragonal phase transitions of $NaNbO_3$, $KNbO_3$, and $Cd_2Nb_2O_7$ lie within the range 400-450°C, the tetragonal—orthorhombic transition temperatures lie within the range 250-300°C, and the transitions to the trigonal modification occur near −70°C.

The behavior of Ti^{4+} is not as definite. In $SrTiO_3$ and $CaTiO_3$, this ion still remains at the center of the oxygen octahedron. However, the temperature of the phase transition of $PbTiO_3$ to the tetragonal modification (~ 500°C) is much higher than the temperature of the corresponding transition of $BaTiO_3$ (120°C), which is due to the strong polarization typical of Pb ions.

This discussion shows that the ability of a given atom to form polar structures in the oxygen-octahedral ferroelectrics depends on its electron configuration. In particular, the d-electrons play an important role in the formation of covalent bonds.

An analysis of the oxygen-octahedral ferroelectrics and antiferroelectris shows that they all contain relatively small cations at the centers of the oxygen octahedra and that these cations have the electron configurations of inert gases after the removal of the s- and d-electrons (ions of this type are formed from atoms with partly filled penultimate shells).

Table 26 lists cations with the electron structure of the inert gas atoms (and hydrogen ions), together with the ionic radii for the coordination number of six. The "framed" ions are those whose electron structure is of the inert-gas type after the removal of the s- and d-electrons. Bold symbols are used to indicate the central ions in the ferroelectrics and antiferroelectrics known at present. The results in Table 26 are of definite interest, although the validity of the hypothesis that all ions with the inert-gas elec-

TABLE 26. Cations with Inert-Gas Electron Structure and Their Ionic Radii (in Å) [3]

Period	Group						
	I	II	III	IV	V	VI	VII
	Valence						
	+1	+2	+3	+4	+5	+6	+7
1	(H)						
2	Li 0.78	Be 0.31	B 0.20				
3	Na 0.98	Mg 0.76	Al 0.57	Si 0.39			
4	K 1.33	Ca 1.06	Sc 0.83	Ti 0.64	V 0.4	Cr 0.3—0.4	Mn 0.46
5	Rb 1.49	Sr 1.27	Y 1.06	Zr 0.77	Nb 0.69	Mo 0.62	Te 0.56
6	Cs 1.65	Ba 1.43	La 1.22	Hf 0.84	Ta 0.68	W 0.62	Re
7	Fr	Ra 1.52	Ac	Th 1.20	Pa	U	

Lanthanides (3+)

Ce	Pr	Nd	Pm Sm	Eu	Gd	Tb	Dy	Ho	Er	Tm	Yb	Lu
1.18	1.16	1.15	1.13	1.13	1.11	1.10	1.05	1.05	1.04	1.04	1.00	0.99

tron structure should form ferroelectrics has not yet been proved and some ferroelectrics (in particular, compounds of Pb with Sn ions at the centers of the oxygen octahedra) contain ions which are not given in this table. Moreover, x-ray diffraction data indicate that, in these compounds, ions at the centers of the octahedra are in a different state of ionization from that assumed in our discussion.

Our analysis of the ferroelectric and antiferroelectric properties of the oxygen-octahedral compounds has been concentrated mainly on the problem of how to explain the changes in the structure associated with the appearance of the electric polarization. The problem why the particular changes take place in these structures can be solved only by taking into account the temperature dependence of all the forces acting in a crystal and the dynamics of the crystal lattice (Chap. VI).

References

1. Yu. N. Venevtsev and G. S. Zhdanov, Izv. Akad. Nauk SSSR, Ser. Fiz., 20:178 (1956).
2a. I. S. Zheludev and L. A. Shuvalov, Kristallografiya, 1:681 (1956).
2b. I. S. Zheludev and L. A. Shuvalov, Izd. Akad. Nauk SSSR, Ser. Fiz., 21:264 (1957).
3. G. A. Smolenskii and N. Ts. Kozhevnikova, Dokl. Akad. Nauk SSSR, 76:513 (1951).
4. A. S. Sonin and I. S. Zheludev, Kristallografiya, 4:487 (1959).
5. A. F. Yatsenko, Izv. Akad. Nauk SSSR, Ser. Fiz., 22:1456 (1958).
6. P. C. Bailey, Thesis, Bristol University (1952).
7. R. N. Cotts and W. D. Knight, Phys. Rev., 96:1285 (1954).
8. B. C. Frazer, H. R. Danner, and R. Pepinsky, Phys. Rev., 100:745 (1955).
9a. A. W. Hornig, R. C. Rempel, and H. E. Weaver, Phys. Rev. Letters, 1:284 (1958).
9b. A. W. Hornig, R. C. Rempel, and H. E. Weaver, J. Phys. Chem. Solids, 10:1 (1959).
10. F. Jona, G. Shirane, F. Mazzi, and R. R. Pepinsky, Phys. Rev. 105:849 (1957).
11. F. Jona, G. Shirane, and R. Pepinsky, Phys. Rev., 98:903 (1955).
12. W. L. Kehl, R. C. Hay, and D. J. Wahl, J. Appl. Phys., 23:212 (1952).
13. H. F. Kay and P. C. Bailey, Acta Cryst., 10:219 (1957).
14. H. F. Kay and P. Vousden, Phil. Mag., 40:1019 (1949).
15. J. T. Last, Phys. Rev., 105:1740 (1957).
16. W. Low and D. Shaltiel, Phys. Rev. Letters, 1:51 (1958).
17. R. T. Mara, G. B. B. M. Sutherland, and H. V. Tyrell, Phys. Rev., 96:801 (1954).
18. H. D. Megaw, Ferroelectricity in Crystals, Methuen, London (1957).
19. R. G. Rhodes, Acta Cryst., 4:105 (1951).
20. E. Sawaguchi, J. Phys. Soc. Japan, 7:110 (1952).
21. E. Sawaguchi, H. Maniwa, and S. Hoshino, Phys. Rev., 83:1078 (1951).
22. G. Shirane, H. Danner, A. Pavlovic, and R. Pepinsky, Phys. Rev., 93:672 (1954).
23. G. Shirane and S. Hoshino, J. Phys. Soc. Japan, 6:265 (1951).
24. G. Shirane, F. Jona, and R. Pepinsky, Proc. IRE, 43:1738 (1955).
25. G. Shirane, R. Newnham, and R. Pepinsky, Phys. Rev., 96:581 (1954).
26. G. Shirane and R. Pepinsky, Phys. Rev., 91:812 (1953).
27. G. Shirane, R. Pepinsky, and B. C. Frazer, Phys. Rev., 97:1179 (1955).
28. R. Ueda and G. Kobayashi, Phys. Rev., 91:1565 (1953).
29. P. Vousden, Acta Cryst., 4:545 (1951).
30. G. S. Zhdanov, Crystal Physics, Oliver and Boyd, Edinburgh and London (1965).
31. W. Känzig, "Ferroelectrics and antiferroelectrics", Solid State Phys. 4:1 (1957).
32. F. Jona and G. Shirane, Ferroelectric Crystals, Pergamon Press, Oxford (1962).
33. J. Fousek, Českoslov. Časopis Fys., A11:495 (1961).
34. B. T. Matthias, Phys. Rev., 75:1771 (1949).
35. W. J. Merz, "Ferroelectricity," in: Progress in Dielectrics, 4:101 (1962).

Chapter III

Structure and Crystal Chemistry of Ferroelectrics and Antiferroelectrics Exhibiting Phase Transitions Involving the Ordering of Structure Elements

Introduction

In Chapter II, we considered the oxygen-octahedral ferroelectrics and antiferroelectrics in which the spontaneous polarization appears at a phase transition because of the displacements of certain ions (the direction of polarization is the same as the direction of the displacements).

Equally important and extensive is another class of ferroelectrics (and antiferroelectrics) in which a transition to the polarized state is due to the ordering of certain structure elements. There are about eighty such materials (Table 27).

The structures of these compounds differ greatly. In ferroelectric and antiferroelectric phosphates, sulfates, fluoroberyllates, cyanides, periodates, and glycine compounds, the spontaneous polarization (and antipolarization) appears as a result of the linear ordering of protons in the hydrogen bonds. These compounds form the first group. The second group consists of tartrates, potassium nitrate, sodium nitrate, dicalcium strontium propionate, and tetramethylammonium chloro- and bromomercurates. In these compounds, the spontaneous polarization appears as a result of the arbitrary ordering of radicals, which takes place by hindered rotation.

TABLE 27. Properties of Ferroelectrics and Antiferroelectrics Exhibiting Phase Transitions Involving the Ordering of Structure Elements

| Compound | | Symmetry of paraelectric phase | | Direction of spontaneous polarization P_s | Phase transition temperature, °C | Symmetry of polarized phase | | Type of phase transition | P_s, $\mu C/cm^2$ | References |
formula	name	space	point			space	point			
KH_2PO_4	Potassium dihydrogen phosphate	$I\bar{4}2d$	$\bar{4} \cdot m$	[001]	-151	Fdd	$2 \cdot m$	2	5	1, 2
KD_2PO_4	Potassium dideuterium phosphate	$I\bar{4}2d$	$\bar{4} \cdot m$	[001]	-60	Fdd	$2 \cdot m$	2	4.8	3, 4
KH_2AsO_4	Potassium dihydrogen arsenate	$I\bar{4}2d$	$\bar{4} \cdot m$	[001]	-176	Fdd	$2 \cdot m$	2	5.0	3
KD_2AsO_4	Potassium dideuterium arsenate	$I\bar{4}2d$	$\bar{4} \cdot m$	[001]	-111	Fdd	$2 \cdot m$	2		5
RbH_2PO_4	Rubidium dihydrogen phosphate	$I\bar{4}2d$	$\bar{4} \cdot m$	[001]	-127	Fdd	$2 \cdot m$	2	5.6	6
RbD_2PO_4	Rubidium dideuterium phosphate	$I\bar{4}2d$	$\bar{4} \cdot m$	[001]	-55	Fdd	$2 \cdot m$	2		7
RbH_2AsO_4	Rubidium dihydrogen arsenate	$I\bar{4}2d$	$\bar{4} \cdot m$	[001]	-162	Fdd	$2 \cdot m$	2		6
RbD_2AsO_4	Rubidium dideuterium arsenate	$I\bar{4}2d$	$\bar{4} \cdot m$	[001]	-95	Fdd	$2 \cdot m$	2		5
CsH_2AsO_4	Cesium dihydrogen arsenate	$I\bar{4}2d$	$\bar{4} \cdot m$	[001]	-130	Fdd	$2 \cdot m$	2		8
CsD_2AsO_4	Cesium dideuterium arsenate	$I\bar{4}2d$	$\bar{4} \cdot m$	[001]	-61	Fdd	$2 \cdot m$	2		5
CsH_2PO_4	Cesium dihydrogen phosphate	$I\bar{4}2d$	$\bar{4} \cdot m$	[001]	-130	Fdd	$2 \cdot m$	2		9
$NH_4H_2PO_4$	Ammonium dihydrogen phosphate	$I\bar{4}2d$	$\bar{4} \cdot m$	[100]	-125	$P2_12_12_1$	2 : 2	1		10
$ND_4D_2PO_4$	Ammonium dideuterium phosphate	$I\bar{4}2d$	$\bar{4} \cdot m$	[100]	-31	$P2_12_12_1$	2 : 2	1		10
$NH_4H_2AsO_4$	Ammonium dihydrogen arsenate	$I\bar{4}2d$	$\bar{4} \cdot m$	[001]	-57	$P2_12_12_1$	2 : 2	1		5
$ND_4D_2AsO_4$	Ammonium dideuterium arsenate	$I\bar{4}2d$	$\bar{4} \cdot m$	[100]	+25,3	$P2_12_12_1$	2 : 2	1		5
$NaKC_4H_4O_6 \cdot 4H_2O$	Rochelle salt	$P2_12_12$	2 : 2	[100]	+24—18	$P2_1$	2	2	0.25	2, 11, 27, 28
$NaKC_4H_2D_2O_6 \cdot 4D_2O$	Deuterated Rochelle salt	$P2_12_12$	2 : 2	[100]	+35—22	$P2_1$	2	2	0.37	12
$LiTlC_4H_4O_6 \cdot H_2O$	Lithium thallium tartrate monohydrate	$P2_12_12$	2 : 2	[100]	-263	$P2_1$	2	2	0.14	2, 13
$LiNH_4C_4H_4O_6 \cdot H_2O$	Lithium ammonium tartrate monohydrate	$P2_12_12$	2 : 2	[010]	-167	$P2_1$	2	2	0.21	2, 13
$NaNH_4C_4H_4O_6 \cdot 4H_2O$	Sodium ammonium tartrate tetrahydrate	$P2_12_12$	2 : 2	[100]	-173	$P2_1$	2	2	0.21	14
$(CH_2NH_2COOH)_3 \cdot H_2SO_4$	Triglycine sulfate (TGS)	$P2_1/m$	2 : m	[010]	49	$P2_1$	2	2	2.7	15, 16, 25, 26
$(CH_2ND_2COOD)_3 \cdot D_2SO_4$	Deuterated triglycine sulfate	$P2_1/m$	2 : m	[010]	62	$P2_1$	2	2	3.0	17
$(CH_2NH_2COOH)_3 \cdot H_2BeF_4$	Triglycine fluoroberyllate	$P2_1/m$	2 : m	[010]	70	$P2_1$	2	2	3.2	17, 18
$(CH_2NH_2COOH)_3 \cdot H_2SeO_4$	Triglycine selenate (TGSe)	$P2_1/m$	2 : m	[010]	22	$P2_1$	2	2	3.1	15
$(ND_2CH_2COOD)_3 \cdot D_2SeO_4$	Deuterated triglycine selenate	$P2_1/m$	2 : m	[010]	34	$P2_1$	2	2		69
$(CH_2NH_2COOH)_2 \cdot HNO_3$	Diglycine nitrate	$P2_1/a$	2 : m	[101]	-67	Pa	m	2	1.5	19, 46

Formula	Name	Prototype space group	Prototype point group	Polar axis	Tc (°C)	Ferroelectric space group	Point group	n	P_s	References
$(CH_2NH_2COOH)_3 \times MnCl_2 \cdot 2H_2O$	Diglycine manganous chloride dihydrate	$P2_1/m$	$2{:}m$	[010]	-55	$P2_1$	2		1.3	20, 46
$CH_2NH_2COOH \cdot AgNO_3$	Glycine silver nitrate			[010]		$P2_1$	2	2	0.55	21, 46
$C(NH_2)_3Al(SO_4)_2 \cdot 6H_2O$	Guanidine ammonium sulfate hexahydrate (GASH)			[0001]		$R3m$	$3 \cdot m$		0.35	22, 23, 24
$C(ND_2)_3Al(SO_4)_2 \cdot 6D_2O$	Deuterated GASH			[0001]		$R3m$	$3 \cdot m$		0.35	22
$C(NH_2)_3Al(SeO_4)_2 \cdot 6H_2O$	Guanidine aluminum selenate hexahydrate			[0001]		$R3m$	$3 \cdot m$		0.45	22
$C(NH_2)_3Ga(SO_4)_2 \cdot 6H_2O$	Guanidine gallium sulfate hexahydrate			[0001]		$R3m$	$3 \cdot m$		0.36	22
$C(NH_2)_3Ga(SeO_4)_2 \times 6H_2O$	Guanidine gallium selenate hexahydrate			[0001]		$R3m$	$3 \cdot m$		0.47	22
$C(NH_2)_3Cr(SO_4)_2 \cdot 6H_2O$	Guanidine chromium sulfate hexahydrate			[0001]		$R3m$	$3 \cdot m$		0.36	22
$C(NH_2)_3Cr(SeO_4)_2 \cdot 6H_2O$	Guanidine chromium selenate hexahydrate			[0001]		$R3m$	$3 \cdot m$		0.47	22
$C(NH_2)_3V(SO_4)_2 \cdot 6H_2O$	Guanidine vanadium sulfate hexahydrate			[0001]		$R3m$	$3 \cdot m$		0.36	29
$(NH_3CH_3)Al(SO_4)_2 \cdot 12H_2O$	Methylammonium aluminum alum	$P2_13$	$3/2$	[001]	-97	$P2_1$	2		0.6	30
$(NH_3CH_3)Cr(SO_4)_2 \cdot 12H_2O$	Methylammonium chromium alum	$P2_13$	$3/2$	[001]	-109	$P2_1$	2		1.0	31
$(NH_4)_2SO_4$	Ammonium sulfate	$Pnam$	$m \cdot 2{:}m$	[001]	-49	$Pna2_1$	$2 \cdot m$	1	0.25	32, 33
$(ND_4)_2SO_4$	Deuterated ammonium sulfate	$Pnam$	$m \cdot 2{:}m$	[001]	-49	$Pna2_1$	$2 \cdot m$	1	0.45	34
$(ND_4)_2BeF_4$	Deuterated ammonium fluoroberyllate	$Pnam$	$m \cdot 2{:}m$	[010]	-94	$Pna2_1$	$2 \cdot m$	1	0.19	34
$(NH_4)_2BeF_4$	Ammonium fluoroberyllate	$Pnam$	$m \cdot 2{:}m$	[010]	-97	$Pna2_1$	$2 \cdot m$	1	0.22	35, 36, 37
$LiH_3(SeO_3)_2$	Lithium trihydrogen selenite	$P2_1/n$ or Pn	$2{:}m$	[401]	-79	Pn	m	1	15	38, 39, 68
$NaH_3(SeO_3)_2$	Sodium trihydrogen selenite	$C2/c$	m				m			40
$K_4Fe(CN)_6 \cdot 3H_2O$	Potassium ferrocyanide trihydrate	$C2/c$	$2{:}2{:}m$	[101]	-25	Cc	m	2	1.4	41, 46
$K_4Fe(CN)_6 \cdot 3D_2O$	Deuterated potassium ferrocyanide trihydrate	$C2/c$	$2{:}2{:}m$	[101]	-18	Cc	m	2	1.5	42
$K_4Mn(CN)_6 \cdot 3H_2O$	Potassium manganocyanide trihydrate	$C2/c$	$2{:}2{:}m$	[101]	-40	Cc	m	2		43
$K_4Os(CN)_6 \cdot 3H_2O$	Potassium osmium cyanide trihydrate	$C2/c$	$2{:}2{:}m$	[101]	-2	Cc	m	2	3.5	43
$K_4Os(CN)_6 \cdot 3D_2O$	Deuterated potassium osmium cyanide trihydrate	$C2/c$	$2{:}2{:}m$	[101]	-2	Cc	m	2	1.3	41
$K_4Ru(CN)_6 \cdot 3H_2O$	Potassium ruthenium cyanide trihydrate	$C2/c$	$2{:}2{:}m$	[101]	-14	Cc	m	2	1.1	42
$K_4Ru(CN)_6 \cdot 3D_2O$	Deuterated potassium ruthenium cyanide trihydrate	$C2/c$	$2{:}2{:}m$	[101]	-7.3	Cc	m	2	1.3	41

TABLE 27. (Cont.)

Compound (formula)	Compound (name)	Symmetry of paraelectric phase (space)	Symmetry of paraelectric phase (point)	Direction of spontaneous polarization P_s	Phase transition temperature, °C	Symmetry of polarized phase (space)	Symmetry of polarized phase (point)	Type of phase transition	P_s, $\mu C/cm^2$	References
$N(CH_3)_4 \cdot HgBr_3$	Tetramethylammonium tribromomercurate			[010]		$P2_1$	2		1.0	44
$N(CH_3)_4 \cdot HgCl_3$	Tetramethylammonium trichloromercurate			[010]		$P2_1$	2		1.4	44
$LiNH_4SO_4$	Lithium ammonium sulfate		$m \cdot 2:m$		+10				0.5	45
$NaNH_4SO_4 \cdot 2H_2O$	Sodium ammonium sulfate dihydrate	$P2_12_12$	2:2	[001]	−171				0.15	46
$(NH_4)_2Cd_2(SO_4)_3$	Diammonium dicadmium sulfate	$P2_13$	3/2	[100]	−178	$P2_1$	2		1.2	46, 47
$(NH_4)In(SO_4)_2 \cdot 12H_2O$	Ammonium indium alum	$P2_13$	3/2	[111]	−146	$P2_1$	2		0.4	48
$(NH_4)Fe(SO_4)_2 \cdot 12H_2O$	Ammonium iron alum	$P2_13$	3/2	[111]	185				1.0	48
$(NH_4)V(SO_4)_2 \cdot 12H_2O$*	Ammonium vanadium alum	$P2_13$	3/2	[111]	157				0.4	48
$ND_4Fe(SO_4)_2 \cdot 12D_2O$	Deuterated ammonium iron alum	$P2_13$	3/2	[111]	185					48
$Li(N_2H_5)SO_4$	Lithium hydrazine sulfate	$P2_1/c$	2:m	[001]	−3	$Pbn2_1$	$2 \cdot m$		0.3	45, 46
$RbHSO_4$	Rubidium hydrogen sulfate	$P2_1/c$	2:m	[001]	−119	Pc	m	2	0.8	46, 49, 50
$(NH_4)HSO_4$	Ammonium hydrogen sulfate	$C2/c$	2:m	[001]	−15, −150	$P1$; Pc	1; m	1	0.3	46, 51
$NH_4O_2CClCH_2$	Ammonium monochloroacetate	$Pbnm$	$n \cdot 2:m$	[10Ī]		Cc or Pc	m	1	0.3	46, 52
CSN_2H_4	Thiourea				−104, −97; −93, −71			1		53
$Ca_2Sr(CH_3CH_2COO)_6$	Dicalcium strontium propionate	$P4_12_12$ or $P4_32_12$	4:2	[001]	8, 5	$P4_1$	4	2	0.65	46, 54
$CaB_3O_4(OH)_3 \cdot H_2O$	Colemanite	$P2_1/a$	2:m	[010]	−3, −7	$P2_1$	2			55, 56
$Mg_3B_7O_{13}Cl$	Boracite		3/4		275					57, 58, 59
$NaNO_2$	Sodium nitrite	$Immm$	$m \cdot 2:m$	[001]	165	Imm	$2 \cdot m$	1	2.0	46, 60, 61, 62
$(NH_4)_2H_3IO_6$	Ammonium periodate	$R\bar{3}, R\bar{3}m$	$6, 6 \cdot m$		−20					63
$Ag_2H_3IO_6$	Silver periodate	$R\bar{3}m$	$6 \cdot m$		−20					64
KNO_3	Potassium nitrate	$R\bar{3}m$	$6 \cdot m$	[001]	125, 115; 126	$R3m$	$3 \cdot m$		8.0	46, 65
K_2SnBr_6	Potassium hexabromostannate									67
$SbSI$	Antimony sulfoiodide	$Pnam$	$m \cdot 2:m$	[001]	+22					70

*Pepinsky recently discovered ferroelectric properties in various alums: $(CH_3NH_3)Ca(SO_4)_2 \cdot 12(H_2O)$, $(CH_3NH_3)In(SO_4)_2 \cdot 12(H_2O)$, $(CH_3NH_3)Fe(SO_4)_2 \cdot 12(H_2O)$, $(CH_3NH_3)V(SO_4)_2 \cdot 12(H_2O)$, $(CH_3ND_3)Al(SO_4)_2 \cdot 12(H_2O)$, $(CONH_2NH_3)Cr(SO_4)_2 \cdot 12(H_2O)$, $(CH_2NH_3)Al(SeO_4)_2 \cdot 12(H_2O)$. These compounds have not yet been fully investigated; they are cubic and their ferroelectric phase transition temperatures range from −170 to −70°C [66].

References in Table 27

1. G. Bush and P. Scherrer, Naturwiss., 23:737 (1935).
2. H. D. Megaw, Ferroelectricity in Crystals, Methuen, London (1957).
3. W. Bantle, Helv. Phys. Acta, 15:373 (1942).
4. B. Zwicker and P. Scherrer, Helv. Phys. Acta, 17:346 (1944).
5. C. C. Stephenson, J. M. Corbella, and L. A. Russell, J. Chem. Phys., 21:1110 (1953).
6. B. T. Matthias, W. J. Merz, and P. Scherrer, Helv. Phys., Acta, 20:273 (1947).
7. B. T. Matthias, Phys. Rev., 85:723 (1952).
8. B. C. Frazer and R. Pepinsky, Phys. Rev., 91:246 (1951).
9. F. Seidl, Tschermak's Miner. Petrogr. Mitt., 1:432 (1950).
10. B. T. Matthias, Phys. Rev., 85:141 (1952).
11. J. Valasek, Phys. Rev., 17:475 (1921); 19:478 (1922).
12. J. Hablützel, Helv. Phys. Acta, 12:489 (1939).
13. B. T. Matthias and J. K. Hulm, Phys. Rev., 82:108 (1951).
14. Y. Takagi and Y. Makita, J. Phys. Soc. Japan, 13:272 (1958).
15. B. T. Matthias, C. E. Miller, and J. P. Remeika, Phys. Rev., 104:849 (1956).
16. V. Janovec, B. Březina, and H. T. Arend, Českoslov. Časopis Fys., 10:63 (1960).
17. S. Hoshino, T. Mitsui, F. Jona, and R. Pepinsky, Phys. Rev., 107:1255 (1957).
18. R. Pepinsky, Y. Okaya, and F. Jona, Bull. Am. Phys. Soc., 2:220 (1957).
19. R. Pepinsky, K. Vedam, S. Hoshino, and Y. Okaya, Phys. Rev., 111:430 (1958).
20. R. Pepinsky, K. Vedam, and Y. Okaya, Phys. Rev., 110:1309 (1958).
21. R. Pepinsky, Y. Okaya, D. P. Eastman, and T. Mitsui, Phys. Rev., 107:1538 (1957).
22. A. N. Holden, B. T. Matthias, W. J. Merz, and J. P. Remeika, Phys. Rev., 98:546 (1955).
23. V. M. Gurevich, I. S. Zheludev, and I. S. Rez, Kristallografiya, 4:718 (1959).
24. I. S. Zheludev and V. S. Lelekov, Kristallografiya, 7:463 (1962).
25. V. M. Gurevich and I. S. Zheludev, Kristallografiya, 6:135 (1961).
26. I. S. Zheludev, A. A. Filimonov, V. A. Yurin, and N. A. Romanyuk, Kristallografiya, 6:676 (1961).
27. V. A. Yurin and I. S. Zheludev, Kristallografiya, 4:253 (1959).
28. I. S. Zheludev and R. Ya. Sit'ko, Kristallografiya, 1:689 (1956).
29. J. P. Remeika and W. J. Merz, Phys. Rev., 102:295 (1956).
30. R. Pepinsky, F. Jona, and G. Shirane, Phys. Rev., 102:1181 (1956).
31. W. Känzig, "Ferroelectrics and Antiferroelectrics", Solid States Phys., 4:1 (1957).
32. B. T. Matthias and J. P. Remeika, Phys. Rev., 103:262 (1956).
33. V. A. Koptsik, B. A. Strukov, A. A. Sklyankin, and M. E. Levina, Izv. Akad. Nauk SSSR, Ser. Fiz., 24:1228 (1960).
34. S. Hoshino, K. Vedam, Y. Okaya, and R. Pepinsky, Phys. Rev., 112:405 (1958).
35. R. Pepinsky and F. Jona, Phys. Rev., 105:344 (1957).
36. B. A. Strukov and V. A. Koptsik, Kristallografiya, 7:234 (1962).
37. B. A. Strukov, N. D. Gavrilova, and V. A. Koptsik, Kristallografiya, 6:780 (1961).
38. R. Pepinsky and K. Vedam, Phys. Rev., 114:1217 (1959).
39. K. Vedam, Y. Okaya, and R. Pepinsky, Phys. Rev., 119:1252 (1960).
40. R. Pepinsky, K. Vedam, Y. Okaya, and F. Unterleitner, Bull. Am. Phys. Soc., 4:63 (1949).
41. S. Waku, H. Hirabayashi, H. Toyoda, H. Iwasaki, and R. Kiriyama, J. Phys. Soc., Japan, 14:973 (1959).
42. S. Waku, K. Masuno, and T. Tanaka, J. Phys. Soc. Japan, 15:1698 (1960).
43. S. Waku, K. Masuno, T. Tanaka, and H. Iwasaki, J. Phys. Soc. Japan, 15:1185 (1960).

44. E. Fatuzzo and R. Nitsche, Phys. Rev., 117:936 (1960).
45. R. Pepinsky, K. Vedam, S. Hoshino, and Y. Okaya, Phys. Rev., 111:1508(1958).
46. K. Vedam, Current Science, 29:79 (1960).
47. F. Jona and R. Pepinsky, Phys. Rev., 103:1126 (1956).
48. S. Pepinsky: see W. Merz, "Ferroelectricity," in: Progress in Dielectrics, 4:101 (1962).
49. R. Pepinsky, K. Vedam, S. Hoshino, and Y. Okaya, Phys. Rev., 111:1508 (1958).
50. B. A. Strukov, V. A. Koptsik, and V. D. Ligasova, Fiz. Tverd. Tela, 4:1334 (1962).
51. B. T. Matthias, Phys. Rev., 85:723 (1952).
52. Pepinsky, R., Okaya, Y., and Mitsui, T., Acta Cryst., 10, 600 (1957).
53. Solomon, A. L., Phys. Rev., 104:1191 (1956).
54. Matthias, B. T., and Remeika, J. P., Phys. Rev., 107:1727 (1957).
55. Goldsmith, G. J., Bull. Am. Phys. Soc., 1:322 (1956).
56. Wieder, H. H., J. Appl. Phys., 30:1010 (1959).
57. Corre, Y. Le, J. Phys. Radium, 18:629 (1957).
58. Jona, F., Bull. Am. Phys. Soc., 4:63 (1959).
59. Sonin, A. S., and Zheludev, I. S., Kristallografiya, 8:57 (1963).
60. Zheludev, I. S., and Sonin, A. S., Izv. Akad. Nauk SSSR, Ser. Fiz., 22:1441 (1958).
61. Sawada, S., Nomura, S., Fujii, and Ioshida, I., Phys. Rev. Letters 1:320 (1958).
62. Sonin, A. S., Zheludev, I. S., and Dobrzhanskii, G. F., Izv. Akad. Nauk SSSR,
     Ser. Fiz., 24:1209 (1960).
63. Helmholtz, L., J. Am. Chem. Soc., 59:2036 (1937).
64. Gränicher, H., Meir, W. M., and Petter, W., Helv. Phys. Acta, 27:216 (1954).
65. Sawada, S., Nomura, S., and Fujii, S., J. Phys. Soc. Japan, 13:1549 (1958).
66. Merz, W., "Ferroelectricity," in: Progress in Dielectrics, Vol. 4, 101 (1962).
67. Galloni, E. E., de Benyacar, M. R., and de Abelefo, M. J., Z. Krist., 117:470 (1962).
68. Berlincourt, D., Cook Jr., W. R., and Rander, M. E., Acta Cryst., 16:163 (1963).
69   Toyoda, H., Repts. Electr. Commun. Lab., 7:416 (1959).
70. Nitsche, R., and Merz, W. J., J. Phys. Chem. Solids, 13:154 (1960).

We can divide ferroelectrics and antiferroelectrics exhibiting linear ordering into four classes, in which the main structure element, participating in the formation of the hydrogen bonds, is:

1) a kinked chain of atoms: this class includes glycine compounds, ammonium chloroacetate, and thiourea;

2) an octahedron: this class includes alums and alum-type compounds, such as double sulfates and selenates of guanidine and trivalent metals, hexacyanides of potassium, and metals of group VIII, as well as antiferroelectric ammonium and silver periodates;

3) a tetrahedron: this class includes phosphates and arsenates of alkali metals and ammonium, as well as numerous sulfates, fluoroberyllates, and selenates;

4) a pyramid: only two compounds belong to this class — sodium and lithium selenides.

§1. Crystallochemical Properties of Ferroelectrics and Antiferroelectrics with Linear Ordering of Hydrogen-Bond Protons

A. Ferroelectrics and Antiferroelectrics in Which a Kinked Chain of Atoms Is the Main Structure Element Participating in the Formation of Hydrogen Bonds. Among the numerous ferroelectric compounds of glycine which belong to this class, the complete structure of the ferroelectric phase has been determined only for triglycine sulfate $(NH_2CH_2COOH)_3 \cdot H_2SO_4$, which is one of three ferroelectric isomorphous molecular compounds of glycine with inorganic acids. The ferroelectric phases of these compounds have the space group $P2_1$ (point group 2) and the paraelectric phases have the space group $P2_1/m$ (point group 2:m). Each unit cell contains two molecules of the $(NH_3CH_2COOH)_3 \cdot H_4AB_4$ composition, where A = S, Se, Be, and B = O or F. The parameters of the unit cells of these compounds are listed in Table 28.

The complete structure of triglycine sulfate (often abbreviated to TGS) was determined by Hoshino, Okaya, and Pepinsky [26], who used x-ray and neutron-diffraction methods. The structure represents complex packing of glycine molecules and sulfate ions linked by the hydrogen bonds $O-H-...O$ and $N-H-...O$. The sulfate ion does not exhibit tetrahedral symmetry because of the formation of hydrogen bonds with the oxygen atoms in this ion. Out of three glycine molecules, one has the usual amphoteric configuration with an NH_3^+ group lying outside the plane of other atoms: the other two are monoprotonated and are planar (within the limits

TABLE 28. Parameters of Unit Cells of Ferroelectric Compounds of Glycine with Inorganic Acids

Formula	a, Å	b, Å	c, Å	β, deg
$(NH_2CH_2COOH)_3 \cdot H_2SeO_4$	9.54	12.92	5.86	110
$(NH_2CH_2COOH)_3 \cdot H_2SO_4$	9.64	12.75	5.90	111
$(NH_2CH_2COOH)_3 \cdot H_2BeF_4$	9.59	12.75	5.70	112

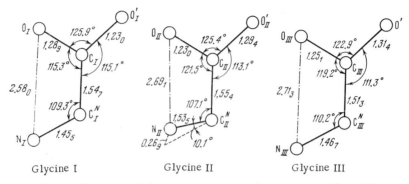

Fig. 47. Configurations of the glycine molecules in triglycine sulfate. Glycine
I and III are planar monoprotonated glycinium ions; glycine II is an amphoteric
glycinium ion. The distances are given in Å.

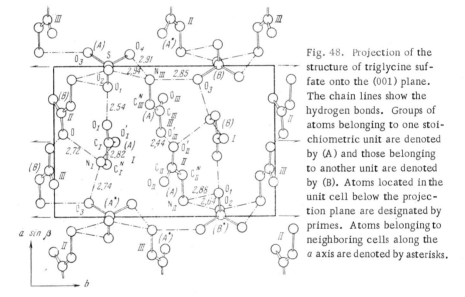

Fig. 48. Projection of the structure of triglycine sulfate onto the (001) plane. The chain lines show the hydrogen bonds. Groups of atoms belonging to one stoichiometric unit are denoted by (A) and those belonging to another unit are denoted by (B). Atoms located in the unit cell below the projection plane are designated by primes. Atoms belonging to neighboring cells along the a axis are denoted by asterisks.

of the experimental error). The configurations of the glycine molecules are shown in Fig. 47. Thus, the correct chemical formula of triglycine sulfate is $(NH_3^+CH_2COOH)_2 \cdot (NH_3^+CH_2COO^-) \cdot SO_4^{2-}$, where the first part of the formula represents glycine molecules I and III (they can be called glycinium ions) and the second part represents an amphoteric glycine ion or simply glycine.

The system of hydrogen bonds in triglycine sulfate is shown in Fig. 48. The glycinium ion I(A), located near the $y = \frac{1}{4}$ plane, forms the following hydrogen bonds: one $O-H\ldots O$ bond 2.54 Å long, with the $O_I(A)$ atom of the sulfate ion, and three $N-H\ldots O$ bonds with $O_3(A^*)$, $O'_I(A)$, and $O'_{II}(B)$, which are 2.74, 2.82, and 2.72 Å long. Two glycine molecules, located near the $y = \frac{1}{2}$ plane, are bound by the strong hydrogen bond $O-H\ldots O$, 2.44 Å long, formed by $O'_{III}(A)$ and $O'_{II}(A)$ atoms. An atom of nitrogen $N_{II}(A)$ also forms three hydrogen bonds $N-H\ldots O$ with $O_2(B^*)$. $O_1(B^*)$, and $O_4(A^*)$ atoms. A similar system of hydrogen bonds is formed also by another nitrogen atom $N_{III}(A)$: a bond 2.94 Å long with $O_2(A)$, a bond 2.91 Å long with $O_4(A)$, and a bond 2.85 Å long with $O_3(B)$.

The ferroelectric properties of triglycine sulfate are due to the ordering of protons in hydrogen bonds, which produces dipoles in the glycine molecules and sulfate ions. The occurrence of such ordering has been demonstrated by a study of the critical scattering of x rays near the Curie point. It is interesting to note that the symmetry planes perpendicular to a twofold axis are distributed at random in the structure because of some disorder in the positions of the glycine molecules of type I.

The determination of the "absolute structure configuration," i.e., the determination of a correspondence between the directions of polarization and the directions of displacements of the atoms and ions participating in the formation of dipole moments is of great importance in studies of the nature of the spontaneous polarization and of the mechanism of the polarization switching (reversal) in ferroelectrics. The absolute configuration of triglycine sulfate has been found from the anomalous scattering of x rays. It has been shown that the hydrogen bond $O-H\ldots O$ between $O'_{III}(A)$ and $O'_{II}(A)$ atoms, of length 2.43 Å, plays the most important role in the process of polarization switching in triglycine sulfate. A schematic diagram showing the displacements of atoms during polarization switching is shown in Fig. 49. If the polarization is directed along the positive direction of the b axis, as shown in this figure, the hydrogen atom in the $O-H\ldots O$ bond lies closer to the $O'_{III}(A)$ atom than to the $O'_{II}(A)$ atom. In this case, glycine II has the configuration of an amphoteric ion. After polarization reversal, the hydrogen atom moves closer to the $O'_{II}(A)$ atom and glycine III becomes an amphoteric ion. Thus, polarization switching in triglycine sulfate is associated with the displacement of the hydrogen atom along the line of the $O-H\ldots O$ bond, which transforms a glycine ion to an amphoteric ion. Such a change in the glycine group configuration rotates, via the system of hydrogen

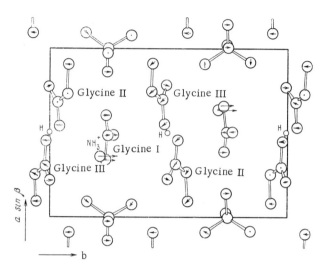

Fig. 49. Changes in the positions of atoms in triglycine sulfate which accompany reversal of the polar axis b. Arrows indicate the directions and magnitudes of atomic displacements.

bonds, the sulfate ions and this gives rise to, again via the system of the hydrogen bonds, a displacement of the NH_4^+ group of glycinium I by about 1 Å along the b axis so that glycinium I assumes a symmetrical position relative to the $y = 1/4$ plane.

Investigations of the infrared and Raman spectra of triglycine sulfate yield important information on the structure of this compound [28]. It has been established that $[SO_4]^{2-}$ has a very low symmetry in triglycine sulfate crystals: at best, it may have one symmetry plane. The ion itself does not play an important role in the ferroelectric properties of triglycine sulfate. The results of structure investigations by diffraction methods have confirmed the presence, in addition to amphoteric ions, of un-ionized COOH groups. The Raman spectra are not greatly affected by the transition through the Curie temperature (+49°C), but it has been found that the C-H (2958 cm^{-1}) and COO (1675 cm^{-1}) frequencies increase when the temperature is raised in the paraelectric region starting from the Curie point (see Chap. VI, §4).

The structure of triglycine selenate $(NH_2CH_2COOH)_3 \cdot H_2SeO_4$ and triglycine fluoroberyllate $(NH_2CH_2COOH)_3 \cdot H_2BeF_4$ have not yet been determined. However, since they are isomorphous with triglycine sulfate and their physical properties are similar, their structures are unlikely to differ greatly from that of triglycine sulfate.

Figure 50 shows a photograph of a model of the structure of glycine silver nitrate $(NH_2CH_2COOH)AgNO_3$. At room temperature, in the paraelectric phase, this compound belongs to the space group $P2_1/a$ (point group 2:m) with the following unit cell parameters a = 5.53 Å, b = 19.58 Å, c = 5.51 Å, β = 100°, Z = 4 [35]. The structure consists of kinked glycine molecule chains, planar triangular ions $[NO_3]^-$, and Ag^+ ions. According to the relationships governing changes in the space symmetry of ferroelectrics (§ 2), the space group of glycine silver nitrate below the Curie point (−55°C) should be $P2_1$ (point group 2).

The structure of ammonium monochloroacetate $CH_2ClCOONH_4$ has not yet been determined. However, it is known that at room temperature, in the paraelectric phase, this compound has the space group $C2/c$ (point group 2:m). The unit cell parameters are a = 8.42 Å, b = 11.63 Å, c = 9.82 Å, β = 110°, Z = 8 [36].

Careful investigations have established that thiourea $(NH_2)_2CS$ exhibits four phase transitions at −104, −97, −93, and −71°C. Thus, thiourea has five different phases: ferroelectric phase I below −104°C; antiferroelectric phase II between −104 and −97°C; fer-

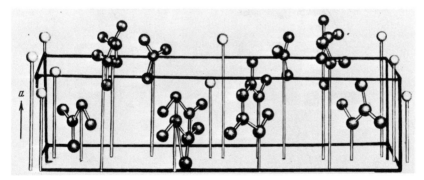

Fig. 50. Model of the structure of glycine silver nitrate $(NH_2CH_2COOH)AgNO_3$. The white spheres represent the silver atoms; the kinked chains of black spheres are the glycine molecules; triangles of black spheres are the $[NO_3]^-$ groups.

roelectric phase III between -97 and $-93°C$; paraelectric or antiferroelectric phase IV between -93 and $-71°C$; antiferroelectric phase V above $-71°C$ [24]. The structure of phase V at room temperature has been investigated by many workers using x-ray and electron-diffraction methods. At room temperature, thiourea is orthorhombic and its space group is $Pbnm$ (point group m·2:m) and the unit cell parameters are a = 5.52 Å, b = 7.655 Å, c = 8.537 Å, Z = 4. Figure 51 shows schematically the configuration of thiourea molecules. The packing of thiourea molecules is classical. All atoms of one $(NH_2)_2CS$ molecule, with the exception of a hydrogen atom H_{II}, lie in a single plane. This H_{II} atom projects from the SCN_2 plane by 0.2 Å. The structure of thiourea includes weak hydrogen bonds $N-H-...S$ [2]. According to x-ray diffraction investigations, phase I at $-153°C$ has an orthorhombic unit cell with the parameters a = 5.494 Å, b = 7.516 Å, c = 8.519 Å, Z = 4. The difference between this structure and that at room temperature consists of small displacements of atoms within the molecules and fairly large rotations of the molecules as a whole. Thus, at room temperature, the angle between the normal to the plane of the molecule and the b axis is 63.6°, while at $-153°C$ this angle is 70.6 and 60.5° for the two types of molecule

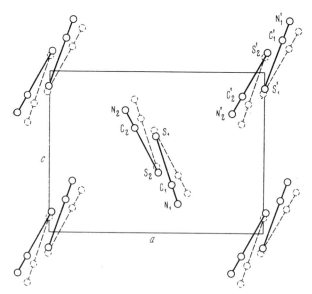

Fig. 51. Structure of thiourea projected onto the (010) planes.

present in the structure. Investigations of the proton resonance in thiourea have shown that the N−H bond length is 1.06 Å and the H−N−H angle is 119°. According to these investigations, the molecule is planar and rotates about the C−S bond. However, we must assume that rotation is also possible about the C−N bond but it is masked by the rotation about the S−N bond. Only very slight changes in the line width and value of the second moment (for any direction of the magnetic field H_0 relative to the a, b, and c axes) take place in the proton resonance at the phase transition to the next (II) phase. This is in good agreement with the planar configuration of the thiourea molecule [19]. The mechanism of the polarization in thiourea has not yet been finally determined but there are grounds for assuming that its ferroelectric properties are associated with a relative displacement of the whole $(NH)_2CS$ molecule and not of its constituent atoms.

B. Ferroelectrics and Antiferroelectrics in Which an Octahedron is the Main Structure Element Participating in the Formation of Hydrogen Bonds. This group includes ammonium and methylammonium alums whose complete structure in the paraelectric phase had been determined only for methylammonium aluminum alum $(CH_3NH_3)Al(SO_4)_2 \cdot 12H_2O$ with the Curie point at −97°C (this compound is also known as methylammonium aluminum sulfate dodecahydrate or MASD). X-ray diffraction investigations have shown that positive ions $[Al(H_2O)_6]^{3+}$, $(CH_3NH_3)^+$, negative ions $[SO_4]^{2-}$, and six molecules of water of crystallization form a cubic structure in this alum. The space group is $P2_13$ (point group 3/2) and the unit-cell parameter is 12.50 Å [30]. Figure 52 shows schematically the spatial distribution of atoms in one-eight of the unit cell. $[Al(H_2O)_6]^{3+}$ ions are almost regular octahedra with the trigonal symmetry. Methylammonium ions have six different configurations and are distributed at random around the body diagonal of the cubic cell. They are surrounded by six oxygen atoms forming a strongly distorted octahedron. Molecules of the water of crystallization form two nonequivalent hydrogen bonds O−H...O: one of them is formed with the oxygen atom of a free water molecule and its length is 2.62 Å, while the other is formed with the oxygen atoms of the $[SO_4]^{2-}$ ion and its length is 2.64 Å. Other oxygen atoms of the water molecules form the O−H...O hydrogen bonds with two oxygen atoms of the $[SO_4]^{2-}$ group and their lengths

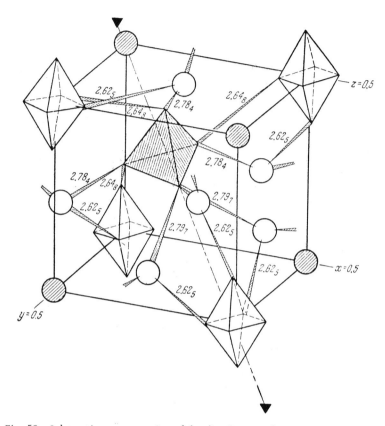

Fig. 52. Schematic representation of the distribution of molecules in methyl-ammonium aluminum alum. One-quarter of the unit cell is shown. Hydrogen bonds are represented by shaded wedges; the white circles represent water of crystallization; the shaded tetrahedron is the SO_4 group; the octahedra are the $[Al(H_2O)_6]$ groups; the centers of gravity of the CH_3NH_3 ions are represented by shaded circles. The dimensions of the octahedra are reduced so that the structure could be displayed more clearly. The distances are given in Å.

are 2.79 and 2.78 Å. The structure of the ferroelectric phase has not yet been determined, but it has been demonstrated that below $-97°C$ methylammonium aluminum alum has the space group $P2_1$ (point group 2).

The structures of other ferroelectric ammonium alums have not yet been fully determined. However, a general idea about their structure can be obtained by considering potash (potassium) alum

$KAl(SO_4)_2 \cdot 12H_2O$, which is isomorphous with the paraelectric phases of ammonium alums. The structure of potash alum [29] can be represented as consisting of $[K(H_2O)_6]^+$ and $[Al(H_2O)_6]^{3+}$ octahedral groups and of $[SO_4]^{2-}$ tetrahedral groups. The $[K(H_2O)_6]^+$ groups are located at the centers of the edges and at the center of the unit cell, while $[Al(H_2O)_6]^{3+}$ groups are located at the corners and centers of the faces, and the $[SO_4]^{2-}$ groups occupy centers of each one-eighth of the cell. The O –H...O hydrogen bonds link the oxygen atoms of the water molecules and the oxygen atoms of the $[SO_4]^{2-}$ groups. We may assume that the structures of ammonium alums include, in addition to these hydrogen bonds, another system of N–H...O bonds.

The first important information on the structure of isomorphous compounds of guanidine sulfates with trivalent metals were obtained by the geometrical-analysis method. The coordinates of the octahedral $[Al(H_2O)_6]^{3+}$ and tetrahedral $[SO_4]^{2-}$ groups, as well as of the guanidinium ions $[C(NH_2)_3]^+$ – which are planar triangles –were determined in [1]. The ferroelectric modification (at room temperature) of guanidine aluminum sulfate hexahydrate (GASH) belongs to the trigonal class 3·m. Its formula is $C(NH_2)_3Al(SO_4)_2 \cdot 6H_2O$; the space group is $R3m$ and the unit cell contains three molecules. No phase transitions have been recorded for this compound. It may be assumed that the ferroelectric phase transition occurs at high temperatures, but it cannot be observed because GASH decomposes at about 200°C. Investigations of the proton magnetic resonance in GASH have shown that, above 199°K, at least some of the proton groups rotate about a threefold axis at a frequency of at least 10^5 cps.

According to Tables 10-12, the high-temperature point groups of GASH may be $\bar{6}/4$, $3/\bar{4}$, m·3:m, and 6·m. Since the space group of GASH is $R3m$, we find from Tables 13-15 that the high-temperature phase of GASH can only have the point groups $\bar{6}/4$, $3/\bar{4}$, or $\bar{6}$·m; the m·3:m group is not permissible by the symmetry considerations.

The complete structure of guanidine gallium sulfate hexahydrate (GGSH), which is isomorphous with GASH, has recently been determined by x-ray diffraction [23]. The formula of this compound is $C(NH_2)_3Ga(SO_4)_2 \cdot 6H_2O$ and its structure is trigonal with the space group $R3m$ (point group 3·m) and the unit cell param-

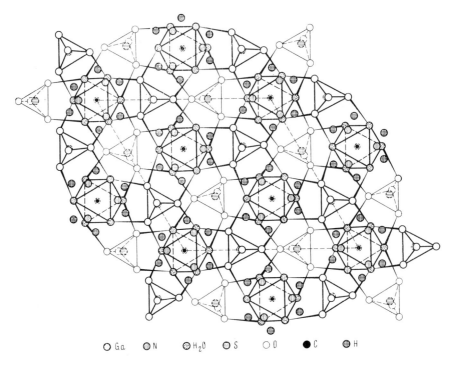

O Ga   ⊕ N   ⊛ H₂O   ⊖ S   O O   ● C   ⊕ H

Fig. 53. Projection of the structure of guanidine gallium sulfate hexahydrate onto the (001) plane.

eters are a = 11.82 Å, c = 9.13 Å, Z = 3. Projection of the unit cell onto the (001) plane is given in Fig. 53. The structure consists of packed $[Ga(H_2O)_6]^{3+}$ octahedral groups with Ga^{3+} ions lying on the threefold axis. Sulfur atoms, belonging to the $[SO_4]^{2-}$ tetrahedra, lie in planes of symmetry. The hydrogen bonds O −H ... O, 2.54-2.64 Å long, join the water molecules, surrounding the Ga^{3+} ions, and the oxygen atoms in the sulfate ions.

This group of compounds includes also hexacyanides of potassium and metals of group VIII. The structures of $K_4Fe(CN)_6 \cdot 3H_2O$ and $K_4Ru(CN)_6 \cdot 3H_2O$ are monoclinic with the space group $C2/c$ (point group 2:m). The lattice parameters for the first compound are a = 9.32 Å, b = 16.84 Å, c = 9.32 Å, $\beta \sim 90°$, Z = 4. The structure is a layered assembly of $[Me(CN)_6]^{4-}$ octahedral groups and almost regular squares consisting of K^+ ions [7].

Antiferroelectric ammonium and silver periodates also belong to this group. The structure of the room-temperature (paraelectric) phase of $(NH_4)_2H_3IO_6$ is trigonal; a = 5.43 Å, $\alpha = 78°35'$, Z = 1. The space group of this compound is $R3$ (point group $\bar{6}$).* The unit-cell sites are occupied by almost regular $[IO_6]^{5-}$ octahedra which are joined by the O –H ... O hydrogen bonds 2.6 Å long. $[NH_4]^+$ ions are located along a threefold rotation-reflection axis. The projection of the structure, without ammonium ions, onto the (0001) plane is shown in Fig. 54 [25].

At $-20°C$, ammonium periodate $(NH_4)_2H_3IO_6$ transforms into the antiferroelectric modification. When the structure is described in terms of the hexagonal symmetry, it is found that the a axis of the new (multiple) unit cell is doubled but the c axis remains unchanged. If the structure is described in terms of the trigonal symmetry, it is found that the unit cell after the transition still remains trigonal but it is now of the body-centered type with all the axes doubled compared with their dimensions before the transition. Moreover, the cell is rotated by 180° about the threefold axis, compared with its initial position.

Neither the space nor the point groups of the antiferroelectric phase have been determined but indirect investigations suggest that the symmetry is centrosymmetric.

---

* According to other investigators, $(NH_4)_2H_3IO_6$ has the space group $R\bar{3}m$ (point group $\bar{6}\cdot m$).

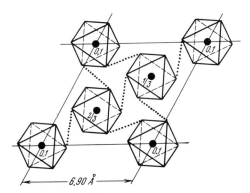

Fig. 54. Projection of the $(NH_4)_2H_3IO_6$ structure onto the (0001) plane. The dotted lines show the hydrogen bonds.

There are grounds for assuming that the antiferroelectric properties of ammonium periodate are associated with the ordering of protons in the hydrogen bonds, which gives rise to dipoles at $[IO_6]^{5+}$

Silver periodate $Ag_2H_3IO_6$, which is isomorphous with ammonium periodate at room temperature, has the following unit-cell parameters: a = 5.44 Å, α = 66°21'. Near −50°C, silver periodate undergoes a phase transition which alters the structure so that [in contrast to $(NH_4)_2H_3IO_6$] the parameters of the multiple unit cell are doubled along the a and c axes.

C. Ferroelectrics and Antiferroelectrics in Which a Tetrahedron is the Main Structure Element Participating in the Formation of Hydrogen Bonds. The most thoroughly investigated compounds of the group are alkali dihydrogen phosphates and arsenates, which are

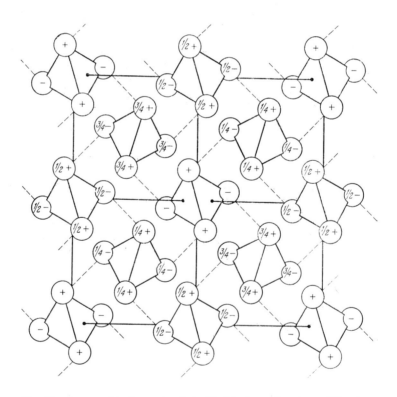

Fig. 55. System of hydrogen bonds in KH_2PO_4 (paraelectric modification, K atoms not shown).

ferroelectric, and ammonium dihydrogen phosphates and arsenates, which are antiferroelectric. Numerous x-ray and neutron-diffraction investigations have established finally the detailed structure and the mechanism of the phase transition in KH_2PO_4 [21, 10a]; this compound is often abbreviated to KDP.

At room temperature, KH_2PO_4 crystallizes in the $\bar{4} \cdot m$ class of the tetragonal system; its space group is $I\bar{4}2d$, and the unit cell parameters are a = 7.453 Å, c = 6.959 Å, and Z = 4. The structure consists of a three-dimensional network of $[PO_4]^{4-}$ groups, joined by the O$-$H...O bonds: the two upper atoms of one $[PO_4]^{4-}$ tetrahedron are joined to the two lower oxygen atoms of two other tetrahedra, while the two lower oxygen atoms of the first tetrahedron are joined to the upper oxygen atoms of two other tetrahedra. The system of hydrogen bonds is shown in Fig. 55. At room temperature, the hydrogen bond O$-$H...O is 2.48 Å long, which indicates that the bonding is very strong, and hydrogen atoms are not ordered but distributed at random between two equilibrium positions separated by 0.5 Å along the bond length. Below the Curie point, the positions of the protons are ordered, i.e., all of them are located either near the lower or upper oxygen atoms of the $[PO_4]^{4-}$ tetrahedra, with the hydrogen atom located at 0.21 Å from the center of the hydrogen bond. This ordering of the protons is shown schematically in Fig. 56, which gives the projection of the neutron-scattering density onto the (001) plane. Such ordering disturbs the distribution of the internal crystal fields and gives rise to dipole moments of the $[PO_4]^{4-}$ tetrahedra. The ordering of the protons is accompanied by an increase of the hydrogen bond length to 2.51 Å and considerable displacements of phosphorus and potassium atoms, which make a considerable contribution to the spontaneous polarization. The direction of the spontaneous polarization coincides with the direction of the displacement of phosphorus in a tetrahedron and is opposite to the direction of the displacement of potassium. The hydrogen ion itself does not contribute to the spontaneous polarization since it is displaced along the hydrogen bond, which is perpendicular to the ferroelectric axis. However, the structure has the property that, in the ordered state, the positive charge of the hydrogen ion induces polarization of the PO_4 group along the c axis.

Below the Curie point ($-151°C$), KH_2PO_4 belongs to the space group Fdd (point group $2 \cdot m$) of the orthorhombic symmetry with

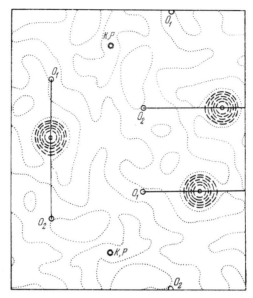

Fig. 56. Fourier projection of potassium dihydrogen phosphate KH_2PO_4 onto the (001) plane. The dashed circles represent negative contours and the dotted curves represent zero contours. Only the hydrogen atoms are shown [10b].

axes rotated by 45° relative to the crystallographic axes in the paraelectric state.

No detailed investigations of the structure of KH_2AsO_4, RbH_2PO_4, RbH_2AsO_4, CsH_2PO_4, and CsH_2AsO_4 have been carried out, but it is known that they are isomorphous with KH_2PO_4 in the paraelectric and ferroelectric phases. The absolute configurations of alkali dihydrogen compounds have been investigated using potassium dihydrogen arsenate as an example, and it has been found that arsenic atoms are shifted along the positive direction of polarization but potassium atoms are shifted in the opposite direction.

At room temperature, the paraelectric phase of $NH_4H_2PO_4$ is isomorphous with KH_2PO_4 and it belongs to the same space group; the unit-cell parameters of ammonium dihydrogen phosphate are a = 7.479 Å and b = 7.516 Å. The structure is again a three-dimentional network of $[PO_4]^{4-}$ tetrahedra, linked by the O–H...O bonds 2.51 Å long, and $[NH_4]^{+}$ tetrahedra, linked by the N–H...O bonds (2.88 Å long) with the oxygen atoms of the $[PO_4]^{4-}$ groups [27, 43]. Below the Curie point, i.e., below −125°C, the lengths of the O −H ... O bonds remain practically the same but the four N − H ... O hydrogen bonds become unequal (their lengths are 3.04, 2.76, 2.99, and 2.88 Å). As in KH_2PO_4, the ordering of the protons in the hydrogen bonds in ammonium dihdrogen phosphate takes place below the phase-transition temperature but this ordering is much more complex than in the potassium compound and it has not yet been determined completely.

The space group of $NH_4H_2PO_4$ in the antiferroelectric modification (below −125°C) is $P2_12_12_1$ (point group 2:2). The direction of polarization in the original unit cell coincides with one of the twofold axes of the crystal. The multiple-cell structure of this compound appears as follows: the centers of the cells, equivalent to sites above the transition temperature, are shifted away from the sites after the transition to the antiferroelectric state.

The structure of none of the numerous ferroelectric sulfates and fluoroberyllates has been determined fully. Ammonium sulfate and fluoroberyllate have for a long time been assumed to have the same K_2SO_4-type structure at room temperature. However, it has recently been shown that the ferroelectric phases of these two compounds are essentially different. At room temperature these compounds have the orthorhombic symmetry and the space group $Pnam$ (point group m·2:m). The unit-cell parameters of $(NH_4)_2SO_4$ are a = 7.783 Å, b = 10.594 Å, c = 5.975Å, and the parameters of $(NH_4)_2BeF_4$ are a = 7.626 Å, b = 10.426 Å, c = 5.914 Å. The structures consist of $[NH_4]^+$, $[SO_4]^{2-}$, $[BeF_4]^{2-}$ tetrahedra linked by the N−H ... O and N−H ... F hydrogen bonds. The general nature of the structure of $(NH_4)_2BeF_4$ is shown in Fig. 57. At room temperature, $(NH_4)_2BeF_4$ has a multiple-cell structure formed by doubling the cell parameters along the b and c axes. In this case, the space group of the true unit cell should be $Acam$ [32]. However, electron-diffraction studies of $(NH_4)_2BeF_4$ have shown no multiple-cell structure. Ammonium phosphate exhibits (sometimes) a multiple-cell structure at room temperature.

The ferroelectric phase transitions of $(NH_4)_2SO_4$ and $(NH_4)_2BeF_4$ occur at −49 and −97°C, respectively. The direction of spontaneous polarization in ammonium phosphate coincides with the c axis and in fluoroberyllate with the b axis. The point group of these crystals in the ferroelectric phase (below −49 and −99°C,

Fig. 57. Model of the structure of $(NH_4)_2BeF_4$.

respectively) is 2·m (Table 11). It is evident from Table 17 that the space group of $(NH_4)_2SO_4$ can be *Pmn* and the space group of $(NH_4)_2BeF_4$ can be *Pna* . The highest value of the refractive index of these crystals is found along the spontaneous polarization direction.

Investigations of the near infrared spectra of ammonium sulfate and fluoroberyllate have demonstrated that ammonium ions do not rotate at room temperature. It has also been established that the proton magnetic resonance is not affected by the phase transition at the Curie point. At room temperature, both crystals have similar magnetic resonance lines but at low temperatures, the lines are different. This is due to the fact that the ferroelectric phases of these two compounds are not isomorphous. The magnetic resonance lines of ammonium fluoroberyllate are not affected by variation of temperature between +150 and −180°C. An estimate of the frequency of the effective switching of $[NH]^{4+}$ at −180°C, deduced from measurements of the second moment, exceeds 10^5 cps. An additional sharp line of variable width appears in ammonium sulfate below −110°C. The magnetic resonance line splits into two easily resolved components, the wide one of which is associated with the "freezing" of motion within ammonium ions, and the other (narrow) is associated with switching of these ions as a whole [13].

Ammonium hydrogen sulfate NH_4HSO_4 is ferroelectric between two phase transitions at -3 and $-119°C$. Pepinsky, Vedam, Hoshino, and Okaya [38] have determined the space groups and the lattice parameters of all the phases. Above $-3°C$, paraelectric NH_4HSO_4 is monoclinic (pseudo-orthorhombic), its space group is $P2_1/c$ (point group 2:m), and the lattice parameters are a = 14.51Å b = 4.54 Å, c = 14.90 Å, β = 120°18', Z = 8. In the ferroelectric phase, NH_4HSO_4 is also monoclinic, belongs to the space group $P2_1$ (point group 2) and has the following cell parameters: a = 14.26 Å, b = 4.62 Å, c = 14.80 Å, β = 121°18'. Below $-119°C$, ammonium hydrogen sulfate belongs to the triclinic system, has the space group $P1$ (point group 1), and the cell parameters a = 14.24 Å, b = 4.56 Å, c = 15.15 Å, β = 123°24'. We may assume that the structure of NH_4HSO_4 includes two systems of hydrogen bonds: $O-H...O$ and $N-H...O$.

It is also known that dicadmium diammonium sulfate $Cd_2(NH_4)_2(SO_4)_3$ is paraelectric at room temperature and has the langbeinite structure with the cubic-cell parameter a = 10.35 Å. The ferroelectric phase transition occurs at $-184°C$.

D. Ferroelectrics and Antiferroelectrics in Which a Pyramid is the Main Structure Element Participating in the Formation of Hydrogen Bonds. This group includes, at present, only two compounds – $LiH_3(SeO_3)_2$ and $NaH_3(SeO_3)_2$. These compounds are monoclinic at room temperature. Lithium trihydrogen selenite exhibits no phase transition [37] and its room-temperature ferroelectric phase belongs to the space group Pn (point group m); its unit-cell parameters are: a = 6.26 Å, b = 7.89 Å, c = 5.43 Å, β = 105.2°, Z = 4. The structure of $LiH_3(SeO_3)_2$ has been determined by Vedam, Okaya, and Pepinsky [48] by x-ray diffraction. They have shown that $[SeO_3]^{2-}$ ions have the pyramidal structure and are joined by the $O-H...O$ hydrogen bonds, oriented perpendicularly to the ferroelectric axis, in the same way as in potassium dihydrogen phosphate and in triglycine sulfate. Recently [46] the structure of this compound has been investigated by neutron diffraction. This study has confirmed the pyramidal structure of $[SeO_3]^{2-}$ ions and the presence of two systems of the $O-H...O$ hydrogen bonds 2.52 and 2.57 Å long. Moreover, it has been found that hydrogen atoms are localized at double potential minima with the coordinates x = 0.35,

y = 0.15, z = 0.91, and x = 0.42, respectively. These results are
in agreement with the NMR data. The appearance of the ferroelectric properties in lithium trihydrogen selenite may be similar
to the appearance of the spontaneous polarization in potassium
dihydrogen phosphate.

Another sulfate, $RbHSO_4$, is isomorphous with NH_4HSO_4, but it
has only one Curie point, $-15°C$. The structure of this compound
has not yet been determined. However, it is known that this crystal is monoclinic at room temperature in the paraelectric phase;
at this temperature, its space group is $P2_1/m$ (point group 2:m)
and its cell parameters are a = 14.36 Å, b = 4.62 Å, c = 14.81 Å,
β = 121°, Z = 8. We may assume that this compound also has the
$O-H...O$ hydrogen bonds [37].

Sodium trihydrogen selenite $NaH_3(SeO_3)_2$ is ferroelectric below $-79°C$. At room temperature, in the paraelectric phase, it
belongs to the space group $P2_1/n$ (point group 2:m) and in the ferroelectric phase it belongs to group $P1$ [47]. According to other
workers, $NaH_3(SeO_3)_2$ has the space group Pn (point group m) at
room temperature; its unit-cell parameters at this temperature
are: a = 5.90 Å, b = 4.82 Å, c = 10.19 Å, β = 91°20', Z = 2. The
structure consists of Na^+ ions, pyramidal $[HSeO_3]^-$ ions, and
H_2SeO_3 molecules. These molecules are linked by the $O-H...O$
hydrogen bonds, 2.52-2.80 Å long, and they form a chainlike system [9a, 9b].

Lithium hydrazine sulfate $Li(N_2H_5)SO_4$ is a ferroelectric with
its Curie point at 164°C. Its structure is orthorhombic, its space
group is $Pbn2_1$ (point group 2·m), and the cell parameters are
a = 8.97 Å, b = 9.91 Å, c = 5.18 Å, Z = 4 [39]. The structure of
this compound has been recently determined from x-ray diffraction and NMR data [17, 46]. The Li and S atoms are located at the
centers of oxygen tetrahedra which are joined by their vertices
and form a three-dimensional framework with large open chan-
nels occupied by hydrazinium (N_2H_5) ions oriented along the c axis.
Each NH_2 group of a hydrazinium ion forms an $N-H...N$ bond,
3.02 Å long, with a neighboring group of the same kind. The trans-
fer of a proton from one potential well to another can explain the
polarization reversal in this ferroelectric. Interesting data have
been obtained on the rotation of $[NH_3]^+$ and NH_2 groups in this compound. The $[NH_3]^+$ group begins to rotate about the $N-N$ bond at

temperatures ranging from -180 to $-140°C$. The NH_2 group also rotates, beginning from $100°C$, and a phase transition of the second kind is observed at about $164°C$.

The reported experimental data on the structures of ferroelectrics and antiferroelectrics with linear ordering consists mainly of information on the principal structure motifs and the main interatomic distances governing these arrays. The fine features of the structures, representing small changes in the interatomic distances and the nature of the mobility of the structure elements giving rise to the spontaneous polarization, are still not known for the majority of these structures. The main distinguishing characteristic of the ferroelectric and antiferroelectric structures considered here is the disorder of the structure elements above the Curie point (in the case of compounds which do not exhibit the Curie point, we can only postulate the theoretical occurrence of the paraelectric phases) and the order of these elements in the ferroelectric and antiferroelectric phases. The structures become ordered by the ordering of the protons in the hydrogen bonds typical of this group of compounds. The ordering of the protons produces such a distribution of internal fields in these crystals that dipole moments appear at the main elements of the structure. This can be seen clearly in the structures of triglycine sulfate and potassium dihydrogen phosphate. Thus, the displacements of the protons in the hydrogen bonds initiate the polarization of unit cells in ferroelectrics and antiferroelectrics. The experimental data, obtained in investigations of the absolute configurations of ferroelectric crystals, show that the principal contribution to the dipole moments of the main structure elements is not made by protons but by other atoms and ions, such as atoms of phosphorus, arsenic, and potassium in potassium dihydrogen phosphate and arsenate. The two stable equilibrium positions of protons in hydrogen bonds correspond to two possible directions of the polarization in ferroelectrics, and a change in the position of a proton corresponds to a polarization reversal. This can be seen quite easily in the case of triglycine sulfate and potassium dihydrogen phosphate.

The ferroelectrics and antiferroelectrics considered in the present section are characterized by the presence of the following hydrogen bonds: $O-H...O$ (this is the main type of bond), $N-H...O$, $N-H...F$, and $N-H...S$. The last bond is found only in

thiourea and its occurrence has not yet been confirmed. Structures of the group of compounds considered here have both strong
hydrogen bonds (the length of the O –H ... O bonds in triglycine
sulfate is 2.43 Å and in potassium dihydrogen phosphate is 2.48 Å)
and weak hydrogen bonds (in methylammonium aluminum alum
the O –H ... O bond lengths are 2.62-2.78 Å, and in guanidine aluminum sulfate hexahydrate they are 2.54-2.64 Å).

Another equally important property of the ferroelectrics and
antiferroelectrics of this type is the pseudosymmetry of their
structures. The pseudosymmetric structures are those which can
be obtained from structures of higher symmetry by slight displacements of atoms or ions. Atoms or ions which occupy special positions in the high-symmetry paraelectric phases shift to general
positions in pseudosymmetric structures. This destroys certain
symmetry axes and planes and, consequently, lowers the symmetry. The pseudosymmetry of the structures of the ferroelectrics
and antiferroelectrics considered here is mainly due to the ordering of the protons in the hydrogen bonds and, to a lesser extent,
it is also due to the displacements of other atoms or ions. Thus,
the basic structure motifs change very little in the ferroelectric
and antiferroelectric phase transitions, i.e., at transitions which
give rise to pseudosymmetry. The structures considered have
easily deformable structure motifs of definite symmetry: kinked
chains of atoms of triclinic symmetry; octahedra of cubic or lower
symmetry; tetrahedra and pyramids of trigonal or tetragonal
symmetry. The symmetry of these elements should change easily
when the internal field in a crystal is altered. The following elements are found most frequently in the ferroelectrics and antiferroelectrics of the group considered: glycine molecules
(NH_2CH_2COOH), whose configuration changes easily from amphoteric to glycinium ions; $[SO_4]^{2-}$ sulfate ions, whose symmetry
changes easily under the influence of the formation of hydrogen
bonds, in which oxygen atoms of these ions participate; $[NH_4]^{+}$
ammonium ions; phosphate $[PO_4]^{3-}$ and arsenate $[AsO_4]^{3-}$ ions.
The symmetry of all these ions changes easily, like that of sulfate
ions, due to the formation of hydrogen bonds, and dipoles are
formed by these ions when the internal field in the crystal is altered.

The ferroelectrics and antiferroelectrics considered in the
present section crystallize in heterodesmic structures, i.e., structures with bonds of different strengths. Atoms or ions in the main

structure elements are joined by mixed bonds, which are nearly covalent in the ferroelectric and antiferroelectric phases. These structure elements are bound by ionic, van der Waals, and hydrogen bonds. In this sense, the structures of ferroelectrics and antiferroelectrics do not differ in any way from the structures of other chemical compounds.

§ 2. Crystallochemical Properties of Ferroelectrics and Antiferroelectrics with Arbitrary Ordering of Structure Elements

We shall now consider the principal properties of ferroelectrics in which radicals may be ordered in an arbitrary manner below the Curie point. These compounds include double tartrates, potassium nitrate, sodium nitrite, dicalcium strontium propionate, tetramethylammonium chloro- and bromomercurates.

Early x-ray investigations of Rochelle salt $KNaC_4 \cdot H_4O_6 \cdot 4H_2O$ established that its symmetry group at room temperature is $P\,2_12_12$ (point group 2:2). It was shown later that the polar ferroelectric phase, limited by the upper ($+24.5°C$) and lower ($-18°C$) Curie points, is monoclinic and has the space group $P2_1$ (point group 2). The monoclinic angle is $90°3'$ at $11°C$. The most accurate values of the unit-cell parameters of Rochelle salt in the para- and ferroelectric phases are given in Table 29 [45].

A general idea of the structure can be obtained by examining Fig. 58 [the projection on the (001) plane is taken from [12b]]. In this projection, the oxygen atoms are designated by numbers ranging from 1 to 10: the oxygen atoms in carboxyl and hydroxyl groups are denoted by 1 to 6 and those in the water molecules by 7 to 10. The structure of Rochelle salt can be represented as consisting of

TABLE 29. Unit-Cell Parameters of Rochelle Salt (in Å) [45]

Parameters	−50 °C	+20 °C	+35 °C
a	11.315	11.867	11.878
b	14.203	14.236	14.246
c	6.195	6.213	6.218

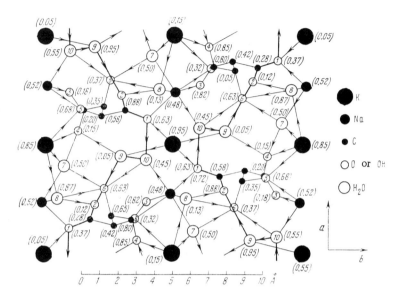

Fig. 58. Projection of the Rochelle salt structure onto the (001) plane. The numbers give the heights of the atoms along the [001] axis, expressed in fractions of the unit-cell parameter. The heavy lines represent hydrogen bonds [12b].

alternating layers of cations and anions, including the water of crystallization. The cation layers consist of sodium atoms, occupying general positions, and potassium atoms, occupying two pairs of special positions. The sodium atoms have a coordination number of six. They are surrounded by two carboxyl atoms of oxygen, a hydroxyl group, and three water molecules. The K_1 atoms $(0, 0)$ have a coordination number of eight. They are surrounded by two carboxyl atoms of oxygen and two water molecules. The other potassium atoms, $K_2 (0, 1/2)$, also have a coordination number of eight. They are surrounded by two carboxyl atoms of oxygen, two hydroxyl groups, and four water molecules. The tartrate ions are kinked chains of carbon atoms lying in two mutually perpendicular planes. The whole structure has infinite helical chains of the O−H...O hydrogen bonds between the molecules of the water of crystallization and the oxygen atoms of the anions. According to [12b], the hydrogen bonds have the following lengths: $O_1 - (H_2O)_{10} = 2.56$ Å, $(H_2O)_{10} - (H_2O)_9 = 2.86$ Å, and $(H_2O)_9 - O_2 = 3.07$ Å.

The presence of chains of hydrogen bonds, including the strong $O_1 - (H_2O)_{10}$ bond, oriented almost parallel to the ferroelectric a axis, is used in [12b] to explain the spontaneous polarization and switching: the $O_1 - (H_2O)_{10}$ bond is regarded as a dipole whose direction changes when a proton is transferred to a symmetrical potential well.

Three-dimensional x-ray [31, 4] and neutron-diffraction [21, 41] analyses have provided considerable information on the structure of Rochelle salt. X-ray diffraction studies of all three phases of Rochelle salt have not confirmed the earlier suggestions of the displacements of potassium atoms from special positions and the strong anisotropy of the thermal vibrations of these atoms along the a axis. It has been established that the $O_1 - (H_2O)_8$ bond is 0.2 Å shorter than originally thought and this has necessitated an increase in the coordination number of this atom from four to six. Six oxygen atoms form a distorted octahedron with an average distance from the center of 3.1 Å. The coordination number of the sodium atoms is six [12a, 12b]. The lengths of the Na−O bonds are basically the same for all three phases.

The tartrate ion consists of two planar groups (Fig. 59): one comprises C_1, C_2, O_1, and O_5 atoms, the other C_3, C_4, O_3, O_4, and O_6 atoms. The angle between the two groups in the high-temperature phase is 47.9°, in the ferroelectric phase it is 47.7°, and in the low-temperature phase it is 45.9° (not 60° as reported earlier). The planar configuration of the tartrate groups is not disturbed in any of the three phases, except that the C_4 atom projects by 0.07 Å from the plane of the second group in the ferroelectric phase.

This three-dimensional x-ray and neutron-diffraction analysis has confirmed basically the system of hydrogen bonds suggested in

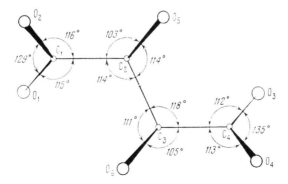

Fig. 59. Configuration of a tartrate anion.

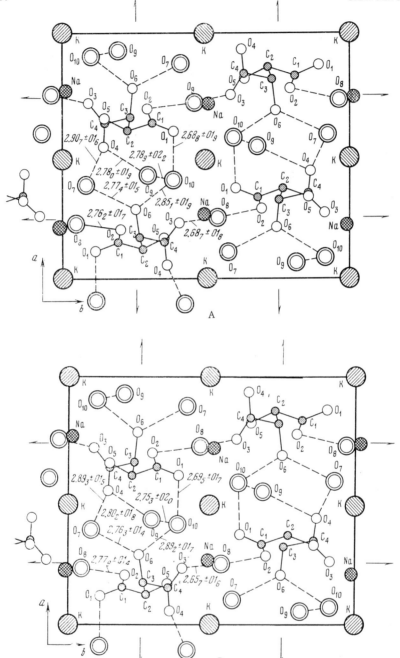

Fig. 60. Projection, onto the (001) plane, of the Rochelle salt structure in the high-temperature (A) and ferroelectric (B) phases. The dashed lines represent the hydrogen bonds.

[12b], except that the water molecule $(H_2O)_8$ has been found to be bound to the O_2 and O_3 atoms and not to the O_2 and O_6 atoms, as suggested earlier. Figures 60A and 60B show the projections on the (001) plane of the structure of Rochelle salt in the high-temperature and ferroelectric phases; the dashed lines show the hydrogen bonds. It follows from these figures that the hydrogen bonds are not affected by a ferroelectric phase transition, with the exception of the O_6-O_{10} and O_3-O_8 bonds.

The most important result obtained by the neutron-diffraction method is the determination of the role of the hydrogen bonds in the appearance of the spontaneous polarization. It is found that the $O_1-(H_2O)_{10}$ hydrogen bond is one of the longest in the structure and the proton in this bond does not play any role in the appearance of the spontaneous polarization, contradicting the suggestions of Bevers and Hughes [12a, 12b]. The main role in the appearance of the ferroelectric properties of this compound is played by dipoles associated with the hydroxyl group $(OH)_5$ and, to some extent, by the water molecule $(H_2O)_8$. Neutron-diffraction studies have indicated that these two groups have two possible orientations in the structure. In one orientation, the $(OH)_5$ group is directed toward the carboxyl oxygen O_4, which is in the next unit cell. In the other orientation, this group is not directed to any specific atom, but the proton of the group shifts to a site of the highest electronegativity. The $(H_2O)_8$ water molecules can behave in a similar manner. As a result of this orientation, the protons in the hydroxyl groups shift by 1 Å along the ferroelectric axis. All these changes in the proton positions are accompanied by shifts of other atoms in the structure, particularly by shifts of the tartrate ions. This transfers the charge from the first to the second carboxyl group in the tartrate ion. Such a redistribution of the charge is the cause of a shift of the proton of the $(OH)_5$ to a more strongly electronegative site in the structure. Thus, the mechanism responsible for the appearance of the spontaneous polarization in Rochelle salt is, to some extent, similar to that suggested by Kurchatov [5]. On this basis, we can understand why numerous spectroscopic investigations have failed to indicate changes in the hydrogen bonds at the ferroelectric phase transitions. The latest spectroscopic studies [8] and the NMR data [6] are in good agreement with this mechanism of the ordering of the $(OH)_5$ group and of the $(H_2O)_8$ water molecule.

The results of investigations of the proton magnetic resonance in Rochelle salt crystals at 24°C and below −18°C support the hypothesis of the motion of protons outside the ferroelectric range of temperatures and, to some extent, in the ferroelectric phase [14].

The structure of another ferroelectric, sodium ammonium tartrate tetrahydrate $NaNH_4C_4H_4O_6 \cdot 4H_2O$, has not yet been determined in the paraelectric or ferroelectric phases. However, it is known that, at room temperature, sodium ammonium tartrate has the same structure as Rochelle salt and the same space group $P\,2_12_12$; these unit-cell parameters are a = 12.15 Å, b = 14.40 Å, c = 6.18 Å [12a]. We may assume that this compound has a system of the N−H ... O hydrogen bonds formed by ammonium ions. A ferroelectric transition is observed in this compound at −164°C. The ferroelectric axis is the b axis. The space and point groups below the phase-transition temperature are identical with the corresponding groups of Rochelle salt.

In the group of ferroelectric tartrate monohydrates, the structure of the paraelectric phase has been determined fully only for lithium ammonium tartrate monohydrate $LiNH_4C_4H_4O_6 \cdot H_2O$. At room temperature, this compound has the space group $P2_12_12$; Z = 4; the unit-cell parameters are: a = 7.878 Å; b = 14.642 Å, c = 6.426 Å [40]. Figure 61 shows the projection of the structure of $LiNH_4C_4H_4O_6 \cdot H_2O$ onto the (001) plane. The striking feature of the structure is its very close similarity to the structure of Rochelle

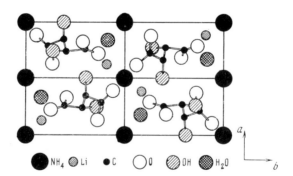

Fig. 61. Projection of the structure of $LiNH_4C_4H_4O_6 \cdot H_2O$ onto the (001) plane. The positions of the hydrogen atoms are not known.

salt. The tartrate anions have the same configuration and are located in the structure exactly as in Rochelle salt. However, water molecules $(H_2O)_{7,9,10}$ are absent. As in the Rochelle salt structure, ammonium ions occupy two special positions and are denoted by $(NH_4)_1$ and $(NH_4)_2$. The coordination number of $(NH_4)_1$ is
eight. This ammonium ion is surrounded by four oxygen atoms
which form the $N-H...O$ hydrogen bonds with the ammonium ion,
and four oxygen atoms which form van der Waals bonds. The
$N...O$ interatomic spacings are 2.84 Å (hydrogen bonds) and 3.02
Å. The coordination number of $(NH_4)_2$ is six. This ion is surrounded by four carboxyl oxygen atoms located at distances of
2.99 Å and two hydroxyl oxygen atoms at 2.90 Å. These spacings
also indicate the presence of the $N-H...O$ hydrogen bonds.
$LiNH_4C_4O_6 \cdot H_2O$ undergoes a ferroelectric phase transition at
$-167°C$. The direction of the spontaneous polarization coincides
with the b axis. The space group is $P2_1$, and the point group is
2 [41]. The structure of another ferroelectric tartrate, lithium
thallium tartrate monohydrate $LiTlC_4H_4O_6 \cdot H_2O$, has not yet been
determined.

The structure of dicalcium strontium propionate $Ca_2Sr(C_2H_5CO_2)_6$
in the paraelectric phase at room temperature is tetragonal; the
space group is $P4_12_12$ or $P4_32_12$ (point group 4:2); the unit-cell
parameters are a = 12.48 Å, c = 17.28 Å, Z = 4 [20, 33]. The main feature of this structure is the possibility of rotation of the C_2H_5 groups,
whose ordering accounts for the phase transition. Below the Curie
point (+19°C) this compound belongs to the space group $P4_1$ (point
group 4).

The structures of the ferroelectrics tetramethylammonium
trichloromercurate $N(CH_3)_4HgCl_3$ and tetramethylammonium tri-
bromomercurate $N(CH_3)_4HgBr_3$ are described by White [49].
These structures are monoclinic with the space group $P2_1$ (point
group 2); the unit-cell parameters are: a = 8.68 Å, b = 15.75 Å,
c = 7.69 Å, β = 93.0° for the first compound and a = 9.05 Å, b =
15.90 Å, c = 7.94 Å, β = 93.6° for the second compound. The structure of $N(CH_3)_4HgBr_3$ consists of tetramethylammonium ions and
$HgBr_3$ groups. The structure of these groups is nearly planar
rather than pyramidal. The Hg atoms project from the Br plane
by 0.32-0.31 Å. The tetramethylammonium ions are approximately
tetrahedral with the $N-C$ spacing of 1.35 Å. It is interesting to
consider the mechanism of polarization switching in this com-

pound. The switching process is associated with dipoles formed
by the HgBr$_3$ groups due to the projection of the Hg atoms from
the plane of the Br atoms. When the polarity of the field is reversed, the configuration of HgBr$_3$ changes to its mirror reflection and the dipole orientation is reversed. Such a change of the
structure requires atomic displacement by 0.7 Å and it can take
place without an appreciable change in the atomic packing.

The structure of KNO$_3$ in the ferroelectric region (125–115°C)
is trigonal: a = 4.365 Å, α = 76°56', Z = 1. The space group of
this compound is $R3m$ and the point group is $\bar{6} \cdot m$. The K atoms
occupy the vertices of the trigonal cell (Fig. 62). A planar triangular group [NO$_3$]$^-$ is located nearly at the center of the cell.
Above the Curie point, the NO$_3$ groups rotate about a threefold
axis, but in the ferroelectric region such rotation is difficult [11].
The structure of KNO$_3$ has not been investigated in greater detail.

The ferroelectric phase (at room temperature) of sodium nitrite, NaNO$_2$, is orthorhombic with the following unit-cell parameters: a = 3.55 Å, b = 5.38 Å, c = 5.56 Å, Z = 2. The space group
is Imm and the point group is 2·m. The high-temperature paraelectric phase, which exists above 165°C, is also orthorhombic;
its space group is $Immm$ and its point group is m·2:m. The structure of NaNO$_2$ is relatively simple and is characterized by the

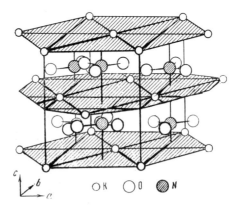

Fig. 62. Schematic representation of the distribution of atoms in the ferroelectric phase
of KNO$_3$ at 120°C.

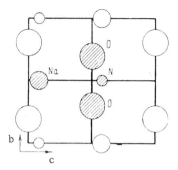

Fig. 63. Projection of the structure of $NaNO_2$ onto the (001) plane. The shaded circles represent atoms lying in the x = 1/2 plane.

presence of $[NO_2]^-$ ions which are planar triangles (within the limits of the experimental error). The relative positions of these groups and of Na^+ ions are shown in Fig. 63. Each Na^+ ion is surrounded by two oxygen atoms at a distance of 2.52 Å and four oxygen atoms at a distance of 2.47 Å. The triangular $[NO_2]^-$ ion has the following parameters: the N−O bond length is 1.24 Å and the O−N−O bond angle is 114.2°. The distance between the oxygen and sodium atoms is practically unaffected by the transition to the paraelectric phase. However, the N−O bond length increases by 0.2 Å and the O−N−O bond angle decreases considerably. The ferroelectric properties are due to the ordering of the $[NO_2]^-$ groups [15, 42a, 42b, 44, 50]. It is now known that an antiferroelectric phase exists above the ferroelectric Curie point.

Some compounds with the general formula ABX (A = Sb, Bi; B = S, Se; X = Cl, Br, I), particularly SbSCl and SbSBr, exhibit ferroelectric properties. The structure of SbSCl has been determined approximately [18], while the structure of SbSBr in the paraelectric phase is known more accurately [16]. At room temperature, these compounds are orthorhombic; the space group is *Pnam*; the point group is m·2:m; the unit-cell parameters are: a = 8.26 Å, b = 9.79 Å, c = 3.97 Å. The structure is a chain of the type

$$\diagdown \underset{\diagup}{\overset{\diagdown}{Sb}} \diagup \overset{Br}{\underset{\diagdown}{}} \diagdown \underset{\diagdown}{\overset{\diagup}{Sb}} \diagup \overset{Br}{\underset{\diagdown}{}} \diagdown \underset{\diagup}{\overset{\diagup}{Sb}} \diagdown$$

It is not clear how the spontaneous polarization appears in these two compounds.

The main distinguishing characteristic of the group of ferro-electrics considered in the present section is the ordering of radicals by hindered rotation below the Curie point. The spontaneous polarization in such compounds can appear only if the ordered radicals have dipole moments. Above the Curie point, the structures are unpolarized because of the arbitrary orientation of these dipole moments. Moreover, polarization switching in the ferroelectric state of these compounds is possible if they are two stable ordering states. The spontaneous polarization is due to the ordering of the water molecules (in tartrates), of the C_2H_5 radical (in propionate), and of $[NO_3]^-$, $[NO_2]^-$, and $[(CH_3)_4]^+$ ions.

Like the ferroelectrics and antiferroelectrics exhibiting linear ordering, the materials considered in the present section have heterodesmic pseudosymmetric structures. The main structure elements are easily deformable linear chains, tetrahedra, pyramids, and triangles. The chemical bonds in these ferroelectrics do not differ in any way from bonds in other compounds.

§3. Dipole Arrays in Ferroelectrics and Antiferroelectrics with Orderable Structure Elements [3]

When we consider the structures described in §§ 1 and 2 of the present chapter, we find that their symmetry is lower than the structures of ferroelectrics and antiferroelectrics with the oxygen-octahedral type of structure. The structures considered in the present chapter are usually orthorhombic or monoclinic in the paraelectric region and monoclinic in the polarized state. The low symmetry of these compounds may simplify or complicate the possible dipole arrays. The simplification is due to the fact that, in the case of low-symmetry structures, there are few directions which are crystallographically equivalent to the spontaneous polarization axis. As a rule, only two antiparallel directions of the P_s vectors are possible in these structures. The complication of the dipole arrays in low-symmetry structures is associated with the fact that there are frequently situations in which we have to consider cells whose enantiomorphic signs are different. One of these cases has been encountered in Chap. II in connection with the dipole arrays in the structure of $NaNbO_3$. We shall now consider

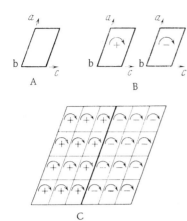

Fig. 64. Unit cell of triglycine sulfate in the paraelectric modification (A), right- and left-handed cells of domains with opposite orientations of the spontaneous polarization (B), and a dipole array in two domains (C).

the dipole arrays of both antiferroelectrics and ferroelectrics described in the present chapter (Chap. III).

Figure 64A shows the monoclinic unit cell of triglycine sulfate in the paraelectric modification. The symmetry of the cell is 2:m. Two opposite directions of the polarization along a twofold axis give rise to two different unit cells of symmetry 2 (Fig. 64B). We can call them the right- and left-handed cells. They can be distinguished as follows: if we view the cell from the positive end of the electric dipole, we find that in one cell the acute angle between the long and short edges is described by clockwise motion from the long to short edges, while in the other cell the same angle is described by anticlockwise motion. Reversal of the direction of polarization in each of these cells is accompanied by a change of the sign of the enantiomorphism. Figure 64C shows the dipole array in two neighboring domains. The sign of the enantiomorphism of these domains is shown by semicircular arrows and the associated positive or negative signs. The direction indicated by the semicircular arrows is determined by viewing all the cells from the same (for example, positive) ends of the dipoles.

In § 1 of the present chapter, we discussed the possible point symmetry groups of guanidine aluminum sulfate in the paraelectric region. Morphological investigations of this crystal (Chap. IV) show that the macroscopic structure of the domain-split state is one of the suggested symmetry groups, namely, $\overline{6}\cdot m$. The point group of the crystal (domain) in the ferroelectric state is $3\cdot m$.

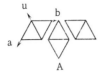

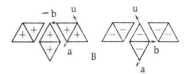

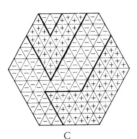

Fig. 65. Dipole array in the structure of guanidine aluminum sulfate. A) unit cells of a hypothetical high-temperature modification; B) unit cells with opposite orientations of the spontaneous polarization; C) a dipole array in the ferroelectric modification and boundaries between domains.

Figure 65 shows the dipole array in the structure of guanidine aluminum sulfate, which is in agreement with this symmetry. Figure 65A gives the three possible equivalent orientations of the unit cell of a rhombohedral crystal in the hexagonal setting; Fig. 65B shows the possible variants of the polarization for these orientations; Fig. 65C shows the dipole arrays and the boundaries between arrays of opposite orientation (domains). The dipole array is repeated along the c axis (normal to the plane of the figure): the layer under that shown in the figure consists of dipoles with the same orientations as those in the layer above. The dipole array in guanidine gallium sulfate is identical with the array in guanidine aluminum sulfate because the two compounds are isomorphous.

Interesting results can be obtained from an analysis of the dipole arrays of antiferroelectric periodates. In §1 of the present chapter, we pointed out that the possible point symmetry groups of $(NH_4)_2H_3IO_6$ are $\bar{6} \cdot m$ or $\bar{6}$ and that the dimension of the unit cell of this compound doubles along the a axis at the antiferroelectric transition but the dimension along the c axis is not affected. In the case of $Ag_2H_3IO_6$, we only know definitely that after the ferroelectric phase transition the dimensions of the unit cell are doubled along the a and c axes.

The dipole arrays of $(NH_4)_2H_3IO_6$ and $Ag_2H_3IO_6$ are shown in Fig. 66. Figure 66A shows a possible arrangement of the unit cells before the phase transition. In the absence of polarization,

all these cells are equivalent. Figures 66B, 66D, and 66F show
multiple cells, of the type illustrated in Fig. 66a, after the antiferroelectric phase transition, i.e., after the polarization of these
multiple cells along the c axis. Each of these cells is a unit cell
in an antiferroelectric domain; the unit cells in different domains
are different (Fig. 66H) and a cell in one domain cannot be transformed by translation alone into a cell in another domain.

Assuming that under each unit cell in the upper layer of
$(NH_4)_2H_3IO_6$ (Fig. 66H) there is a layer of unit cells with the same
orientation of the dipole moment, i.e., that there is no multiple-
cell structure along the c axis, we find that the symmetry group
of this crystal in the high-temperature state should be $\bar{6}\cdot m$ and not
$\bar{6}$.

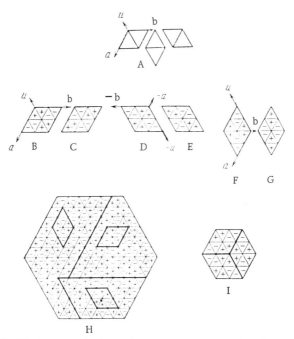

Fig. 66. Dipole arrays in the multiple-cell structure of antiferroelectric
periodates: A) a unit cell in the paraelectric modification; B, D, F)
multiple unit cells in $(NH_4)_2H_3IO_6$ and multiple unit cells in the first layer in $Ag_2H_3IO_6$; C, E, G) multiple unit cells in the second layer in
$Ag_2H_3IO_6$; H) dipole arrays, domain boundaries, and multiple unit cells;
I) ideal dipole arrays consisting of three multiple cells of different orientations (symmetry of this array is $\bar{6}\cdot m$).

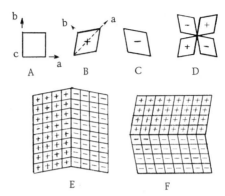

Fig. 67. Dipole arrays in KH_2PO_4: A) a unit
cell in the paraelectric modification; B, C)
identical unit cells with the opposite orientations of P_s in the ferroelectric modification; D) a combination of polarized cells
having the symmetry group $\bar{4}{\cdot}m$ in the paraelectric modification; E, F) variants of dipole arrays with domain boundaries along the
(100) and (010) planes.

If we assume that $Ag_2H_3IO_6$ has a multiple-cell structure also
along the c axis, we find that the unit cells shown in Figs. 66B,
66D, and 66F in the first layer correspond to the unit cells shown
in Figs. 66C, 66E, and 66G in the next layer. An assembly of such
cells forms the symmetry group $m{\cdot}3{:}m$. Obviously, $Ag_2H_3IO_6$ has
the same point symmetry group in the paraelectric phase because
(Chap. IV) ideally after the phase transition this crystal returns
to the symmetry of the original phase (in the macroscopic sense).
This applies also to antiferroelectrics if all the domains in this
structure are equivalent (as in Fig. 66I). The dipole array in the
structure of $Ag_2H_3IO_6$ is the same as in the structure of $(NH_4)_2H_3IO_6$
(Fig. 66H) but in the case of silver periodate each cell in the first
layer has a cell with the opposite polarization in the second layer;
the polarization of the cells of the third layer is the same as in
the first layer.

Figure 67 shows the original and phase-transition-distorted
cells of KH_2PO_4 and the dipole arrays which appear in this structure. The original tetragonal cell (Fig. 67A) becomes orthorhombic (group $2{\cdot}m$) after the appearance of the spontaneous polariza-

tion along the 4 axis. This distortion of the cell can be regarded as a result of a piezoelectric deformation due to the appearance of the spontaneous polarization.

The cells with opposite polarizations in potassium dihydrogen phosphate (Figs. 67B and 67C) are indistinguishable (except for a rotation). The four cells shown in Fig. 67D represent the ideal orientation of dipoles in a crystal after the phase transition and they correspond to the point symmetry group $\bar{4} \cdot m$, which is identical with the symmetry group before the transition.

The dipole arrays in real structures of KH_2PO_4 can be represented by a combination of any pairs of cells in Fig. 67D with opposite signs of polarization (close packing of the cells is assumed). The dipole arrays of two (out of four possible) combinations are shown in Figs. 67E and 67F. The boundaries between cells with different directions of antipolarization (between domains) are always the (100) or (010) planes. These are the planes of symmetry present in the crystal before the phase transition. The coordinate system of a domain is rotated by 45° relative to the system of coordinates of the original crystal (see § 1 in the present chapter). Moreover, the c axis of the tetragonal structure becomes the b axis in the orthorhombic structure.

The dipole array in antiferroelectric $NH_4H_2PO_4$ (below $-125°C$) is shown in Fig. 68. The tetragonal cell (Fig. 68A) becomes monoclinic and acquires the symmetry group 2 after the appearance of the spontaneous polarization along a twofold axes.* The distortion of the cell at the transition point can be found by considering its piezoelectric deformation due to the appearance of the spontaneous polarization along the a and b axes. This distortion can be regarded as a shearing of the cell in the ac or bc plane, resulting in a change of the original angle (90°) between the a and c or b and c axes. We must change the axes in the new cell: the a axis, along which the spontaneous polarization appears, now becomes the b axis; the c axis is not affected (Figs. 68B and 68C). An ideal multiple cell in the antiferroelectric modification is shown in Fig. 68D. This cell should have the symmetry of the original crystal (group $\bar{4} \cdot m$) and it therefore follows that the cells shown in Fig. 68B and 68C have different signs of enantiomorphism; one of them is right-handed and the other left-handed. Only in this case can we retain

---

*It is assumed that a and b are twofold axes.

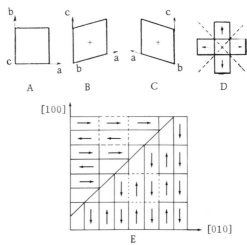

Fig. 68. Dipole arrays in antiferroelectric $NH_4H_2PO_4$; A) a unit cell in the paraelectric modification; B) a right-handed cell with the polarization (in the original arrangement) along [100]; C) a left-handed cell with the polarization (in the original arrangement) along [010]; D) a combination of polarized cells of group $\bar{4}\cdot m$; E) dipole arrays, unit cells, and domain boundaries in the antiferroelectric modification.

two planes of symmetry passing through the $\bar{4}$ axis. The conclusion that the cells have the opposite signs of enantiomorphism follows also from the fact that the [100] and [010] directions in a crystal are reflection-equivalent but cannot be made to coincide.

In a real structure, corresponding to each of the antiferroelectric domains, we have only one type of orientation of P (Chap. IV). A given multiple cell, which represents one of the two possible types of polarization, consists of four old cells (four subcells) and has (according to structure investigation) the 2:2 symmetry (Fig. 68E). Each of the domains consists of cells of the same sign of enantiomorphism; different domains have the opposite signs of enantiomorphism.

Relatively simple dipole arrays are encountered in ferroelectrics whose paraelectric phase is of the m·2:m symmetry and whose ferroelectric phase has the symmetry group 2·m due to the appearance of the spontaneous polarization along one of the twofold axes [$(NH_4)_2BeF_4$, $NaNO_2$, etc.]. The oppositely polarized or-

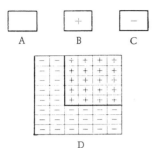

Fig. 69. Dipole arrays in ferroelectrics whose paraelectric modifications have the m·2:m symmetry [$(NH_4)_2BeF_4$, $NaNO_2$]: A) a unit cell in the paraelectric modification; B-C) identical cells polarized in opposite directions in the ferroelectric modification; D) dipole arrays and domain boundaries.

thorhombic cells can be made identical after rotation (Figs. 69B and 69C) and the dipole arrays in different domains can have boundaries which are parallel to the cell faces (Fig. 69D).

The dipole arrays in Rochelle salt are of considerable interest. The original orthorhombic cell of the 2:2 symmetry (Fig. 70A) becomes monolinic after the phase transition (due to the appearance of the spontaneous polarization along the a axis) and its symmetry is then 2. The monoclinic distortion of the cell can be explained by a piezoelectric deformation which accompanies the electric polarization. The change in the cell requires a change in the nomenclature of the axes so that the orthorhombic a axis becomes the monoclinic b axis and conversely; the c axis is not affected (Fig. 70B). The oppositely oriented cells have the same sign of enantiomorphism (Figs. 70B and 70C). The original symmetry of the crystal (group 2:2) can be obtained by a combination of monoclinic

Fig. 70. Dipole arrays in the structure of Rochelle salt: A) a unit cell in the paraelectric modification; B-C) identical unit cells in the ferroelectric modification with opposite orientations of the spontaneous polarization vector P_s; D) a combination of cells having the symmetry group of the paraelectric modification 2:2; E-F) dipole arrays and possible domain boundaries along (010) and (001) (expressed in indices of the paraelectric modification).

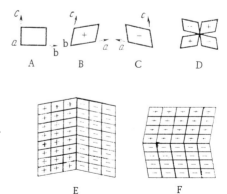

polarized cells (Fig. 70D). Pair combinations in the close packing of neighboring cells of opposite polarity give rise to orientations of boundaries between domains along the (001) and (010) planes. Two (out of the four possible) such combinations are shown in Figs. 70E and 70F).

The dipole arrays in the structure of dicalcium strontium propionate $Ca_2Sr(C_2H_5CO_2)_6$ should be very simple. The tetragonal cell with the 4:2 symmetry remains tetragonal after the appearance of the polarization along a fourfold axis and it acquires a symmetry of class 4 (Figs. 71A-C). The cells with opposite polarization are identical and the boundaries between the arrays of opposite orientations coincide with the (100) and (010) planes (Fig. 71D).

The dipole arrays described in the present section are in agreement with the experimentally established symmetries in the paraelectric and ferroelectric (or antiferroelectric) phases. A dipole array represents the final result of a rearrangement of the structure; it corresponds to orientations of the spontaneous polarization vectors directed from the centers of gravity of negative charges to the centers of gravity of positive charges. In this sense, the dipole moments represent also real displacements of atoms, molecules, and ions in a crystal. In some cases, the appearance of the dipole moments may be associated with the displacements of specific particles. Thus, it is shown in §§ 1 and 2 of the present chapter that the appearance of polarization in triglycine sulfate is accompanied by the displacement of the NH_4^+

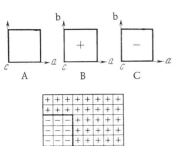

Fig. 71. Dipole arrays in dicalcium strontium propionate: A) a unit cell in the paraelectric modification; B-C) identical unit cells in ferroelectric modification with opposite orientations of the spontaneous polarization; D) dipole arrays and domain boundaries.

group of glycinium I along the b axis; the appearance of polarization in KH_2PO_4 may be attributed to the displacement of phosphorus and potassium atoms along the c axis, etc. However, we must not forget that the phase transitions in all the ferroelectrics and antiferroelectrics described in the present chapter cannot be described simply by the unidirectional displacements of certain particles in a crystal. Phase transitions in these crystals are associated with ordering of the structure elements, which are the hydrogen atoms in the case of triglycine sulfate and KH_2PO_4, the water molecules in Rochelle salt, etc. Only such ordering produces a change in the structure, which results in the polarization of the cells.

References

1. L. A. Varfolomeeva, G. S. Zhdanov, and M. M. Umanskii, Kristallografiya, 3: 368 (1958).
2. V. F. Dvoryankin and B. K. Vainshtein, Kristallografiya 5:589 (1960).
3. I. S. Zheludev, Proc. Indian Acad. Sci., A57:361 (1963).
4. I. Krstanovic, Y. Okaya, and R. Pepinsky, Bull. Acad. Serbe Sciences Arts, Cl. Sci. Math. Natur., Sci. Natur., 32(9):149 (1963).
5. I. V. Kurchatov, Ferroelectrics [in Russian], GTTI, Moscow (1933); French translation: Le Champ Moléculaire dans les Diéléctriques (le Sel de Seignette), Hermann, Paris (1936).
6. A. G. Lundin, K. S. Aleksandrov, G. M. Mikhailov, and S. P. Gabuda, Izv. Akad. Nauk SSSR, Ser. Fiz., 24:1195 (1960).
7. V. A. Pospelov and G. S. Zhdanov, Zh. Fiz. Khim., 21:405 (1947).
8. A. I. Stekhanov, Z. A. Gab'ichidze, and E. A. Popova, in: Hydrogen Bond [in Russian], Nauka, Moscow (1964), p. 127.
9a. Chou Kung-Tu and T'ang Yu-Ch'i, Acta Scient. Natur. Univ. Pekin., 4:201 (1958).
9b. Chou Kung-Tu and T'ang Yu-Ch'i, Scientia (K'o Hsüeh T'ung Pao), No. 10, p. 299 (1957).
10a. G. E. Bacon and R. S. Pease, Proc. Roy. Soc. (London), A230:359 (1955).
10b. G. E. Bacon and R. S. Pease, Proc. Roy. Soc. (London), A220:397 (1953).
11. T. F. W. Barth, Z. Physik. Chem. (Leipzig), 43B:448 (1939).
12a L. A. Beevers and W. Hughes, Nature, 146:96 (1940).
12b. L. A. Beevers and W. Hughes, Proc. Roy. Soc. (London), A177:251 (1941).
13. R. Blinc and I. J. Levstek, J. Phys. Chem. Solids, 12:295 (1960).
14. R. Blinc and A. Prelesnik, J. Chem. Phys., 32:387 (1960).
15. G. B. Carpenter, Acta Cryst., 5:132 (1952).
16. G. D. Christofferson and G. D. McCullough, Acta Cryst., 12:14 (1959).
17. J. D. Cuthbert, I. D. Brown, and H. E. Petch (Abstracts of Papers presented at Sixth Intern. Congress and Symposia on Crystallography, Rome, 1963), Acta Cryst., 16:A184 (1963).

18.   E. Dönges, Z. Anorg. Allgem. Chem., 263:112, 280 (1950).
19.   S. Emsley and J. A. S. Smith, (8e Colloque Ampère, London, 1959), Archives des Sciences, 12 (Fasc. spec.) 122 (1959).
20.   E. Ferroni and P. Orioli, Gazz. Chim. Ital., 89:732 (1959).
21.   B. C. Frazer, M. McKeown, and R. Pepinsky, Phys. Rev., 94:1435 (1954).
22.   B. C. Frazer and R. Pepinsky, Acta Cryst., 6:273 (1953).
23.   S. Geller and D. P. Booth, Z. Krist., 111:117 (1959).
24.   G. J. Goldsmith and J. G. White, J. Chem. Phys. 31:1175 (1959).
25.   H. Helmholtz, J. Am. Chem. Soc., 59:2036 (1937).
26.   S. Hoshino, I. Okaya, and R. Pepinsky, Phys. Rev., 115:323 (1959).
27.   R. O. Keeling and R. Pepinsky, Z. Krist., 106:236 (1955).
28.   R. S. Krishnan and P. S. Narayanan, Programme and Abstracts of Intern. Symp. on Protein Structure and Crystallography, Madras, 1963.
29.   H. Lipson and C. A. Beevers, Proc. Roy. Soc. (London), A148:664 (1935).
30.   Y. Okaya, M. S. Ahmed, R. Pepinsky, and V. Vand, Z. Krist., 109:367 (1957).
31.   Y. Okaya, R. Pepinsky, I. Shibuya, I. Krstanović, K. Vedam, S. Hoshino, T. Mitsui, B. Singh, M. Kay, and B. C. Frazer (Abstracts of Papers presented at Fifth Intern. Congress on Crystallography, Cambridge, 1960), Acta. Cryst., 13: 1073 (1960).
32.   Y. Okaya, K. Vedam, and R. Pepinsky, Acta Cryst., 11:307 (1958).
33.   P. Orioli and M. Pieroni, Ricerca Scientifica, 29:295 (1959).
34.   R. Pepinsky and K. Vedam, Phys. Rev., 114:1217 (1959).
35.   R. Pepinsky, Y. Okaya, D. P. Eastman, and T. Mitsui, Phys. Rev., 107:1538 (1957).
36.   R. Pepinsky, Y. Okaya, and T. Mitsui, Acta Cryst., 10:600 (1957).
37.   R. Pepinsky and K. Vedam, Phys. Rev., 117:1502 (1960).
38.   R. Pepinsky, K. Vedam, S. Hoshino, and Y. Okaya, Phys. Rev., 111:1508(1958).
39.   R. Pepinsky, K. Vedam, Y. Okaya, and S. Hoshino, Phys. Rev., 111:1467 (1958).
40.   A. J. J. Sprenkels, Proc. Koninkl. Nederlands Akad. Wetenschap., 59B:221 (1956).
41.   G. Shirane, F. Jona, and R. Pepinsky, Proc. IRE, 43:1738 (1955).
42a. B. Strijk and C. H. MacGillavry, Rec. Trav. Chim., 62:705 (1943).
42b. B. Strijk and C. H. MacGillavry, Rec. Trav. Chim., 65:127 (1946).
43.   L. Tenzer, B. C. Frazer, and R. Pepinsky, Acta Cryst., 11:505 (1958).
44.   M. R. Truter, Acta Cryst., 7:73 (1954).
45.   A. R. Ubbelohde and I. Woodward, Proc. Roy. Soc. (London), A185:448 (1946).
46.   J. H. Van den Hende and H. P. Boutin (Abstracts of Papers presented at Sixth Intern. Congress and Symposia on Crystallography, Rome, 1963), Acta. Cryst., 16:A30 (1963).
47.   K. Vedam, Current Sci., 29:79 (1960).
48.   K. Vedam, Y. Okaya, and R. Pepinsky, Phys. Rev., 119:1252 (1960).
49.   J. G. White, Acta Cryst., 16:397 (1963).
50.   G. E. Ziegler, Phys. Rev., 38:1040 (1931).
51.   I. S. Zheludev and L. A. Shuvalov, Trudy In-ta Kristallografii Akad. Nauk SSSR, No. 12, p. 59 (1956).
52.   I. S. Zheludev and L. A. Shuvalov, Kristallografiya, 1:681 (1956).
53.   Z. V. Zvonkova and Yu. Tashpulatov, Kristallografiya, 3:553 (1958).

54. W. Känzig, "Ferroelectrics and antiferroelectrics," Solid State Phys., 4:1 (1957).
55. W. P. Mason, Piezoelectric Crystals and Their Application to Ultrasonics, Van Nostrand, New York (1950).
56. A. S. Sonin and I. S. Zheludev, Kristallografiya, 4:487 (1959).
57. A. S. Sonin and I. S. Zheludev, in: Physics of Dielectrics (Proc. Second All-Union Conf., Moscow, 1958) [in Russian], Izd. AN SSSR, Moscow (1960), p. 366.
58. V. V. Udalova, Kristallografiya, 6:629 (1961).
59. L. A. Shuvalov, K. S. Aleksandrov, and I. S. Zheludev, Kristallografiya, 4:130 (1959).
60. L.A. Shuvalov and A. S. Sonin, Kristallografiya, 6:323 (1961).
61. C. J. Calvo, J. Chem. Phys., 33:1721 (1960).
62. L. Demény and I. Nitta, Bull. Chem. Soc., Japan, 3:128 (1928).
63. E. Fatuzzo and R. Nitsche, Phys. Rev., 117:936 (1960).
64. J. Fousek, Českoslov. Časopis. Fys., A11:495 (1961).
65. H. Gränicher, W. M. Meier, and W. Petter, Helv. Phys. Acta, 27:216 (1954).
66. O. Hassel, Z. Elektrochem., 31:523 (1925).
67. S. B. Hendricks, Am. J. Sci., 14:269 (1927).
68. S. B. Hendricks, J. Am. Chem. Soc., 50:2455 (1928).
69. H. von R. Jaffe, 51:43 (1937).
70. F. C. Kracek, T. F. W. Barth, and C. J. Ksanda, Phys. Rev., 40:1034 (1932).
71. R. S. Krishnan and K. Balasubramian. Proc. Indian Acad. Sci., A48:138(1958).
72. N. R. Kunchur and M. R. Truter, J. Chem. Soc., p. 2551 (1958).
73. H. A. Levy, S. W. Peterson, and S. H. Simonsen, Phys. Rev., 93:1120 (1954).
74. H. D. Megaw, Ferroelectricity in Crystals, Methuen, London (1957).
75. H. Mueller, Phys. Rev., 57:829 (1940).
76. R. S. Pease and G. E. Bacon, Nature, 173:443 (1954).
77. R. Pepinsky, Y. Okaya, and F. Jona, Bull. Am. Phys. Soc., 2:220 (1957).
78. R. Pepinsky, Y. Okaya, and F. Unterleitner (Abstracts of Papers presented at Fifth Intern. Conf. on Crystallography, Cambridge, 1960), Acta. Cryst., 13: 1071 (1960).
79. S. W. Peterson, H. A. Levy, and S. H. Simonsen, J. Chem. Phys., 21:2084 (1953).
80. I. Shibuya and T. Mitsui, J. Phys. Soc. Japan, 16:479 (1961).
81. G. Shirane, F. Jona, and R. Pepinsky, Proc. IRE, 43:1738 (1955).
82. L. Taurel, C. Delain, and C. Guérin, Compt. Rend., 246:3042 (1958).
83. B. E. Warren and H. M. Krutter, Phys. Rev., 43:500 (1933).
84. J. West, Z. Krist., 74:306 (1930).
85. E. A. Wood and A. N. Holden, Acta Cryst., 10:145 (1957).
86. R. W. G. Wyckoff and R. D. Corey, Z. Krist., 81:386 (1932).

Chapter IV

Domain Structure of
Ferroelectrics and Antiferroelectrics

Introduction

Assemblies of spontaneously polarized unit cells form regions known as domains. All the unit cells within a domain in a ferro-electric are oriented identically. Consequently, each domain has a macroscopic spontaneous electric polarization. The directions of the spontaneous polarizations of neighboring domains in a fer-roelectric make definite angles with one another. Domain walls (boundaries) in ferroelectrics should be considered not only as having geometrical form but also as being electrically neutral and corresponding to a minimum of the energy of a crystal. Conse-quently, the dipoles in neighboring domains should be oriented in such a way that, at a wall, the projection of the polarization vector of one domain should be equal in magnitude and opposite in sign to the projection of the polarization vector of another (neighboring) domain.

Ferroelectrics have multiple unit cells. Such cells are formed by neighboring cells of the paraelectric modification (subcells), having antiparallel orientations of the polarization. Multiple unit cells of neighboring domains are different. In some cases, this difference is manifested by different directions of the subcell po-larization in neighboring domains (for example, in $PbZrO_3$); in other cases, multiple cells not only have different directions of the subcell polarization but also different signs of enantiomorph-ism (for example, $NH_4H_2PO_4$). Antiferroelectric domains do not exhibit macroscopic polarization.

Real ferroelectrics and antiferroelectrics consist of domains, i.e., they have a domain structure, below the relevant phase transition temperature. In a simplified approach it is assumed that domains of a given compound are in the form of identical "bricks" oriented with the same probability along various crystallographically equivalent directions. In real crystals, external factors, growth conditions, etc., may disturb the uniformity of the domain structure.

A ferroelectric crystal splits into domains because such splitting lowers the free energy by reducing the electrostatic energy of the spontaneous polarization charges. However, domain splitting cannot be continued without limit because a definite energy is required for the formation of domain walls. The splitting of a crystal into domains stops when the energy gained by reduction of the electrostatic energy becomes equal to the energy lost in the formation of walls. These considerations apply to an open-circuited crystal. However, the splitting into domains occurs also in short-circuited crystals if only because the polarization, which arises at different points in a crystal at the Curie temperature, is equally likely to assume any of the various crystallographically equivalent directions. This equiprobable distribution of the polarization directions is responsible for the splitting of antiferroelectric crystals into domains (in the case of antiferroelectrics, there is no reduction in the electrostatic energy because antiferroelectric domains are not polar). In some real crystals, the splitting into domains depends strongly on the presence of stressed regions, defects, as well as on external electric and mechanical fields, etc.

The presence of domains in ferroelectric crystals was predicted, on the basis of indirect observations, much earlier than domains were actually observed experimentally. They were predicted on the basis of the following observations: a low value of the coercive field, polarization jumps (similar to Barkhausen jumps in ferromagnets), some multiple-cell structure lines in x-ray diffraction patterns of ferroelectrics, etc. The first direct observarions of domains were made in the late thirties on Rochelle salt. X-cut Rochelle salt crystals were sprinkled with charged powders (used earlier to study the polarization of pyroelectrics) and this procedure revealed oppositely polarized stripes. Domains were later investigated optically in $BaTiO_3$, Rochelle salt, and other crystals. Many new methods have since been developed for investigating the domain structure of crystals. The methods are described in this chapter (§2).

Experimental investigations of ferroelectric and antiferroelectric domains are concerned mainly with three topics: domain geometry (orientations, sizes, shapes of walls, etc.), changes in domains under the influence of temperature, and domain motion in external mechanical and electric fields. The first topic has been considered partly at the end of Chap. II and in Chap. III in connection with the dipole arrays in some ferroelectrics and antiferroelectrics. We shall now discuss briefly the geometrical features of domains. Later in this chapter we shall consider results of investigations of the static domain structure of ferroelectrics and antiferroelectrics and we shall describe changes in this structure with temperature. We shall also discuss domain walls. The role of domains in various physical properties of crystals (polarization, piezoelectric effect, electrostriction, etc.) is considered in the second volume of this book.

§1. Some Aspects of Domain Geometry

The point group symbols in Tables 7-11 (Chap. II) are followed by a number of directions (enclosed in parentheses) which are crystallographically equivalent to the direction along which the spontaneous polarization is actually oriented. We can easily see that an assembly of domains oriented uniformly over all possible crystallographically equivalent directions has the same macroscopic symmetry group (i.e., the group of the whole ferroelectric crystal split into domains) as before the transition, i.e., the

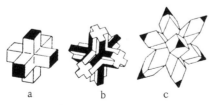

Fig. 72. Schematic representation of the possible orientations of domains in BaTiO$_3$ crystals (class $\bar{6}/4$) after transitions: $\bar{6}/4 \rightarrow$ 4·m (a), $\bar{6}/4 \rightarrow 2·$m (b), and $\bar{6}/4 \rightarrow 3·$m (c).

symmetry group of the paraelectric modification. Thus, after it has split into domains, a ferroelectric crystal reverts macroscopically to its original symmetry and its macroscopic properties (for example, elastic, piezoelectric, and other properties) should be considered using the "old" symmetry. Figure 72 shows assemblies of $BaTiO_3$ domains in all three ferroelectric modifications of this compound (tetragonal, orthorhombic, and trigonal): all these assemblies have the same point symmetry $\bar{6}/4$, which is the symmetry of the paraelectric modification of barium titanate.

A set of crystallographically equivalent directions is a set of possible orientations of the spontaneous polarization in individual domains. The number of crystallographically equivalent directions is given by the expression

$$n = \frac{N_1}{N_2},\qquad\qquad(IV.1)$$

where N_1 and N_2 are the orders of the groups of the whole crystal and of a single domain, respectively. The relationship (IV.1) is valid for directions which are not of the polar vector type. Along the nonpolar directions we can have domains with antiparallel polarizations. This gives rise to "180°" walls between such domains. The number of equivalent directions for the polar vector orientations is half the number given by Eq. (IV.1). The 180° walls cannot exist between domains polarized along the polar vector directions.

If we consider ferroelectric domains as twins, we can show that the symmetry elements of twinning are those elements of a crystal which are lost on transition from a single domain to the whole crystal. This circumstance explains why a crystal reverts to is original symmetry after splitting into domains.

A detailed consideration of each of the equivalent directions yields the values of the possible angles between domains (between directions of their spontaneous polarization P_s) and the orientations of the walls between domains. Bearing in mind the fact that in real crystals the components of domain twins are combined in pairs, we can find all the possible combinations. In other words, for each specific crystal we can solve all the problems associated with the domain-structure geometry. Thus, for example, in crystals of class $\bar{6}/4$ (BaTiO$_3$ case) the transition $\bar{6}/4 \rightarrow 4 \cdot$m permits combinations with the 180° walls (antiparallel orientation in neighboring domains) as well as the 90° walls [mutually perpendicular orientations with the walls along (110) planes]. In the case of the $\bar{6}/4 \rightarrow 3 \cdot$m transition, the directions of P$_s$ in neighboring domains can make angles of 70°35', 109°28', and 180°, and, in the $\bar{6}/4 \rightarrow 2 \cdot$m case we can have 60°, 90°, 120°, and 180° domain walls.

It is not surprising that domains can be "right-handed" or "left-handed" because they can have the symmetry of any of the pyroelectric classes whose symmetry elements include only simple rotation axes. A more interesting observation is that a given crystal can have domains of two enantiomorphous modifications. This can be seen easily in the case of transitions which occur, for example, in the classes 6:m, 4:m, 3:m, 2:m. Here, the opposite directions of P$_s$ along an axis of symmetry (these directions are equivalent in all three classes) give rise to enantiomorphous modifications of domains (some right-handed and some left-handed).

The relative scarcity of the experimental data on the structure and properties of antiferroelectrics prevents us from drawing final conclusions about laws governing the domain orientation in these materials. Therefore, our discussion will be limited to some aspects of the domain geometry of antiferroelectrics. Bearing in mind the multiple-unit cell structure of antiferroelectrics, we may conclude that the general relationships governing the orientation of the P$_s$ vectors of subcells in antiferroelectrics are exactly identical with the relationships governing the orientation of domains in ferroelectrics. It follows, in particular, that below the phase-transition point an antiferroelectric has the symmetry of the original high-temperature phase. Consequently, the characteristic features of the phase transitions involving a change in the direction (and magnitude) of P$_s$ in antiferroelectrics are exactly the same as the characteristics of the analogous transitions in ferroelectrics. In other words, if we consider an antiferroelectric domain as one original unit cell (the cell before the transition and the formation of a multiple cell), we find that all the relationships governing the orientation of the P$_s$ vectors of the subcells of such antiferroelectric "domains" are identical with the analogous relationships for ferroelectrics. This is the foundation of any discussion of the structure of antiferroelectric domains.

In view of the conclusions drawn in the preceding paragraph, we must consider in more detail the multiple-cell structure in antiferroelectrics. We note that the number of subcells in a multiple cell is governed by the number of crystallographic directions which are equivalent to a given direction of the spontaneous polarization. This follows from the fact that all the equivalent directions of P_s in a multiple cell should be represented in the same way. The number of such directions (for different directions of P_s) can be found for nonpolar crystals using Tables 7-11 or similar data tabulations. Antiferroelectrics are characterized by assemblies which give rise to structures compensated in respect of the dipoles. This means that multiple cells in antiferroelectrics have the point symmetry of the nonpolar centrosymmetric classes or of the polar-neutral classes.

We must point out that perfect three-dimensional periodicity of a multiple unit cell is very unlikely to be encountered in real crystals if only because of packing considerations. Therefore, in many cases a multiple unit cell does not represent all the possible subcells but only some of them. In the simplest cases we have combinations of two antiparallel cells, two cells whose polarizations are inclined at some angle to each other, etc.

The multiplicity of various combinations of subcells, forming a given multiple unit cell, means that the domain structure of antiferroelectrics is, generally speaking, more complex than that in ferroelectrics. Therefore, the terms "domain" and "twin component" do not have simple meanings in the case of antiferroelectrics. We shall assume that in an antiferroelectric domain the orientation of P_s in unit cells is of the same type (but not of the same direction). In neighboring domains (which have the same type of orientation of P_s) the directions of the polarization meet at some definite angle. Antiferroelectric domains do not give rise to the macroscopic polarization. Some idea of the nature of orientation of dipoles in neighboring domains in an antiferroelectric can be gained from Fig. 73A.

The presence of domains in antiferroelectrics, each of which represents the orientation of P_s of some unit cells, frequently impedes correct interpretation of the experimentally determined multiple-cell structures and symmetries of crystals observed after a phase transition.

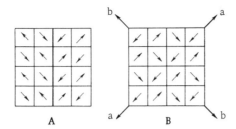

Fig. 73. Schematic representation of the orientation of dipoles in antiferroelectric domains:
A) a compensated structure; B) a combination of compensated (antiferroelectric) and uncompensated (ferroelectric) structures.

In addition to ferroelectrics and antiferroelectrics, there is a class of compounds which is called ferrielectrics, weak ferroelectrics, or cone ferroelectrics. Such crystals exhibit ferroelectric properties along some directions and antiferroelectric properties along other directions. Weak ferroelectrics (or ferrielectrics) can be considered as partly compensated antiferroelectrics. In fact, antiferroelectrics containing domains which represent only some of the possible combinations, can exhibit ferroelectric properties (uncompensated dipole structure) along some directions of an external field and antiferroelectric properties (compensated dipole structure) along other directions. This is illustrated in Fig. 73B, which shows that the direction of the a–a diagonals of the large square, representing an assembly of dipoles, is compensated, whereas the b–b direction is uncompensated. Hence, we can expect to observe ferroelectric properties (weak ferroelectricity) along the b–b direction and antiferroelectric properties along the a–a direction. In some cases it is assumed that ferrielectrics are characterized by uncompensated structure of the type shown in this figure. Obviously, weak ferroelectricity is possible in those ferroelectrics in which the energies of the parallel and antiparallel interaction of dipoles are similar.

§ 2. Methods for Investigating Domain Structure of Crystals

A. Charged-Powder Method. In this method, charged-powder particles are attracted (by the electrostatic interaction) to bound charges associated with the spontaneous polarization. There are several variants of this method. Thus, domains in Rochelle salt (described in the introduction to the present chapter) have been investigated using a mixture of red lead oxide and sulfur (lycopodium is sometimes added to such a mixture), which become oppositely charged during mixing: red lead oxide becomes positively charged and sulfur becomes negative. Since the components of a powder mixture have different colors (lead oxide is red and sulfur is yellow), the surface of a ferroelectric crystal becomes coated with colored stripes, which represent (reasonably accurately) the domain structure. In simple experiments only red oxide or sulfur alone is used.

The domain structure can be made visible by direct deposition of a mixture of powders (or one powder) on a crystal or by immersion of a crystal in a liquid dielectric (kerosene, alcohol, carbon tetrachloride) containing a fine suspension of the charged powder. The use of a liquid produces a clearer pattern. Figure 74 shows photographs of a Y-cut triglycine sulfate crystal which was immersed in a fine suspension of red lead oxide in carbon tetrachloride in order to delineate the unipolar structure of blocks

Fig. 74. Visualization of domains by the precipitation of charged particles on Y-cut triglycine sulfate: a) powder pattern on one side of a plate; b) the same pattern on the opposite side. It is evident from Fig. 74 that the opposite sides of unipolar blocks differ greatly in the intensity of their coloring [10].

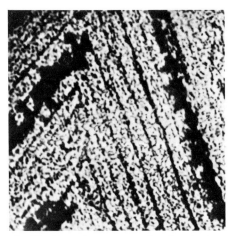

Fig. 75. Domain structure of an $(NH_4)_2SO_4$
crystal made visible by the dew method on
a surface cut at right-angles to the c axis.
Domain walls are oriented along (430)
planes [14b].

in this crystal. Within each block we can distinguish spots of different degrees of blackening, which represent different domains.

The domain structure can also be investigated by the deposition of smoke particles and by freezing water droplets (this is
known as the modified dew method, Fig. 75).

When a ferroelectric crystal is stored for a long time at a
constant temperature the bound charges of the domains are compensated by charges attracted from air or by internal charges
which move due to finite electrical conductivity of a crystal. Consequently, it is frequently necessary to heat a crystal before the
"visualization" of its domains by powders. Such heating produces
an additional charge resulting from the pyroelectric effect and this
charge can easily be made visible. Charges captured from air
can sometimes be removed by passing a crystal quickly through
the flame of a burner.

The powder method can be used to determine reliably the nature of the domain structure of a crystal, the directions of domain
polarization, etc. However, charged powders may be deposited
also at those points on a crystal where piezoelectric charges appear due to local stresses. This makes it possible to study inhomogeneities of the crystal structure, but it complicates the inter-

pretation of the domain structure. The main disadvantages of the powder method are: 1) it cannot be used to investigate changes in the domain structure during heating (cooling) or due to application of electric and mechanical fields; 2) the resolving power is low (it depends on the powder-particle dimensions, their coagulation ability, uniformity of the powder layer deposited on a crystal, etc.).

B. Etching Method. The etching rates of opposite ends of domains, i.e., of the ends having opposite signs of the bound spontaneous polarization charge, are different. This difference gives rise to a relief on the surface of a crystal as well as to etch figures which are of different shape at the opposite ends of a domain.

The etching method, used first to investigate the domain structure of BaTiO$_3$ [25], has been employed successfully in studies of the static domain patterns in triglycine sulfate, guanidine aluminum sulfate, and sodium nitrite. The possibilities of this method can be seen from Figs. 76 and 77, which show the 180° domains in BaTiO$_3$ and NaNO$_2$, respectively. The different degree of etching of the opposite ends of crystals, corresponding to the opposite signs of the spontaneous polarization, is self-evident from the formal point of view, but the actual etching mechanism is usually quite complex. Thus, a study of the etching of domains in NaNO$_2$ has shown that the different degree of etching of opposite ends is

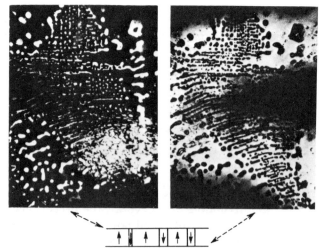

Fig. 76. Upper and lower surfaces of a BaTiO$_3$ crystal plate, etched in HCl, showing the 180° domains [25].

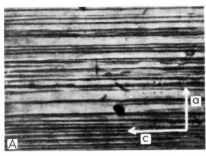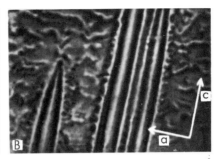

Fig. 77. Etch figures (obtained using NaOH etchant) showing the domain structure of NaNO₂: a) lamellar domains; b) wedge-shaped domains [38].

due to the electrostatic interaction between the etchant ions and the polarization charges. Alkali etchants (NaOH) etch more rapidly the positive ends of domains because the density of anions at these ends is higher. The negative ends of dipoles are etched more rapidly in acid solutions. It is interesting to note that the positive ends of domains in $BaTiO_3$, which is insoluble in water, are etched more rapidly in acid etchants (HCl) than the negative ends.

In some cases, particularly when optical methods for the investigation of domains are inapplicable (these methods will be discussed later), the etching method is very useful and gives good results. However, the selection of the etchant and of the etching conditions are a difficult and time-consuming task. We must mention also that the etching method cannot be used at all in studies of dynamic changes in domains.

C. Electroluminescence Method. This method was suggested quite recently by Zheludev et al. [4]. The procedure is as follows. An electrode is deposited by any of the well-known methods on one of the ground surfaces of a crystal plate, cut at right-angles to its ferroelectric axis. A small soft brush is used to deposit on the opposite surface of the plate a thin layer of liquid paste made of a powder of ZnS (electroluminescent phosphor) and silicone oil. A rigid transparent electrode is placed on the top of the paste layer and pressed tightly against the crystal plate. A glass plate, coated with a conducting film of stannic oxide (this film must be in contact with the paste), can be used as the transparent electrode. Such an assembly is a capacitor with a two-layer di-

electric, consisting of a ferroelectric plate and a phosphor layer.
When a sinusoidal voltage is applied to such a capacitor, the ratio
of the field intensities in the two dielectric layers is given, in the
first approximation (ignoring dielectric losses and higher harmonics of the field), by the following expression:

$$\frac{E_p}{E_f} = \frac{\varepsilon_f}{\varepsilon_p} \, ,$$

where E_p and E_f are the amplitudes of the fundamental harmonics
of the field intensities in the phosphor and ferroelectric layers,
respectively; ε_p is the permittivity of the phosphor; ε_f is the
permittivity of the ferroelectric, corresponding to the principal
harmonic of oscillations of the charge.

If the ferroelectric plate is electrically uniform, the whole
phosphor paste layer emits green luminescence when the field E_p
exceeds the excitation threshold field. The electric uniformity of
the ferroelectric plate is governed primarily by the uniformity of
its oriented polarization, which makes the greatest contribution to
the permittivity of the ferroelectric (for the sake of simplicity,
we can ignore the possible nonuniformity of the electric displacement). Consequently, the luminescence brightness will be the same
at all points of the paste layer only if there is no domain switching
or if the switching is uniform throughout the sample. In the lat-
ter case, $\varepsilon_f \gg \varepsilon_p$, and, therefore, practically all the applied voltage is concentrated in the phosphor layer.

Let us now assume that domains of one sign only are switched
in the ferroelectric plate, whereas domains of the opposite sign
are "clamped." Figure 78a shows antiparallel domains in the schematic form of rectangular slabs, traversing the whole sample. Let
us assume that switching occurs only in the domains with the spontaneous polarization vectors P_s directed upward. The permittivity
of those parts of the plates which are occupied by the "clamped"
domains decreases strongly, which reduces the field E_p in those
parts of the phosphor layer which lie immediately above the "clamped"
domains and, consequently, this will reduce strongly the intensity
of the luminescence in these regions of the phosphor layer. When
the amplitude of the external field is selected in a suitable manner,
the luminescence of the phosphor layer above the clamped domains
disappears completely and a striped pattern, shown in Fig. 78b, is

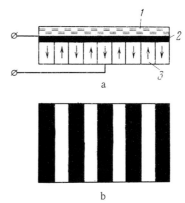

Fig. 78. Schematic representation of a sample (a) and the observed domain pattern (b) in the electroluminescence method. 1) Transparent electrode; 2) electroluminescent phosphor; 3) ferroelectric.

observed through the transparent electrode; this pattern corresponds to the domain structure of the ferroelectric plate shown in Fig. 78a.

The clamping of domains of one sign can be achieved by a constant voltage, which must be applied to a two-layer capacitor simultaneously with an alternating voltage. The resultant constant field in the phosphor E_p^c does not affect the ac luminescence; the constant field in the ferroelectric, E_f^c, should be sufficient to establish some preferential orientation of domains so that the volume of domains of one sign is larger than the volume of domains of the opposite sign. In this case, the alternating field E_p produces an alternating change in the volumes of the domains of different signs and the parts of the phosphor layer located directly over the alternately switched regions of the sample begin to luminesce. It must be pointed out that the domain pattern observed in this way does not always represent the static domain structure of the sample; nevertheless, it yields information on the nature of the domain structure in a given crystal.

Figure 79 shows patterns observed by this method for Z-cut guanidine aluminum sulfate in the presence of a positive (Fig. 79a) and negative (Fig. 79b) constant field. It is evident from Fig. 79 that when the polarity of the constant field is reversed, the bright growth pyramids of the lateral faces become dark, which shows that the growth pyramids in guanidine aluminum sulfate crystals are unipolar. Within each pyramid we can distinguish separate stripes corresponding to domains.

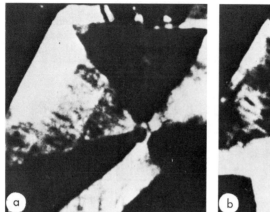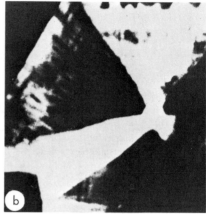

Fig. 79. Unipolar blocks and domains on surfaces of guanidine aluminum sulfate crystals subjected to external positive (a) and negative (b) fields. Temperature 20 °C; magnification 4 × [4].

The electroluminescence method can be used to observe quite easily the domain structure of antiferroelectrics and of some other crystals which are polarized in the antiferroelectric manner because of the presence of some impurities or as a result of irradiation. In this case, the usual hysteresis loop is replaced by a double loop whose nonlinear branches are due to the switching of domains of opposite polarities: the positive branch of the loop is due to the switching of domains in which the direction of the vector P_s coincide — in the absence of external fields — with the negative direction of the abscissa ("negative" domains, Fig. 80), and conversely. In this case, domains can be observed by applying a constant electric field $E_=$, which is approximately equal to the critical field E_{cr} of the double loop, as well as an alternating field $E_\sim$, corresponding to the saturation field of that hysteresis loop which is produced by the field $E_=$ (Fig. 80). A field $+E_=$, applied simultaneously with an alternating field, gives rise to continuous switching of the "negative" domains, while the "positive" domains remain at rest. Consequently, the phosphor luminesces only over the "negative" domains (right-hand side of Fig. 80). When the polarity of $E_=$ is reversed, the bright and dark regions in the pattern are interchanged, i.e., the pattern is reversed (left-hand side of Fig. 80). The two patterns shown in Fig. 80 are a fair representation of the static domain structure because the constant field does not alter the volumes of domains of different signs. The ratio of $E_=$ and $E_\sim$ can best the selected by connecting a sample in a circuit used for oscillographic observation of hysteresis loops and adjusting the values of the fields until two hysteresis loops are observed on the oscillograph screen.

The dynamics of domains can be studied by viewing the phosphor layer through apertures in a rotating disk of a mechanical stroboscope, whose angular frequency is adjusted to equal the fre-

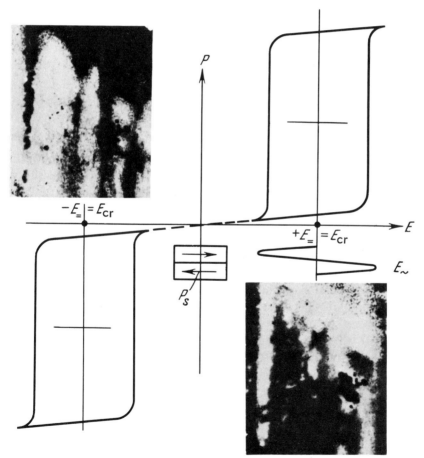

Fig. 80. Domain structure and hysteresis loop of a triglycine sulfate crystal irradiated with γ quanta. Radiation dose $4 \cdot 10^6$ R; temperature $20\,°C$; alternating field frequency 800 cps; magnification $2.5 \times$ [4].

quency of $E_\sim$. Moreover, the domain structure at any phase of the polarization can be studied also by means of a stroboscope synchronized with the applied alternating field.

The electroluminescence method can be used to study domains in any large ferroelectric crystal. However, this method cannot yet compete with the resolving power of other methods (particularly that of the optical and electron-optical methods) because the resolving power of the electroluminescence method is governed by the size of the powder grains in the phosphor layer. The clearest pattern is obtained for samples with large domains penetrating the whole crystal. The advantages of the electroluminescence method are as follows: it is simple and universal, and it can be used to observe domain switching processes as well as the appearance of domains at the phase-transition point.

D. Electron-Optical Methods. Electron-optical methods are not widely used in investigations of the domain structure of ferroelectrics and antiferroelectrics, but there are several reports of successful applications of these methods.

The most useful is the replica method, which is well known in electron microscopy. Carbon replicas usually give good results. Chromium shadowing is often used to increase the contrast of the replica image. Electron-microscopic stereo pairs of images have been employed in some investigations of the surface relief of crystals split into domains. The greatest difficulties in the replica method are encountered in the interpretation of the obtained images since the surface relief of a crystal split into domains is not only due to the phenomena associated with ferroelectric domains (different etching of opposite ends of domains, piezoelectric or electrostrictive deformation of domains due to the appearance of polarization) but also due to other phenomena which have no relation to the domain structure (mechanical stresses which appear during growth of a crystal: uneven cleavage; effects of various treatments). However, the combination of electron-microscopic results (obtained by the replica method) with the results of optical investigations (described in the next subsection) makes it possible to give a correct interpretation of the observed pattern.

Since the resolving power of the replica method is high, large useful magnifications can be obtained and fine details of the domain structure observed.

Electron-microscopic methods open up very interesting possibilities of investigating domains by the determination of electrostatic fields of the spontaneous polarization charges using the "electron mirror" method[13]. In this method, the trajectories of electrons, projected by an electron gun toward an object, are altered by the electric fields of surface charges on the object and this produces an image of the field structure. A ferroelectric crystal can act as a "reflecting" surface. Charging of the investigated crystal by incident electrons is avoided by vacuum-evaporation of a thin (several angstroms) semiconducting film (for example, germanium) on the crystal; the same film is used to apply the voltages required in the focusing system.

An image of the domain structure is formed at the surface of a sample where the electrons are turned back. The primary electron beam density is modulated by electric inhomogeneities of the crystal surface, which are due to the spontaneous polarization, and by geometrical inhomogeneities (primarily due to the relief of the domain walls). In particular, the distribution of dipoles at a 90° domain wall on a (100) face of a $BaTiO_3$ crystal is such that they form a microcapacitor (on one side of the boundary, the spontaneous polarization charge is positive, and on the other, it is negative). The electric field of such a microcapacitor, which extends into vacuum at the domain boundary, is responsible for the formation of an electron-optical image of the domains, as shown in Fig. 81. The same figure includes, for the sake of comparison, an image of the domain structure of the same crystal obtained by the op-

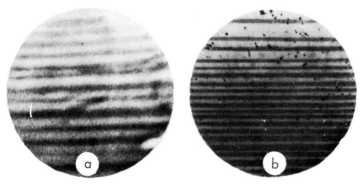

Fig. 81. Electron-optical (a) and optical (b) images of the domain structure of the same crystal of $BaTiO_3$. Magnification 200 × [13].

tical method. The electron mirror method promises, in principle, to provide new ways for the quantitative investigation of spontaneous polarization charges and domain fields.

E. Optical Method. All the methods described so far (with the exception of the electron mirror method) are indirect. Although they have provided useful data, the most reliable and fullest information on the domain structure of ferroelectrics and antiferroelectrics can be obtained only by direct optical observations of crystals in a polarizing microscope.

Several variants for investigating ferroelectric (and antiferroelectric) domains by the optical method have been suggested. The simplest and most important uses the fact that the extinction conditions are different for domains oriented in different ways. This applies only to some crystals, for example, to Rochelle salt: at room temperature the optical indicatrices of the Rochelle salt domains of opposite orientation are rotated relative to one another by an angle of the order of 1-2° (Figs. 70 and 82). This makes it possible to set domains of a given orientation at the extinction position and to observe domains of the opposite orientation. The same behavior is exhibited also by KH_2PO_4 crystals (Fig. 67).

When the extinction positions of domains of opposite orientation are different it becomes possible to investigate macroscopically the processes associated with changes in domains and in their polarization by measuring the light flux passing through a crystal [17]. An illustration of this method is given in Fig. 83,

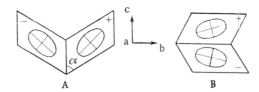

Fig. 82. Orientation of the spontaneous polarization and of the optical indicatrices of unit cells in Rochelle salt domains. The monoclinic angle α is very close to 90° ($\sim$ 89°5') and, therefore, the extinction of all domains with charges of the same sign on an X-cut face is practically instantaneous for: A) ac domains (walls parallel to the ac plane) and B) ab domains (walls parallel to the ba plane).

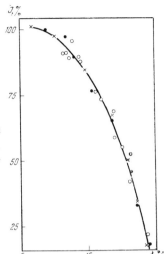

Fig. 83. Temperature dependence of the light flux transmitted by an X-cut Rochelle salt plate. Different designations of points correspond to different heating cycles [11].

which shows the temperature dependence of the light flux passing through X-cut crystalline plates of Rochelle salt. The observed change in the light flux with temperature is due to the temperature dependence of the monoclinicity of the crystal. Comparison of this curve with the results of other experiments shows that it illustrates also the temperature dependence of the spontaneous polarization of Rochelle salt, since the transmission of light (proportional to the monoclinic angle) and the polarization are related by a linear function (§ 3 of the present chapter).

Unfortunately, only a few crystals exhibit the favorable orientation of the optical indicatrices found in Rochelle salt and potassium dihydrogen phosphate. For example, the antiparallel domains in triglycine sulfate, sodium nitrite, and in other crystals have parallel optical indicatrices. The same is true, also, of the 180° domains in BaTiO$_3$. Domains in such crystals can be observed by applying a constant electric field, perpendicular to the direction of polarization [34]. This field makes the domain walls visible because domains are turned in opposite directions by the transverse field. The same result can be achieved also by some special mechanical strains.

Domains of opposite orientation in BaTiO$_3$ can be made visible by depositing semitransparent metallic films on the surface of a crystal; these films act as electrodes and produce optical contrast because of different crystallization conditions on surfaces with opposite signs of the surface charge.

Although the optical indicatrices of the 90° domains in BaTiO$_3$ are inclined to one another, the angle through which they are rotated from 90° is only 36' (this will be discussed in the next section). Consequently, the domains located on either side of a wall are optically extinguished at practically the same time. Nevertheless, using a quarter-wave plate, we can distinguish the positions of orthogonal domains. A 90° wall in BaTiO$_3$ can be distinguished quite clearly in a polarizing microscope even without a quarter-wave plate because of the total internal reflection at the domain walls and because of the birefringence at these walls (due to mechanical stresses). This frequently makes it possible to observe the walls between domains in crystals with the oxygen-octahedral type of structure even without using optical apparatus.

The optical method has obvious advantages and it can be used also (because of its instant response) to study the temperature-induced changes in the domain structure and the behavior of domains in alternating fields. In particular, the optical method, supplemented by stroboscopic illumination and combined with cinematography, makes it possible to investigate the behavior of domains in high-frequenty fields ($\sim 10^5$-10^6 cps).

We shall conclude this review of methods for investigating the domain structure by mentioning x-ray and electron diffraction. These methods can be used to establish, for example, the orientation domains, the angles between them, etc. Successful applications have been reported also of the x-ray microdiffraction method (Lang method) in studies of the domain structure of ferroelectrics. In this method the contrast is due to a local reduction in the primary extinction (which appears at lattice defects) and which enhances the intensity of the diffracted beam of x rays. This method has been applied successfully in studies of the structure of the 90° domains in BaTiO$_3$. A special feature of the method is the possibility of investigating domains in the interior of a crystal. Moreover, the microdiffraction method can be used (in combination with the optical method) to study mechanical stresses at domain boundaries [19].

§3. Real Domain Structure
of Some Ferroelectrics

A. Barium Titanate BaTiO₃. The domain structure
of barium titanate and of other ferroelectrics and antiferroelectrics with the oxygen-octahedral type of structure is quite complex. This is because the high-temperature cubic modifications
of these crystals permit the appearance of the spontaneous polarization along several equivalent directions. This is sometimes
stressed specially by calling these ferroelectrics multiaxial.

The principal geometrical features of the domain structure
of BaTiO₃ (or, more exactly, of the crystal class $\bar{6}/4$, to which barium titanate belongs) are discussed in §1 of the present chapter
(Fig. 72). It is pointed out there that BaTiO₃ can exist in three
ferroelectric modifications: tetragonal with the point symmetry
group 4·m (between +120 and 0°C), orthorhombic with the symmetry 2·m (between 0°C and −80°C), and orthorhombic with the symmetry 3·m (below −80°C).

The dipole arrays in domains of the tetragonal modification
of BaTiO₃ are shown in Fig. 84. The general orientation of the domains (all six possible directions) is shown in Fig. 84a and the
orientation of domains in the case of the 90° walls is shown in
Fig. 84b. The condition for lattice matching at the boundary between two domains gives rise to a slight tetragonality of the cells
(which is approximately 1%) and, therefore, the positions of ex-

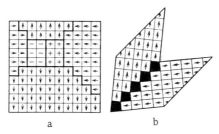

a   b

Fig. 84. Dipole array in domains of the tetragonal modification of barium titanate: a)
view onto the (001) plane; b) orientation of
dipoles and rotation of the lattice in the case
of a 90° domain.

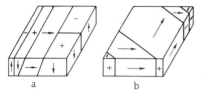

Fig. 85. Distribution of domains in the (001) plane of the tetragonal modification of barium titanate: a) a domain between c domains; b) positions of a domains.

tinction for two "perpendicular" domains differ by a small angle $[2 \tan^{-1} (c/a) = 36']$.

The tetragonal crystals of BaTiO₃ may have antiparallel domains, with the 180° walls, and "perpendicular" domains (whose spontaneous polarizations meet at an angle of 90°), which have the 90° walls. In the first case, the domain walls are planes of the (100) type and, in the second case, the walls are planes of the (110)

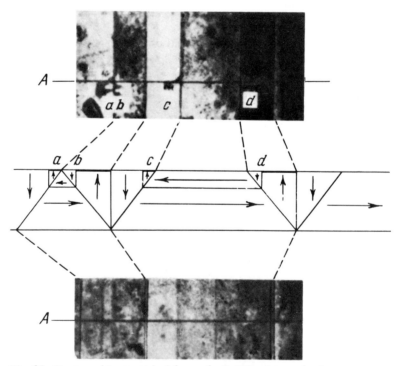

Fig. 86. Upper and lower etched faces of a BaTiO₃ plate and orientation of domains in the interior [25].

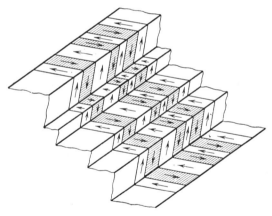

Fig. 87. 180 and 90° domain walls on the surface of a
BaTiO$_3$ crystal [25].

type. In the case of thin BaTiO$_3$ plates the domains are usually
called the c domains if the direction of the spontaneous polarization is perpendicular to the plane of the plate, and the a domains,
if the direction of polarization lies in the plane of the plate. The
orientations of all the a and c domains as well as the walls between
them are shown in Fig. 85. It is evident from this figure that to satisfy

Fig. 88. Interference pattern of BaTiO$_3$ domains obtained under a polarizing microscope [23].

the requirement of the electrical neutrality (and stability) of the
walls, the domains meet at the 90° walls in such a way that the negative end of one domain begins at the positive end of another domain.

The real domain structure of the tetragonal BaTiO$_3$ can be
seen from Figs. 86-90. Figure 86 shows the orientation of do-

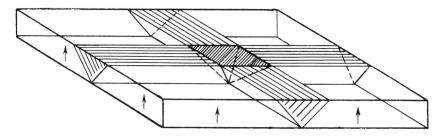

Fig. 89. Intersection of lamellar domains, which gives rise to the interference pattern shown in Fig. 88.

mains in the interior of a crystal (the image was obtained by etching followed by reflection of light from the opposite surfaces of a plate). It is evident from this figure that there are no 90° walls in the interior, i.e., there are no internal stresses in that sample. In this connection, it is worth mentioning that, since the spontaneous deformation of antiparallel domains is the same, there is no electromechanical interaction at the 180° walls.

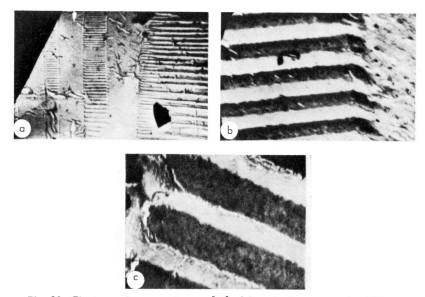

Fig. 90. Electron microscope images [12] of domains in tetragonal BaTiO$_3$, obtained using different magnifications: a) 1000 ×; b) 8000 ×; c) 25,000 ×.

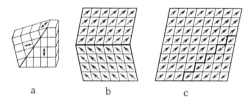

Fig. 91. Dipole arrays in orthorhombic BaTiO$_3$: a)
60° (120°) wall; b) 90° wall; c) 180° wall.

Long (up to 1 cm) and narrow (10^{-3}-10^{-4} cm wide) a-domain stripes with the 90° walls are, in their turn, split into antiparallel domains. A pattern of this type can be observed optically by stressing a crystal mechanically, because this produces opposite piezoelectric polarizations in neighboring antiparallel domains (Fig. 87).

The domains in plates of the tetragonal BaTiO$_3$ sometimes give rise to fairly complex interference patterns when viewed under a polarizing microscope; such a pattern is shown in Fig. 88.

It is evident from Fig. 89 that intersection of domain layers produces pyramidal configurations, which are responsible for the pattern shown in Fig. 88.

The finest details of the domain structure of BaTiO$_3$ can be obtained by the replica technique of transmission electron microscopy. The minimum width of domains found in this way is (3-5) $\times$ 10^{-6} cm (Fig. 90).

When barium titanate is cooled below 0°C, it transforms to the orthorhombic ferroelectric modification. The direction of polarization in this modification coincides with axes of the [110] type. There are altogether twelve such equivalent directions (Fig. 72b). The unit cell is distorted in such a way as if a crystal were transformed instantaneously (at the transition point) from the tetragonal to the cubic form and then only became orthorhombic. It is evident from Fig. 72b that the directions of polarization in domains of the orthorhombic modification can meet at angles of 60°, 90°, 120°, and 180°. Experimental observations confirm the presence of the 90° and 60° (or 120°) walls. The dipole arrays of the orthorhombic BaTiO$_3$, corresponding to these two types of wall and to the third possible (180°) wall, are all shown in Fig. 91. The 60° (or 120°)

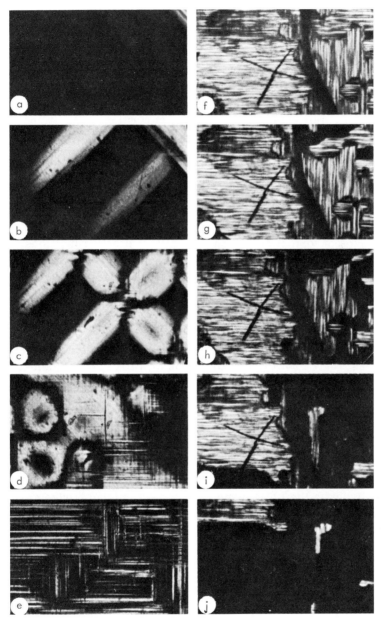

Fig. 92. Cine frames illustrating the appearance, growth, and changes in domains during phase transitions in BaTiO$_3$ crystals at 120°C (frames a-e) and at 5°C (frames f-j). The directions of oscillations in crossed nicols are horizontal and vertical [2].

and 180° walls coincide with planes of the (110) type and the 90°
walls coincide with planes of the (100) type (indices of these planes
are given in the coordinate system of the original paraelectric modification).

There is practically no published information on the domain
structure of the trigonal modification of BaTiO$_3$, which exists below −80°C. However, on the basis of general considerations, we
may conclude that the spontaneous polarization directions in the
neighboring domains of this modification should meet at approximately 70° (110°) and (180°) (Fig. 72c). The 70° (110°) walls between domains should coincide with the (100) planes of a crystal
and the 180° walls should coincide with the (110) planes.

The nucleation of domains and their growth, as well as the
processes of formation of domain walls at phase transitions, are
of considerable interest. We shall consider briefly some of these
processes which occur at the 120°C and 0°C phase transitions in
BaTiO$_3$. The data which we shall consider were obtained in a
cinematographic study of the domain structure at the phase transition points. We shall discuss these data frame by frame.

Figure 92 is a set of cine frames showing the nucleation of
domains, their growth, and formation of walls between domains at
the phase transition of BaTiO$_3$ from the cubic to the tetragonal
modification (near 120°C; Figs. 92a-92e) and from the tetragonal
to the orthorhombic phase (near +5°C; Figs. 92f-92j). Figure 92a
shows the beginning of the cubic-tetragonal transition, which occurs when a crystal is cooled below 120°C. The major part of the
crystal is still cubic and the transition to the tetragonal modification begins in the top right-hand corner. The plane of the image
coincides with the (001) plane and the vertical and horizontal directions in the plane of the paper correspond to the [110] directions; it follows that a fourfold axis of the new tetragonal modification lies in the (001) plane and coincides with the [100] axis of
the crystal (an a–domain is formed). Figures 92b-92d show the appearance of new tetragonal regions having fourfold axes oriented
along the [100] and [010] directions. This is because a cubic crystal has two equivalent directions − [100] and [010] in the (001) plane.
Two tetragonal domains, with mutually perpendicular directions of
the spontaneous polarization, meet and form walls which are inclined at 45° to each of these directions, i.e., walls which coincide

with the (110) planes of a cubic crystal. The formation of such boundaries can be followed easily in Figs. 92b-92d. During the next stage the whole crystal splits into domains whose boundaries coincide with the (110) planes (Fig. 92e).

Cine frames showing a transition of a different $BaTiO_3$ crystal from the tetragonal to the orthorhombic modification are given in Figs. 92f-92j. The orientation of the second crystal is the same as in Figs. 92a-92e. Figure 92f shows the domain structure of a tetragonal crystal in its initial state above 5°C. The tetragonal-orthorhombic phase transition begins near 5°C. This transition is not gradual and does not take place simultaneously throughout a crystal but is in the form of sudden rapid transitions of small regions.

Figures 92g-92i demonstrate the various stages of the transition to the orthorhombic modification during subsequent cooling. It is evident from these frames that the boundaries between individual orthorhombic regions (which are dark in Fig. 92) coincide with the [110] directions of a cubic crystal. If an orthorhombic crystal is rotated between crossed nicols, it becomes transparent when the [100] axis of the cubic modification coincides with the direction of oscillations for one of the nicols; in this position the formerly dark regions can be seen to be split into smaller regions (domains) whose boundaries coincide with the directions of the [100] type. It follows that the directions of spontaneous polarization of the orthorhombic modification coincide with the directions of the [110] type and that the domains form 90° walls.

B. Triglycine Sulfate $(CH_2NH_2COOH)_3 \cdot H_2SO_4$. The appearance of the spontaneous polarization in a centrosymmetric paraelectric crystal of triglycine sulfate (group 2:m) produces the same electrostrictive strains in domains with opposite orientations of P_s, which is directed along the b axis. Domains with opposite orientations of the spontaneous polarization have different signs of enantiomorphism (Chap. III), but the optical axes of domains in triglycine sulfate coincide (Fig. 64), which means that they cannot be investigated by the optical method. However, the etching method (various etchants, such as water, acetone, etc., dissolve the positive ends of domains more strongly than the negative ends) and the charged-powder method have made it possible to investigate these domains quite thoroughly.

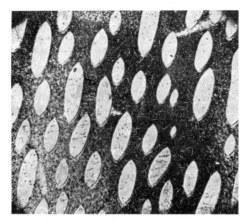

Fig. 93. Typical domain structure, revealed
by etching a Y-cut triglycine sulfate plate
and subjected to external influences [8].

Although the domain structure of triglycine sulfate depends
considerably on the crystal growth conditions (particularly on the
growth temperature), the domains in the majority of crystals which
have not been subjected to electric or mechanical fields are in the
shape of rods, with lenticular cross sections, oriented along the Y
axis. Domains with the same orientation of the spontaneous polari-

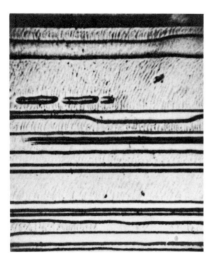

Fig. 94. Different form of domain
walls, revealed by etching a Y-cut triglycine sulfate crystal [8].

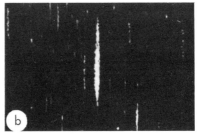

Fig. 95. Spindle-shaped domains in a triglycine sulfate plate. The spontaneous polarization axis is oriented along the spindle axis. a) Image obtained by etching; b) image obtained by charged-powder method [22].

zation form a field (matrix) which encloses domains of the opposite orientation (Fig. 93). The long axis of the lenticular cross section is oriented along the a axis of a crystal and lies approximately in the optical plane. Electric fields and mechanical stresses alter the static domain structure, transforming it from rods into lamellas perpendicular to the c axis. The thickness of these lamellas is approximately 10^{-4} cm and their length is a few tenths of a centimeter (Fig. 94).

Large domains usually grow right through Y-cut plates about 1 mm thick (Fig. 74a). Such plates contain domains which do not emerge on the surface and which are spindle-shaped (Fig. 95).

Applications of the etching method to triglycine sulfate have shown that there are etchants which reveal both domains and dislocations in this crystal. This makes it possible to establish some correlation between the static domain structure and the positions of dislocations (Fig. 96).

Interesting investigations of the nucleation of a large number of new domains on surfaces of Y-cut plates of triglycine sulfate and within such plates have been carried out during rapid cooling and heating. It is found that many new domains, which are formed on the surfaces of plates during rapid cooling, are due to the field of free charges (which compensate bound charges) directed opposite to the domain field existing before cooling. During rapid heating the field of free charges on the surfaces of plates coincides in direction with P_s, and within the plates it is opposite to the P_s; this produces a large number of new domains in the interior of a plate.

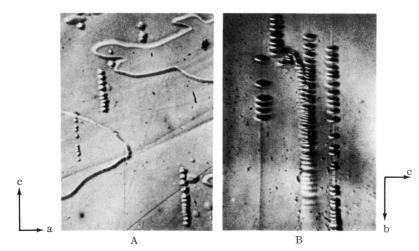

c

a

c

b

A   B

Fig. 96. A) Y-cut triglycine sulfate crystal showing no correlation between points of emergence of dislocations and domain boundaries. B) Cut close to (100) shows that points of emergence of dislocations can lie along domain boundaries [9].

C. Rochelle Salt $NaKC_4H_4O_6 \cdot 4H_2O$. The domain of Rochelle salt has been investigated by many methods, but the fullest results have been obtained by the optical method. Section 2 of the present chapter mentions that a polarizing microscope can be used to reveal domains in Rochelle salt which have different extinction positions (Fig. 82).

Distortion of the orthorhombic cell of Rochelle salt and its phase transformation into the monoclinic form can be analyzed most simply by treating it as a consequence of piezoelectric deformation of a crystal.* However, changes in the optical properties of this crystal, particularly the rotation of the optical indicatrices of neighboring domains by an angle 2φ relative to one another, should be regarded as a consequence of the electro-optical properties of Rochelle salt crystals. We can show that for crystals of class 2:2, in which the spontaneous polarization appears along the X axis, the angle between the indicatrices of neighboring

---

*This deformation consists of a shear r_{23}, as a result of which a crystal (or, more accurately, a domain) acquires the symmetry of class 2; all the domains have the same sign of enantiomorphism.

domains of opposite orientation can be found from the following relationship:

$$\tan 2\varphi = \frac{2r_{41}^{*}P_{s}}{\alpha_1 \left(\dfrac{1}{n_y^2} - \dfrac{1}{n_z^2} \right)}, \qquad \text{(IV.2)}$$

where r_{41}^{*} is the electro-optical coefficient of a free crystal; n_y and n_z are the refractive indices of a crystal along the Y and Z axes, respectively; α_1 is the polarizability along the a axis. The value of the angle 2φ is about 1-2° in the middle of the temperature range limited by the two Curie points of Rochelle salt, which corresponds to $r_{41}^{*} \approx (2\text{-}3)\times 10^{-8}$ cgs esu. Different investigators give different values for the angle 2φ at the same temperature. It is known that the second and subsequent cooling cycles yield values of 2φ which are lower than the value obtained in the first cooling cycle; this is due to an increase of order in the domain structure resulting from repeated cooling. The temperature dependence of the angle 2φ for an X-cut plate of Rochelle salt, plotted using values obtained after several cooling cycles, is shown in Fig. 97.

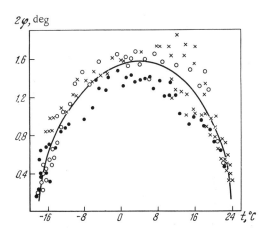

Fig. 97. Temperature dependence of the angle between extinction positions of neighboring domains in an X-cut Rochelle salt crystal. Different heating and cooling cycles are represented by different points [7].

It follows from Eq. (IV.2) that for small angles (such as φ) the value of φ should depend linearly on P_s if the refractive indices n_y and n_z, as well as the quantity r_{41}^*, are independent of temperature in the interval between the two Curie points. The temperature dependence of P_s (Fig. 118) is similar to the dependence shown in Fig. 97. Moreover, as mentioned in §2 of the present chapter, the linear relationship between the monoclinic angle α and P_s in the temperature range between the two Curie points makes it possible to investigate the nature of the temperature dependence of the spontaneous polarization of a crystal using the temperature dependence of the transmitted light flux (Fig. 83).

The domains in a real Rochelle salt crystal are lamellas parallel to the (010) and (001) planes, i.e., to the a c and a b planes. They are known as the a c and a b domains (Fig. 82). According to Fig. 70, these two types of domain should be observed simultaneously on X-cut crystals of Rochelle salt (Fig. 98). However, it must be pointed out that because of the anisotropy of the (110) plane the energy of formation of the a b and a c domain boundaries is different: the a b domains are more stable, as indicated by the

Fig. 98. Boundaries between a b and a c domains in an X-cut
Rochelle salt crystal.

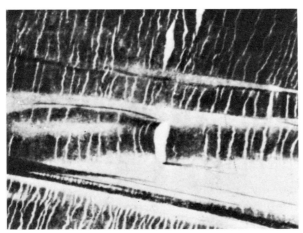

Fig. 99. Microcracks in an X-cut Rochelle salt crystal (image obtained using the electron-microscope replica method; 8000 ×) [12].

lower energy of their walls, compared with the energy of the ac domain walls. In particular, the upper Curie point of the ac domains is somewhat lower than the corresponding point of the ab domains.

The strain energy, associated with the simultaneous existence of the ab and ac domains, is reduced by the formation of wedge-shaped domains. However, these two types of domain cannot be made to fit tightly and this gives rise to blocks (each of which contains one type of domain) which are separated by microcracks (Fig. 99).

The domain structure of Rochelle salt depends strongly on the crystal growth conditions, the presence of impurities, imperfections, and of stresses, the previous history of a crystal, etc. The relative stability of the domain structure of Rochelle salt is related to these dependences: the brief heating of a crystal to a temperature above the upper Curie point does not alter significantly the original domain structure, as found by observations carried out after cooling below the upper Curie point. Only prolonged heating, which guarantees the redistribution of stresses, diffusion imperfections, etc., may produce a new domain structure. Such a new structure in a Rochelle salt crystal may be due to partial decomposition of the crystal during its annealing. However, if the annealing is carried out in an atmosphere which prevents a change in the composition of the Rochelle salt, no significant changes take place in the domain structure.

Investigations of the influence of impurities and nuclear radiations on the properties of Rochelle salt show that the domain structure itself produces conditions favoring its stability: the spontaneous polarization field orders impurities in accordance with the orientation of domains; the long relaxation time of these ordering processes ensures that a crystal reverts to its original domain structure after heating.

It is known that the faces of a crystal adsorb in different ways the impurities present in a solution from which the crystal is grown. This produces more favorable growth conditions for some faces and less favorable conditions for others; a grown crystal shows sectorial structure and hourglass-shaped impurity inclusions. If the temperature during growth is varied in steps, it is frequently found that this produces a steplike precipitation of impurities in sectors. All this is observed very clearly in the growth of Rochelle salt crystals because they are very strongly anisotropic. In particular, investigations show that the formation of the ab and ac domains depends strongly on the pyramid which grows at a given point in a crystal. Consequently, samples cut from different growth pyramids may have different domain structures; the orien-

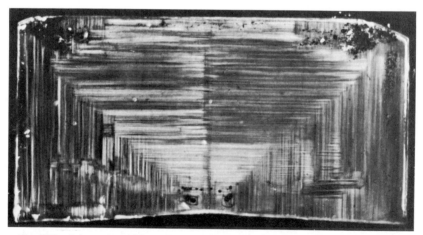

Fig. 100. Orientation of domains in different growth pyramids of a Rochelle salt crystal [15].

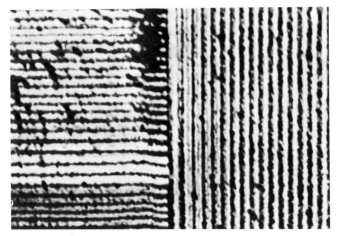

Fig. 101. Domain structure of KH_4PO_4 crystals observed by the "dew" method on a cut perpendiculat to the c axis [14a].

tation of the walls between the domains may coincide with the orientation of growth striations in a crystal (Fig. 100).

The nature of the walls between domains depends, to some extent, on the temperature during the growth of a crystal. Observations show preferential growth of the ab domains in crystals grown at temperatures above the upper Curie point and preferential growth of the ac domains in crystals grown in the temperature range between the two Curie points. However, in both cases, both types of domain are usually produced.

D. Domain Structure of Some Other Crystals. The nature of the structure distortion and the possible orientations of domain walls in a crystal of KH_2PO_4 are discussed in the preceding chapter (Fig. 67). Because of the electro-optical effect, when spontaneous polarization appears in this crystal along the Z axis, the optical indicatrices transform from ellipsoids of revolution into triaxial ellipsoids with semiaxes coinciding with the diagonals of the orthorhombic cells of this crystal. The orthorhombic distortion of a crystal (due to the piezoelectric effect) makes the angles between the axes of the optical indicatrices of neighboring domains deviate from 90° and this makes it possible to distinguish optically the domains with oppositely oriented spontaneous polarizations. A structure in the form of stripes with boundaries oriented along the [100] and [010] directions is observed below the phase-transition temperature under a polarizing microscope (Fig. 101).

We must stress that in crystals belonging to the $\bar{4}\cdot$m class (which includes KH_2PO_4) the domain configurations shown in Figs. 67E and 67F are geometrically and energetically equivalent. This unavoidably gives rise to blocks containing domains of only one configuration. Stresses between such blocks can fracture a crystal, as frequently observed during the cooling of KH_2PO_4 below its Curie point.

A study of the etch figures on Z-cut plates of guanidine aluminum sulfate cut from unipolar blocks (see, for example, Fig. 79) shows that the opposite sides of such plates are etched in a different manner and that the etch figures are rotated in accordance with the domain symmetry 3·m (Fig. 102). Unannealed crystals of guanidine aluminum sulfate have very high internal stresses and these generate a great variety of domains differing in shape and size. Some idea of the complex nature of domains and of the orientation of domain walls in guanidine aluminum sulfate can be gained from Figs. 79 and 103. More detailed studies of the domains in guanidine aluminum sulfate have yet to be carried out.

Fig. 102. Etch figures on two opposite (a and b) sides of a guanidine aluminum sulfate crystal cleaved along the c axis [3].

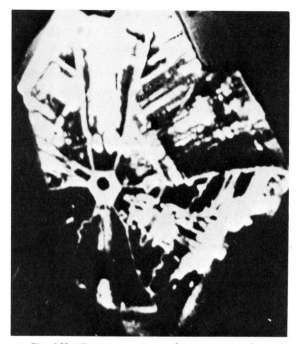

Fig. 103. Domain structure of a Z-cut guanidine
aluminum sulfate crystal observed by the electroluminescence method [16].

Investigations of $NaNO_2$ crystals by the etching method have
established that domains in this crystal, in agreement with structure investigations reported in §1 of Chap. III, exhibit a spontaneous polarization oriented along the b axis. The domain walls lie
in the (100) planes. The general nature of the domain structure
can be seen from the schematic representation given in Fig. 104
(see also Fig. 77). We must point out that $NaNO_2$ crystals, pre-

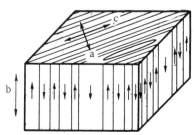

Fig. 104. Schematic representation of
the domain structure of $NaNO_2$. Arrows
indicate the directions of spontaneous
polarization in domains [38].

pared from an aqueous solution, are almost monoclinic before
heating above the Curie temperature and they split into domains
only when such heating is followed by cooling below the Curie point.

We have mentioned in §3 of Chap. III that domain walls coinciding with the (100) and (001) planes may be found in crystals belonging to the m·2:m class after transition to the ferroelectric
phase when the spontaneous polarization appears along one of the
twofold axes. However, examination of the domain structure of
$NaNO_2$ shows that in this crystal the interaction between its component particles is weaker in the (100) plane than in the (001) planes;
this evidently explains why no domain walls are found in the (001) planes.

§4. Domain Structure of Antiferroelectrics

Some information on the domain structure of antiferroelectrics, based on a discussion of dipole arrays, has been given in
Chaps. II and III. The principal features of the domain structure of
antiferroelectrics are discussed also in §1 of the present chapter.

We must add that the splitting of antiferroelectrics into domains is not as self-evident as in the case of ferroelectrics. We
cannot attribute the splitting to a reduction of the electrostatic energy of the spontaneous polarization because antiferroelectric domains are electrically neutral (nonpolar). Consequently, domains
in antiferroelectrics are frequently considered as mechanical
twins. Thus, any boundary between domains, which is permissible
on geometrical grounds, may exist irrespective of the fact that it
is electrically neutral. The domains in antiferroelectric crystals
owe much of their existence to the fact that the directions of polarization (or, more precisely, the directions of antipolarization)
in different parts of a crystal may be different if the nucleation of
the antiferroelectric phase proceeds independently at each point in
a crystal. Regions with different antipolarization directions meet
and form boundaries. The formation of these boundaries relieves
mechanical stresses which are encountered when two such regions
meet. However, in some cases these stresses are so high that
they crack a crystal when it passes through the antiferroelectric
Néel point (also called the antiferroelectric Curie point). This occurs, for example, in $NH_4H_2PO_4$ crystals. Moreover, local imperfections in real crystals give rise to mechanical stresses which
may favor the appearance of antipolarization along different di-

rections which are geometrically permissible and crystallographically equivalent. The splitting of antiferroelectrics into domains tends to lower the energy of these mechanical stresses and thus reduce the internal energy of a crystal.

Experimental investigations of the domain structure have been carried out only for a few antiferroelectrics. The main results of the investigations of $NaNbO_3$, $PbZrO_3$, and WO_3 are reviewed briefly in the present section.

There is as yet no experimental proof that dipoles in domains of the orthorhombic modification of $NaNbO_3$ are oriented as shown in Fig. 42 (antipolarization along the b axis, coinciding with the [010] axis of the cubic subcell). However, this orientation of the dipoles does not contradict the available data on the optical properties of domain twins in $NaNbO_3$. Thus, the published investigations show that below 360°C the orthorhombic axes of domains are rotated by 45° in the (010) plane with respect to the original cubic axes. The components of domain twins, with boundaries oriented along the (100) planes of the cubic modification, give rise to symmetrical extinction in polarized light. The thickness of the regions enclosed between two neighboring planar boundaries is about 0.01 mm. The orientation of the antipolarization along axes of the [100] type permits the existence of domain boundaries along the (110) planes of the cubic modification (§3 of the present chapter). The simultaneous existence of the (100) and (110) boundaries has been confirmed by experimental observations and it is shown schematically in Fig. 105.

When $NaNbO_3$ is heated above 360°C, all the regions exhibiting symmetrical extinction disappear [they are separated by the (110) planes below 360°C]. At these temperatures, a crystal of sodium niobate exhibits optical anisotropy along all directions. Twin regions with parallel extinction have boundaries along the (110) planes.

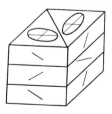

Fig. 105. Extinction positions of domain twins in an orthorhombic crystal of $NaNbO_3$ at room temperature [39].

The components of domain twins are orthorhombic but a rigorous examination of their optical anisotropy shows that they are very nearly tetragonal. Some observations — weak optical anisotropy, the presence of only the parallel extinction, the failure to establish the orthorhombic nature of unit cells by the x-ray diffraction method — give grounds for assuming that above 360°C (right up to the next phase transition) $NaNbO_3$ is a tetragonal antiferroelectric with the antipolarization directed along the [100] axis in the cubic cell.. The b axis is also an antipolarization axis. The experimentally established orientation of the optical axes of domain twins of this modification is shown schematically in Fig. 106.

Investigations of the optical properties of $NaNbO_3$ near 518°C show that the phase transition observed at this temperature is accompanied by a rotation of the "pseudotetragonal" axis and by a change of the optical sign of the crystal.

The domain-twin structure of the orthorhombic $PbZrO_3$ crystals is similar to the domain structure of the orthorhombic $BaTiO_3$. This is natural because the orthorhombic modifications of both crystals are due to the appearance of polarization in cubic paraelectric cells along directions of the [110] type. The only difference between these two compounds is that the unit cell of the orthorhombic $PbZrO_3$ is of the multiple type, whereas $BaTiO_3$ has the unit cell of the cubic modification (Chap. II).

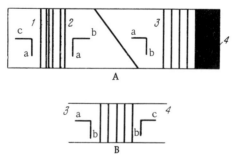

Fig. 106. Domain twins in a crystal of $NaNbO_3$ above 360°C (up to 470°C): A) polarized light, nicols oriented at 45° to extinction positions, region 4 is in an extinction position; B) polarized light, regions 3 and 4 exhibit the same transmission and have the same orientations of domain twin axes [21].

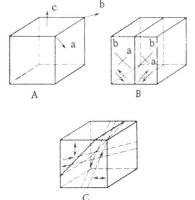

Fig. 107. Boundaries between domain twins, orientation of optical axes, and directions of antipolarization in components of domain twins of orthorhombic PbZrO$_3$: A) selection of axes relative to the cubic structure; B) boundary along a plane of the (100) type; C) boundary along a plane of the (110) type in a cubic cell.

The selection of axes of the orthorhombic PbZrO$_3$, by reference to the cubic cell, is shown in Fig. 107A. Since the antipolarization is oriented along the [110] axis of the cubic cell, domains in PbZrO$_3$ can have geometrically permissible boundaries along the (100) and (110) planes of the cubic cell. The (100) planes separate domain twins in which the directions of antipolarization meet at an angle of 90°. Such boundaries, with symmetrical extinction of domains, have been observed experimentally and are shown schematically in Fig. 107B. In this case, the b axes are the antipolarization axes of domains and, consequently, they meet at an angle of 90°. The (110) planes of the cubic cell separate, in the orthorhombic modification, twins with parallel extinction of the components; the directions of antipolarization of the components meet at an angle of 60° (120°). Such boundaries have been observed experimentally and are shown in Fig. 107C.

Jona, Shirane, and Pepinsky [27] have described experimentally observed boundaries in PbZrO$_3$, which are oriented along the (110) planes of the cubic cell with symmetrical (but not parallel, see Fig. 107C) extinction of components of domain twins. They have also described boundaries between domains lying along the (hk0) planes of the orthorhombic cell (h, k $\neq$ 1). The presence of boundaries of the second type is regarded by Jona et al. as proof of the nonpolarity (dipole compensation) of the ab plane. However, it follows from geometrical considerations that neither of the types of boundary observed by Jona et al. can result from the appearance of antipolarization in a crystal. Nevertheless, such boundaries may be formed when different crystals meet during growth.

The domain structure of WO_3 was discovered before its antiferroelectricity. Early investigations established that the room-temperature domain structure of WO_3 resembles the domain structure of $BaTiO_3$. Moreover, it was found that the domains are highly mobile when a crystal is subjected to mechanical stresses and this gives rise to nearly perfect plasticity. It has also been reported that domains in WO_3 are not affected by electric fields.

Other features of domain twins in WO_3 were investigated later. In particular, it has been found that plates cut perpendicular to the c axis of a crystal (the dipole moment of the subcell practically coincides with this axis, as shown in Fig. 44A) have domain boundaries coinciding with the (110) planes of the cubic cell. The existence of such boundaries can be understood by assuming that in one of two neighboring domains the spontaneous polariza-

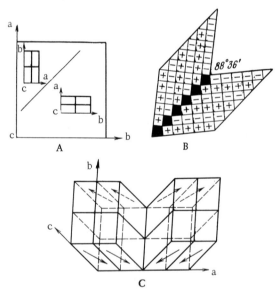

Fig. 108. Boundary along a (110) plane between domains in monoclinic WO_3 at room temperature: A) boundary and orientation of crystallographic axes in domains on both sides of the boundary; B) rotation of cells in neighboring domains because of inequality of the parameters a and c; C) schematic representation of boundaries along planes of the (100) type within one domain.

tion P_s is directed along the [h0l] and [h0$\bar{l}$] axes and in the other domain the spontaneous polarization lies along the [0kl] and [0k$\bar{l}$] axes in the coordinate system of the cubic cell (Fig. 108A). Each of these domains has boundaries parallel and perpendicular to the a and b faces of a crystal. The presence of boundaries along the (100) planes of the cubic cell can be understood by taking into account the equivalence of the polarization directions (in one domain) corresponding to the [h0l] and [h0$\bar{l}$] as well as [h0l] and [h0l] axes (see Fig. 108C). The parts of a crystal between the boundaries in the (100) planes can be regarded as independent submicroscopic domains. The angle between these boundaries is not equal to 90° because of a small distortion of the cell (b $\neq$ a), but is given by 2 tan^{-1} (b/a) = 88°36' (Fig. 108B). The domain width ranges from 0.004 to 0.01 mm, which is approximately the same as the domain width in $BaTiO_3$. Crystals of tungsten trioxide contain lamellar and wedge-shaped domains.

Near 740°C the domain structure changes with the structure of the crystal (see Fig. 44B). Above this temperature a crystal viewed along the c axis becomes dark in the field of view of a microscope because the direction of antipolarization in the new tetragonal modification coincides with the c axis of the crystal.

When WO_3 is cooled from room temperature to about −50°C its domain twin structure changes. The domain boundaries, originally oriented along the (110) planes, become aligned along the (100) planes. Optical investigations show that domain twins in WO_3 below −50°C resemble, in respect of their optical properties, domains in $BaTiO_3$ below −70°C. Hence, we may conclude that the direction of antipolarization in WO_3 below −50°C coincides with the [111] direction of a cubic crystal.

§ 5. Walls Between Domains.

Domain Configurations Corresponding

to a Free-Energy Minimum

A. Domain Walls. A theoretical determination of the energy and thickness of a boundary between domains (a domain wall) is fairly difficult and such determinations have been carried out only for the simplest cases. However, even a simple qualitative analysis of domain walls yields general information on their dimensions and energies and shows that the thickness of a domain wall should – in most cases – be of the order of the lattice constant. Domain walls in ferroelectrics are much thinner than domain walls in ferromagnets, whose thickness is of the order of several hundreds of lattice constants.

Domain walls in ferromagnets are transition regions in which the magnetization vector gradually rotates from one direction to another, which may be opposite (Fig. 109a). The thickness of this transition region depends on the relationship between the exchange and the anisotropy energies. The exchange energy of two neighboring spins is proportional to the square of the angle between the spins and it therefore tends to expand a domain wall. On the other hand, the anisotropy energy tends to contract a domain wall since a thick wall represents an array of a large number of spins oriented along arbitrary rather than preferred directions. The exchange energy of ferromagnets is usually one order of magnitude higher than the anisotropy energy and, therefore, domain walls in ferromagnets are fairly thick.

Ferroelectrics do not have an analog of the magnetic exchange energy. In the presence of electronic and ionic polarization the dominant interaction is that of the electrostatic forces between polarized ions. The energies of interaction for parallel and antiparallel arrays of dipoles in dielectrics are very similar and, therefore, a domain wall in a ferroelectric is relatively thin and cannot be regarded as a continuous region. It follows that the ani-

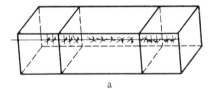

a

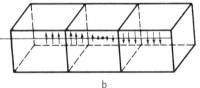

b

Fig. 109. Behavior of the spontaneous magnetization vector M_s (a) and of the spontaneous polarization vector P_s (b) in domain boundaries (walls) of ferromagnetic and ferroelectric crystals.

sotropy energy is the dominant energy in the case of ferroelectric domain walls.

In a strongly anisotropic ferroelectric crystal the polarization vector does not rotate within a domain wall but simply decreases in absolute value without a change of direction, passes through zero, and gradually increases in the opposite direction until it reaches the other side of a wall (Fig. 109b). The anisotropy energy does not contribute to the energy of a domain wall although it governs its structure. In a weakly anisotropic crystal (a highly symmetrical crystal) the polarization vector rotates within a domain wall.

An important contribution to the energy of a domain wall in a ferroelectric is made by the elastic energy. This energy is associated with mechanical stresses due to variation of the polarization within the wall, caused by the piezoelectric effect. The elastic energy usually tends to contract a wall. Its order of magnitude is comparable with the dipole energy.

Several attempts have been made to estimate the energy of a 180° wall in $BaTiO_3$ crystals. Such estimates show that the structure of such a wall is very simple. Although the anisotropy of $BaTiO_3$ is not as high as that of Rochelle salt, KH_2PO_4, and other low-symmetry crystals, it is still sufficiently high to cause a continuous variation of the magnitude of the polarization within a wall. The presence of a thick wall would give rise to a high value of the elastic energy due to the piezoelectric effect. Obviously, the energy of a wall has its minimum value when the spontaneous polarization changes its sign within one unit cell. Since the spontaneous strain (proportional to the square of the spontaneous polarization P_s) is the same on both sides of a wall, the periodicity of the lattice is not affected by the presence of a domain wall.

The contribution of the dipole interaction to the energy of a 180° wall in $BaTiO_3$ is slight. This has been demonstrated by Kinase [28], who carried out a detailed calculation of the local field near a Ti ion for antiparallel and parallel dipole arrays. He assumed that the dipoles were solely due to displacements of Ti ions and he showed that the local field was of the same order in the antiparallel and parallel cases and that it was only slightly higher in the parallel case (Cohen [20] reached the opposite conclusion). Since the local fields in the antiparallel and parallel cases are similar, we can consider the antiparallel (antiferroelectric) state as a limiting case of the polar (ferroelectric) state with domains whose thicknesses are equal to one lattice constant.

Using the model of a 180° wall in BaTiO$_3$ shown in Fig. 109b and employing the local fields at Ti ion sites obtained by Kinase [28], Kinase and Takahashi [30] estimated the field at a domain wall and found that the displacement of ions under the action of this field differed by 0.5% from the displacement of ions within the domain. The distortion of the lattice parameter at the wall does not exceed 0.002%. Thus, the crystal lattice is practically undistorted at a 180° domain wall in BaTiO$_3$, and the crystal has antiparallel orientations of the spontaneous polarization on two sides of the boundary and, therefore, the boundary has a negligible thickness. The energy required for the formation of such a wall was calculated by Kinase and Takahashi assuming that this energy was equal to the difference between the total energy of the lattice at the wall and the energy of a single-domain crystal. Such a calculation gave $\mathscr{E}_w = 1.40$ erg/cm^2.

Taking into account not only the shift of Ti atoms but also the shift of O$_I$ atoms, we find that the thickness of a domain wall is equal to two lattice constants. Allowance for the displacement of O$_{II}$ atoms complicates the problem very considerably. Kinase [29] considered the field at the tip of a wedge-shaped domain and showed that the wall at the tip of the wedge should be thicker than at its sides. According to his estimates, the front wall of a wedge should be about 16 Å thick and its energy should be about 80 ergs/cm^2.

A modification of the well-known Bloch domain-wall model in ferromagnets, based on the assumption that the total energy of a wall is equal to the sum of the energy of the dipole interaction and the anisotropy energy, makes it possible to determine the energy of a wall $\mathscr{E}_w$ from the following expression [35]:

$$\mathscr{E}_w = \frac{A}{t} + Bt, \qquad\qquad (IV.3)$$

where t is the thickness of the wall and A, B are functions of the lattice constant. Using Eq. (IV.3), Merz [35] showed that the wall thickness t in BaTiO$_3$ should be of the order of one lattice constant. The corresponding wall energy should be about 7 ergs/cm^2. The expression for the electrical component of the wall energy in a bcc crystal was obtained by Känzig and Sommerhalder [32]. They assumed that the wall was parallel to a (100) plane and that "frozen" dipoles oriented along the [001] and [00$\bar{1}$] directions were located on the two sides of the wall. In this case, $\mathscr{E}_{dip}$ per 1 cm^2 is

$$\mathscr{E}_{dip} = 0.88 P^2 d, \tag{IV.4}$$

where P is the polarization in the interior of a domain; d is the unit-cell parameter. The energy $\mathscr{E}_{dip}$ represents 0.42 of the polarization energy $[(2\pi/3)P^2 d]$ of a layer whose thickness is d.

A phenomenological analysis of a ferroelectric domain wall, based on the method employed by Landau and Lifshitz for domain walls in ferromagnets, was carried out by Zhirnov [6]. Zhirnov determined the equilibrium orientation of the polarization vector near a wall from the condition of minimum of the thermodynamic potential. Zhirnov derived expressions for the thickness and energy of domain walls and found numerical values of these parameters in many cases. His estimates gave a thickness of 5-20 Å and an energy of about 10 ergs/cm^2 for a 180° domain wall in BaTiO$_3$; these values are close to those found by Merz [35], who also used a phenomenological approach to the problem of domain boundaries.

The internal structure of a 90° wall in BaTiO$_3$ is more complex. Even simple geometrical considerations show that such a boundary should contain anomalously deformed cells (Fig. 84b). The presence of such cells causes expansion of a domain wall because contraction would increase the elastic energy. Moreover, it is difficult to see how an appreciable change in the absolute value of the polarization could occur within such a wall because such a change would give rise to high values of the dipole and elastic energies due to the piezoelectric effect. All this shows that a 90° wall in BaTiO$_3$ should be fairly thick and that the direction of the polarization vector within the boundary should vary continuously. Using the experimentally determined thickness (4000 Å) of a 90° domain wall in BaTiO$_3$, Little [33] employed thermodynamic reasoning to estimate the energy of this wall as approximately equal to 65 ergs/cm^2. On the other hand, Zhirnov [6] estimated (using the method described earlier) the thickness of a 90° domain wall to be 50-100 Å and its energy as 2-4 ergs/cm^2. Fousek and Březina [24] found that the wall energy at the tip of a wedge-shaped 90° domain was about 7.5 ergs/cm^2. Moreover, Fousek and Brezina concluded that the 90° wall model suggested by Zhirnov should be modified in the case of wedge-shaped domains.

Using the experimental results obtained for very small samples of KH_2PO_4 and Eq. (IV.4), Känzig and Sommerhalder [32] estimated roughly the energy and thickness of a domain wall in these
crystals. According to their estimates, the wall energy is about
40 ergs/cm^2 and the wall thickness is equal to two or three lattice
constants. Other investigators have suggested molecular models
of domain walls in KH_2PO_4. According to one of these models, the
polarization vector rotates within a wall by 90° in the width of one
unit cell. Two lattice constants are found to be sufficient for a
wall between domains with antiparallel orientations of P_s. According to another model, the width of a domain wall is equal to one
unit cell parameter, and the wall is unpolarized. Calculations of
the wall energies in these two models are quite complex and will
not be duscussed here [18].

Rochelle salt is very strongly anisotropic, as indicated, in
particular, by the observation that the components ε_2 and ε_3 of the
permittivity along directions perpendicular to the ferroelectric
axis are very small compared with the component of the permittivity along this axis. It follows that the direction of P_s in a wall cannot deviate from the direction of the ferroelectric axis a. A probable model of a domain wall in Rochelle salt is shown in Fig. 109b.
Mitsui and Furuichi [37] calculated the energy of such a wall taking into account the electrostatic dipole interaction and the elastic energy. The electrostatic energy was assumed to have two
components. One component represents a reduction in the polarization energy due to a decrease of P_s in the wall and it tends to
reduce the wall thickness. The other component describes variation of the dipole interaction with variation of the value of P_s. This
component increases with decreasing wall thickness and, therefore, it tends to broaden the wall. The elastic energy is assumed
to be the result of a concentration of the unit cell due to a reduction of the polarization within the domain wall. Obviously, the
elastic energy increases with increasing wall thickness (Mitsui and
Furuichi ignored the contribution of the piezoelectric strain r_{23} to
the energy). Minimizing these three energies, Mitsui and Furuichi
found that the wall energy was $\mathscr{E}_w = 1.4 \times 10^{-10} P_s^3$ ergs/cm^2 and the
wall thickness was t = $1.8 \times 10^{-4} P_s$ cm. These expressions gave
$\mathscr{E}_w = 0.057$ erg/cm^2 and t = 24 Å for the maximum value of P_s at
5°C. A wall of this thickness cannot be treated as a continuous
medium but we can say that the wall is very thin. It can be shown

that the energy associated with the piezoelectric strain, ignored by Mitsui and Furuichi, increases somewhat the wall thickness.

B. Domain Configurations Corresponding to a Minimum of Free Energy. In general, the problem of finding domain configurations of a real crystal, corresponding to a minimum of the free energy, is very complex. The solution can be obtained only for some very simple special cases. In contrast to ferromagnets, closed domain configurations (Fig. 86) are fairly rare in ferroelectrics because of their strong anisotropy. The most frequent case is that of splitting of a crystal into domains with antiparallel orientation of the spontaneous polarization (Rochelle salt, KH_2PO_4, triglycine sulfate, guanidine aluminum sulfate, etc.). Some crystals (Rochelle salt, KH_2PO_4, etc.) split into domains as well as into blocks (Fig. 99) because of the geometrical features of their structure. It is practically impossible to calculate the energy of boundaries between blocks.

In ferroelectric phase transitions of the first kind domains are formed from nuclei. These nuclei appear independently of one another and, consequently, domain configurations which are formed during such a transition do not initially correspond to the absolute minimum of the free energy. In time, such a metastable structure slowly transforms into a more stable configuration: this is known as aging of ferroelectrics (it is observed, for example, in ceramic samples of $BaTiO_3$).

In ferroelectric phase transitions of the second kind no nuclei are formed and a domain structure corresponding to a minimum of the free energy is established more rapidly.

In the simplest case of an open-circuited dielectric crystal, which is not subjected to external electric or mechanical fields, the equilibrium width of a domain can be estimated by assuming that a crystal consists of narrow ($\mathscr{D} \ll h$) 180° domains (Fig. 110). In the ideal case shown in Fig. 110, internal stresses and anisotropy do not contribute to the volume energy of a crystal (this is discussed in subsection A) if the polarization is uniform and identical in all domains. The problem of finding the optimum wall thickness in the ideal case reduces to finding a minimum of the intrinsic electric energy A_{el} of a crystal (the "depolarization energy") and the total energy of its walls $A_{t.w}$.

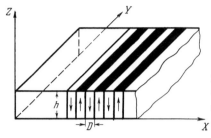

Fig. 110. Model used for calculation of the domain structure corresponding to the energy minimum.

According to Kittel [31], the intrinsic electrostatic energy of a crystal plate (the volume energy per 1 cm^2 of surface) is

$$A_{el} = 2 \cdot 0.85 \, P_s^2 \mathscr{D}. \qquad (IV.5)$$

However, this expression does not include the energy of the field of the surface charges due to the spontaneous polarization P_s, which induce a polarization opposite to P_s. This polarization reduces the depolarization energy, which (according to Kittel [31] and Mitsui and Furuichi [37]) can be included by introducing into Eq. (IV.5) the factor $2/[1 + (\varepsilon_z \varepsilon_x)^{1/2}]$:

$$A'_{el} = \frac{2}{1 + \sqrt{\varepsilon_z \varepsilon_x}} \cdot 2 \cdot 0.85 \, P_s^2 \mathscr{D}. \qquad (IV.6)$$

The induced polarization is important only near the surface of a crystal in a region whose thickness is of the same order of magnitude as the domain width $\mathscr{D}$. It follows from $\mathscr{D} \ll h$ that the volume of a region of nonuniform polarization is small compared with the total volume of the crystal. This makes it possible to neglect the piezoelectric elastic energy due to the nonuniform polarization.

The factor $2/[1 + (\varepsilon_z \varepsilon_x)^{1/2}]$ is similar to the correction μ^* in the case of ferromagnets. This factor can be called ε^* in the ferroelectric case; ε_z and ε_x are permittivities along the ferroelectric axis and at right-angles to it. The value of ε^* is approximately $2/720$ for BaTiO$_3$ at room temperature, $2/10$ for KH$_2$PO$_4$ at $-197°C$, and $2/25$ for Rochelle salt near $10°C$.

The total energy of a wall, per 1 cm^2 of the area of the plate (Fig. 110), is

$$\mathscr{E}_{t.w} = \frac{1}{\mathscr{D}} h \mathscr{E}_w. \qquad \text{(IV.7)}$$

The condition for a minimum of the sum of A_{el} and $\mathscr{E}_w$ yields

$$\mathscr{D} = \left[\frac{\mathscr{E}_w h (1 + \sqrt{\varepsilon_z \varepsilon_x})}{3.4} \right]^{1/2} \frac{1}{P_s}. \qquad \text{(IV.8)}$$

This expression allows us to solve the converse problem, i.e., to determine the surface energy of walls from the known domain widths $\mathscr{D}$. Mitsui and Furuichi [37] heated thoroughly a crystal of Rochelle salt and cooled it slowly from its upper Curie point to 13°C. They found that the domain width was indeed proportional to $h^{1/2}$, i.e.,

$$\mathscr{D} = 1.4 \cdot 10^{-3} h^{1/2},$$

which corresponded to the wall energy $\mathscr{E}_w$ of about 0.12 erg/cm^2. This value is the upper limit of the wall energy because Mitsui and Furuichi ignored the compensation of charges resulting from the leakage during measurements. When the volume conductivity of Rochelle salt is allowed for, it is found that $\mathscr{E}_w$ is about 0.08 erg/cm^2.

Similar experiments have not been carried out for KH_2PO_4 but, substituting into Eq. (IV.8) the calculated value of the wall energy 40 ergs/cm^2 (given in subsection A), we find that the width of domains in this compound is 2.6×10^{-4} cm for $h = 0.1$ cm at $T = 90°K$; this value is in agreement with the experimental data reported by Strukov and Toshev [14].

Equation (IV.8) can be applied only to the equilibrium domain structure of $BaTiO_3$, i.e., to the structure which is obtained after prolonged storage of a crystal at some temperature. An approximate estimate of the domain width for 180° walls in $BaTiO_3$, obtained on the assumption that $\mathscr{E}_w = 7$ ergs/cm^2 and $h = 0.1$ cm, yields a domain width of the order of 2×10^{-4} cm.

Kinase and Takahashi [30] determined the energy of a 180° wall in $BaTiO_3$ ($\mathscr{E}_w = 1.40$ ergs/cm^2) and used this energy to estimate the width of antiparallel domains. Kinase and Takahashi found the condition for equilibrium between the wall energy and the electrostatic energy due to free charges on the surface of a crystal. They considered domain configurations in the form of antiparallel plates, prisms, and cylinders. They found that the domain width for these three configurations was approximately the same [(0.6-1.5) $\times$ 10^{-4} cm] for a crystal slab 0.1 cm thick; this was in good agreement with the experimental data.

Very small ferroelectric crystals are a special case. The surface energy of a domain wall in a very small crystal may be comparable with its volume energy. The presence of narrow domains in very small crystals may not be favored by the energy considerations. In the absence of narrow domains the field of surface charges may extend over a considerable part of the volume of a very small crystal. The polarization inside such a crystal becomes nonuniform and a spontaneous distribution of the piezoelectric strain is established. The introduction of a correction does not give satisfactory results. An analysis shows that the depolarization energy of a spherical single-domain dielectric crystal, which is stored in vacuum in the open-circuited state, is given by

$$A'_{el} = \frac{1}{2} \cdot \frac{4\pi}{3} PV \qquad \qquad (IV.9)$$

(P is the resultant polarization which includes the influence of surface charges; V is the volume), which shows that the depolarization energy is much greater than the absolute energy of a ferroelectric transition

$$QV = \frac{1}{2}(T_0/C)P^2V \qquad \qquad (IV.10)$$

(C is the Curie-Weiss constant and T_0 is the Curie temperature) for any ferroelectric. This means that, under these conditions, the spontaneous polarization cannot appear even below the Curie temperature until the electrostatic energy decreases due to conduction processes or due to the formation of domains. Thus, in the case of KH_2PO_4 crystals, whose conductivity is low at low temperatures (near the transition point), we can prevent the formation of domains by making crystals very small. Jaccard, Känzig, and Peter [26] showed that, when KH_2PO_4 crystals are placed in an insulating medium with a low value of the permittivity, the depolarizing field prevents the appearance of the spontaneous polarization in open-circuited samples if the diameter of such samples (particles) is less than 1500 Å. An estimate of the wall energy

($\mathscr{E}_w = 40$ ergs $/cm^2$), based on this critical size, has been given earlier in the present subsection.

Corresponding phenomena are not observed in small ferromagnetic crystals. The intrinsic magnetostatic energy of such crystals is approximately 10^3 times smaller than the transition energy and, therefore, it cannot suppress the spontaneous magnetization. In this respect, ferroelectrics are similar to some paramagnetic salts which are magnetized spontaneously at extremely low temperatures.

The domain structure and properties of "quenched" ferroelectric crystals (crystals rapidly cooled through the Curie temperature) is of considerable interest. Strong mechanical stresses, which appear in the surfaces of such crystals, split them into very small domains because the formation of domain walls reduces effectively the elastic energy and, therefore, the total internal energy of a crystal. The presence of a very fine domain structure in a crystal makes its properties approach those of antiferroelectrics. These effects have been observed in Rochelle salt [5] and in barium titanate [1].

References

1. I. N. Belyaev, N. S. Novosil'tsev, E. G. Fesenko, and A. L. Khodakov, Dokl. Akad. Nauk SSSR, 83:675 (1952).
2. I. S. Zheludev and V. F. Parvov, Kristallografiya, 1:482-483 (1956).
3. I. S. Zheludev, I. S. Rez, A. S. Sonin, V. V. Gladkin, and V. M. Gurevich, in: Physics of Dielectrics (Proc. Second All-Union Conf., Moscow, 1958) [in Russian] Izd. AN SSSR, Moscow (1960).
4. I. S. Zheludev, A. A. Filimonov, V. A. Yurin, and N. A. Romanyuk, Kristallografiya, 6:676 (1961).
5. I. S. Zheludev and V. A. Yurin, Izv. Akad. Nauk SSSR, Ser. Fiz., 20:211 (1956).
6. V. A. Zhirnov, Zh. Éksp. Teor. Fiz., 35:1175 (1958).
7. V. L. Indenbom and M. A. Chernysheva, Zh. Éksp. Teor. Fiz., 32:697 (1957).
8. V. P. Konstantinova, Kristallografiya, 7:748 (1962).
9. V. P. Konstantinova and M. V. Klassen-Neklyudova, Mechanical Twinning of Crystals [in Russian], Izd. AN SSSR, Moscow (1960).
10. V. A. Meleshina, I. S. Zheludev, and I. S. Rez, Kristallografiya, 5:322 (1960).
11. N. A. Romanyuk and I. S. Zheludev, Kristallografiya, 5:904 (1960).
12. G. V. Spivak, É. Igras, and I. S. Zheludev, Dokl. Akad. Nauk SSSR, 122:54 (1958).
13. G. V. Spivak, É. Igras, I. A. Pryamkova, and I. S. Zheludev, Kristallografiya, 4:123 (1959).
14a. S. D. Toshev, Kristallografiya, 8:680 (1963);
14b. B. A. Strukov and S. D. Toshev, Kristallografiya, 9:426 (1964).

15. M. A. Chernysheva, Dokl. Akad. Nauk SSSR, 91:87 (1953).

16. V. A. Yurin, A. S. Baberkin, and I. S. Zheludev, Kristallografiya, 7:147 (1962).

17. R. Abe, Phys. Soc. Japan, 13:244 (1958).

18. H. M. Bárkla and D. M. Finlayson, Phil. Mag., 44:109 (1953).

19. J. Časlávský and M. Polcatová, Czech. J. Phys., 14:454 (1964).

20. M. H. Cohen, Phys. Rev., 84:368 (1951).

21. L. E. Cross and B. J. Nicholson, Phil. Mag., 46:453 (1955).

22. A. G. Chynoweth and W. L. Feldmann, J. Phys. Chem. Solids, 15:225 (1960).

23. P. W. Forsbergh, Jr., Phys. Rev., 76:1187 (1949).

24. J. Fousek and B. Březina, Czech. J. Phys., 11:261 (1961).

25. J. A. Hooton and W. J. Merz, Phys. Rev., 98:409 (1955).

26. C. Jaccard, W. Känzig, and M. Peter, Helv. Phys. Acta, 26:521 (1953).

27. F. Jona, G. Shirane, and R. Pepinsky, Phys. Rev., 97:1584 (1955).

28. W. Kinase, Progr. Theoret. Phys. (Kyoto), 13:529 (1955).

29. W. Kinase, Busseiron-Kenkyu, 4:721 (1958).

30. W. Kinase and H. Takahashi, J. Phys. Soc. Japan, 12:464 (1957).

31. C. Kittel, Rev. Mod. Phys., 21:541 (1949).

32. W. Känzig and R. Sommerhalder, Helv. Phys. Acta, 26:603 (1953).

33. E. A. Little, Massachusetts Inst. Technology, Report No. 87 (1954).

34. W. J. Merz, Phys. Rev., 88:421 (1952).

35. W. J. Merz, Phys. Rev., 95:690 (1954).

36. B. Matthias and A. von Hippel, Phys. Rev., 73:1378 (1948).

37. T. Mitsui and J. Furuichi, Phys. Rev., 90:193 (1953).

38. S. Nomura, Y. Asao, and S. Sawada, J. Phys. Soc. Japan, 16:917 (1961).

39. E. A. Wood, Acta Cryst., 4:353 (1951).

40. É. Igras, G. V. Spivak, and I. S. Zheludev, Kristallografiya, 4:121 (1959).

41. W. Känzig, "Ferroelectrics and antiferroelectrics," Solid State Phys., 4:1 (1957).

42. E. G. Fesenko, Dokl. Akad. Nauk SSSR, 88:785 (1953).

43. L. A. Shuvalov, K. S. Aleksandrov, and I. S. Zheludev, Kristallografiya, 4:130 (1959).

44. H. Gränicher, W. M. Meier, and W. Petter, Helv. Phys. Acta, 27:216 (1954).

45. A. von Hippel, Rev. Mod. Phys., 22:221 (1950).

46. K. Hirakawa, J. Phys. Soc. Japan, 7:331 (1952).

47. F. Jona and G. Shirane, Ferroelectric Crystals, Pergamon Press, Oxford (1962).

48. H. D. Megaw, Ferroelectricity in Crystals, Methuen, London (1957).

49. G. L. Pearson and W. L. Feldmann, J. Phys. Chem. Solids, 9:28 (1959).

50. S. Sawada, R. Ando, and S. Nomura, Phys. Rev., 82:952 (1951).

51. R. Ueda and T. Ichinokawa, Phys. Rev., 80:1106 (1950).

52. R. Ueda and J. Kobayashi, Phys. Rev., 91:1565 (1953).

53. P. Vousden, Acta Cryst., 4:545 (1951).

Chapter V

Pyroelectric Effect and Associated Phenomena

Introduction

Linear dielectric crystals belonging to the polar classes (such as tourmaline, lithium sulfate, saccharose, etc.) do not undergo phase transitions, but they do exhibit spontaneous polarization throughout the whole range of temperatures in which they exist. Ferroelectrics usually have polar phases in the lower range of temperatures in which they exist. The most important difference between ferroelectrics and linear polar dielectrics (pyroelectrics of the crystal classes, 1, 2, 3, 4, 6, m, 2·m, 3·m, 4·m, 6·m, and those having textures ∞, ∞·m) is that ferroelectrics split into regions of spontaneous polarization (domains) and pyroelectrics do not.

Pyroelectric phenomena are those effects which are associated with changes in the spontaneous polarization of crystals due to a change in their temperature. The converse phenomena are known as electrocaloric effects, representing a change in the temperature of a crystal when an electric field E is applied to it.

Investigations of pyroelectric crystals show that their spontaneous polarization P_s depends strongly on the temperature only at low temperatures; at other temperatures this dependence is weak. The temperature dependence of the pyroelectric coefficient p is similar to the temperature dependence of the specific heat and of the thermal expansion coefficient α.

In Chap. IV we have considered general relationships governing the orientation of domains in ferroelectrics and we have shown

that a crystal split into domains reverts to the macroscopic symmetry of the paraelectric nonpolar phase. This means that a perfect ferroelectric crystal split into domains does not have a macroscopic spontaneous polarization and, therefore, it cannot exhibit a macroscopic pyroelectric effect. However, the spontaneous
polarization and the pyroelectric effect of single domains can be
measured using the optical methods described in Chap. IV; they
can be measured also for a crystal as a whole if the crystal is
transformed to the single-domain state. Electric methods of the
measurement of P_s and, particularly, the method of dielectric hysteresis loops, are used most widely in such studies.

The spontaneous polarization appears (or disappears) at the
temperatures of ferroelectric phase transitions and the pyroelectric effect is strongest at these temperatures. It is also strong at
temperatures corresponding to transitions from one ferroelectric
modification to another.

Antiferroelectric domains are not polar and, therefore, in the
absence of external forces, antiferroelectric crystals do not exhibit spontaneous electric polarization even if they are split into
nonrandomly distributed domains. This means that antiferroelectric crystals do not exhibit pyroelectric properties. However, the
structure of an antiferroelectric may change from nonpolar to polar
in very strong electric fields. This makes it possible to measure
both the magnitude of the spontaneous polarization of the ferroelectric phase induced by an external field as well as the temperature dependence of this polarization. However, no experimental data have yet been published on the induced ferroelectric state.

Variation of the spontaneous polarization P_s with temperature is accompanied by certain physical effects which will be discussed in the present chapter.

§ 1. Equations for the Pyroelectric

and Electrocalorie Effects.

Pyroelectric Properties

of Linear Dielectrics

A. General Information on the Pyroelectric
Effect. The polar classes 6·m, 4·m, 3·m, 2·m, m, 6, 4, 3, 2, 1

(§5, Chap. I) describe the point symmetry of dielectric crystals polarized in the absence of external fields, i.e., crystals which have a finite spontaneous polarization P_s per unit volume. Uniform heating of such crystals may alter the value of P_s. Such a change in the polarization is responsible for the pyroelectric phenomena. The magnitude of the pyroelectric effect can be represented by the change in the spontaneous polarization ΔP_s proportional to (for small changes in the temperature ΔT):

$$\Delta P_s = p\Delta T. \tag{V.1}$$

Thus, the pyroelectric effect in crystals is described by the vector $\mathbf{p}$.

The spontaneous polarization of a crystal P_s can be represented in the form of a dipole moment, defined as the product of the charge per unit volume of a dielectric q and the distance between the centers of gravity of the positive and negative charges l:

$$P_s = ql, \tag{V.2}$$

where l is assumed to be directed from the negative to the positive charge. The change in the value of P_s due to the pyroelectric effect, given by Eq. (V.2), can be regarded as a sum of the primary (true) and secondary (false) effects. The primary or true pyroelectric effect is the change of P_s which is not associated with the piezoelectric polarization.* The change in P_s associated with the piezoelectric polarization is the secondary or false pyroelectric effect. Thus, the sum of the primary and secondary pyroelectric effects is the total effect.

The secondary pyroelectric effect can be calculated most easily from the deformation of a free (unclamped) crystal during uniform heating. Using Eq. (V.2), this effect can be treated as a change in the value of l without a change in q. If the values of P_s at two temperatures T_1 and T_2 are

$$P_s^{T_1} = ql_{T_1},$$
$$P_s^{T_2} = ql_{T_2}, \tag{V.3}$$

---

*Every crystal tends to change its dimensions during heating, and this gives rise to the piezoelectric effect. In a free crystal this effect is due to the resultant deformation and in a clamped crystal it is due to thermal stresses (this point will be discussed later).

the change in the polarization can be written in the form

$$\Delta P_s^{''} = q\Delta l = p''\Delta T \qquad (\Delta T = T_2 - T_1), \qquad (V.4)$$

where $\mathbf{p}^{\pi}$ is the secondary pyroelectric coefficient.

In practice, the separation of the primary and secondary py-roelectric effects is difficult since the experimental measure-ments give the total effect:

$$\Delta P_s = (p' + p'')\Delta T, \qquad (V.5)$$

where $\mathbf{p'}$ is the primary pyroelectric coefficient. The above ex-pression can be given in terms of the components of the vectors:

$$\Delta P_{si} = (p_i' + p_i'')\Delta T \qquad (i = 1, 2, 3), \qquad (V.6)$$

and hence, going over to the differential form, we obtain

$$p = \frac{\partial P_s}{\partial T}, \qquad (V.7)$$

where p is the total pyroelectric coefficient, equal to p' + p".

The characteristics of the thermal expansion of crystals, con-sidered earlier in the book, can be used to determine the direction of the vectors $\mathbf{P}_s$ and possible changes in this vector. It follows from our discussion in Chap. I that the thermal expansion of crys-tals of classes 6·m, 4·m, 3·m, 2·m, 6, 4, 3, and 2 cannot alter the directions of the vectors $\mathbf{P}_s$, which coincide with the symmetry axes, but it can change the magnitudes of these vectors. In crystals of class m, the vector $\mathbf{P}_s$ lies in the reflection plane of these crys-tals; the thermal expansion alters the magnitude and direction of this vector without displacing it from the reflection plane. In crys-tals of class 1, the vector $\mathbf{P}_s$ can occupy any position and the ther-mal expansion alters continuously its magnitude and direction.

Media (textures) which can be described by the symmetry groups ∞·m and ∞ can also exhibit a change in the polarization $\mathbf{P}_s$ during heating (provided this polarization exists at all), i.e., they can also be pyroelectrics.

We can easily see that a scalar force (heating) cannot alter the symmetry of a crystal. This means that the pyroelectric ef-fect cannot appear in crystals which do not exhibit spontaneous polarization. However, heating of a crystal may not be uniform. In this case, the external force is not scalar and the symmetry of a crystal, which need not be pyroelectric before heating, may change so that it can now be described by one of the polar classes. In this case, heating produces electric polarization, which is called the tertiary pyroelectric effect. The tertiary effect can appear in a variety of forms and is highly indeterminate; for these reasons, the textbooks on crystal physics usually mention this effect but do not consider it in detail.

B. Equations for the Pyroelectric Effect. The free energy of a crystal G, considered as a function of mechanical stresses t, electric field E, and entropy S, can be written in the form given by Cady [6]:

$$G = \frac{1}{2} s^E_{hi} t_h t_i + \frac{1}{2} \alpha'_{km} E_k E_m + d_{mh} E_m t_h$$

$$+ \frac{1}{2} \frac{S \rho T}{c} (\Delta S)^2 + \Delta T \alpha_h t_h + \Delta T p_m E_m \qquad (V.8)$$

$$(i, h = 1, 2, \ldots, 6; \; k, m = 1, 2, 3).$$

In this expressions s^E_{hi} stands for the elastic (compliance) constants of a crystal in a constant electric field and at a fixed temperature; α'_{km} is the polarizability of a dielectric at constant deformation; d_{mh} is the piezoelectric strain coefficient; J is the mechanical equivalent of heat; ρ is the density of a crystal; c is the specific heat; α_h is the thermal expansion coefficient; p_m is the pyroelectric coefficient. The six terms in Eq. (V.8) describe, respectively, the elastic energy, electric polarization energy, piezoelectric deformation energy, thermal energy, energy of thermal expansion, and energy of pyroelectric polarization (due to the primary pyroelectric effect).

We shall use Eq. (V.8) to derive equations for the pyroelectric effect. We shall assume that the polarization charge in a pyroelectric crystal is proportional to the change in temperature ΔT. We shall also assume that the crystal is heated uniformly at all times. We shall postulate that, at the initial temperature T_1, the polarization charge is neutralized by the internal conductivity or by some deliberate action so that the surface of the crystal is at zero potential. Thus, the charge which appears in the crystal is proportional to the change in the polarization P_s with a coefficient of proportionality p_m.

Taking the derivative of the free energy G (per unit volume) with respect to E, we obtain

$$\frac{\partial G}{\partial E_m} = P_m = \alpha'_m E_m + d_{mh}t_h + \Delta T p'_m. \tag{V.9}$$

In this expression E_m represents any field (including the external electric field as well as the depolarizing field, generated by the polarization charge). The field E_m can be compensated in experimental measurements and, therefore, we shall ignore the first term in Eq. (V.9).

The second term in Eq. (V.9) describes the piezoelectric polarization of a clamped sample due to stresses generated by heating (the secondary pyroelectric effect). This term can be written in the form

$$d_{mh}t_h = d_{mh}\beta_h\Delta T, \tag{V.10}$$

where β_h is the thermal stress coefficient, which occurs in the equation

$$t_h = \beta_h\Delta T. \tag{V.11}$$

Comparing Eqs. (V.10) and (V.11), we obtain the increase in the polarization due to the secondary pyroelectric effect:

$$d_{mh}\beta_h\Delta T = p''\Delta T, \tag{V.12}$$

where p'' is the secondary pyroelectric coefficient.

The third term in Eq. (V.9) describes the polarization of the crystal due to the primary pyroelectric effect, and the quantity p'_m is the primary pyroelectric coefficient. This coefficient represents only that component of the pyroelectric effect which is not associated with the piezoelectric polarization.

Thus, the change in the polarization of a clamped crystal is, according to Eqs. (V.9) and (V.10),

$$\Delta P_m = (p' + p'') \Delta T. \tag{V.13}$$

The free energy G of a crystal can be regarded as a function of mechanical strain r, electric field E, and temperature T. This function (G_1) is similar to the function G given by Eq. (V.8). Differentiating G_1 with respect to E_m , we obtain an expression

$$\frac{\partial G_1}{\partial E_m} = P_m = \alpha''_{km} E_k + e_{mn} r_n \dotplus p'_m \Delta T, \tag{V.14}$$

which is similar to Eq. (V.9). Here, α''_{km} is the polarizability of a free crystal (a crystal with constant stresses); e_{mn} is the piezoelectric stress coefficient related to the coefficient d_{nk} by the expression $e_{mn} = d_{nk} c^F_{hk}$.

Using the last two terms in Eq. (V.14) and assuming that

$$r_n = \alpha_n \Delta T, \tag{V.15}$$

where α_n is the thermal expansion coefficient, we obtain the equation for the pyroelectric effect in a mechanically free and freely deformable crystal:

$$\Delta P_m = (e_{mn} \alpha_n + p'_m) \Delta T \equiv (p''_m + p'_m) \Delta T, \tag{V.16}$$

where p" is the secondary pyroelectric coefficient, equal to $e_{mn} \alpha_n$. The total pyroelectric coefficient

$$p_m = p'_m + p''_m \tag{V.17}$$

represents the electric moment per unit volume of a crystal due to the primary and secondary pyroelectric effects. This coefficient is positive if an increase in the temperature increases the spontaneous polarization of a crystal P_s .

C. Equation for the Electrocaloric Effect. It follows from thermodynamic considerations that, in addition to the pyroelectric effect, there should be a converse effect. This effect is known as the electrocaloric effect, and it represents a change in the temperature of a pyroelectric crystal when an electric field is applied to it. Analytically, the electrocaloric effect is represented by the coefficient

$$q = \frac{dT}{dE}. \tag{V.18}$$

The quantity q is known as the electrocaloric coefficient (it should not be confused with the symbol q used for charge in subsection A).

Electrocaloric properties can be exhibited only by crystals of the polar classes 1, 2, 3, 4, 6, m, 2·m, 3·m, 4·m, 6·m, and by textures described by the symmetry groups ∞ and ∞·m, since the electric field energy can be transformed directly to the thermal energy only in the polar crystals and textures (it must be pointed out that nonpolar dielectrics can be made polar by the application of an external field and they can then exhibit – usually very weak – pyroelectric and electrocaloric phenomena). The temperature of crystals of other classes of symmetry can also change due to the application of an external electric field (for example, due to electrostrictive or piezoelectric deformations, due to electrical conductivity, etc.), but these changes in temperature have nothing in common with the electrocaloric effect since they are not the result of a direct transformation of the electrical energy into heat.

We shall now derive the equation for the electrocaloric effect. Assuming that the only result of the application of an electric field to a crystal is a change in its heat capacity, we can write the change in the energy of a unit volume of the crystal dU in the form

$$dU = E dP + T dS, \tag{V.19}$$

where dS is the change in the entropy and dP is the change in the polarization due to the application of a field E. Rewriting this expression to obtain T in an explicit form and calculating the derivative dT/dE, we obtain

$$q = \frac{dT}{dE} = -\frac{dP}{dS} = -\frac{\partial P}{\partial T}\frac{\partial T}{\partial S}.$$

Replacing $\partial P / \partial T$ by the pyroelectric coefficient p [see Eq. (V.17)], we find that

$$q = -p\frac{\partial T}{\partial S}.$$

Using the well-known thermodynamic relationship

$$dS = \frac{dQ}{T}, \qquad dQ = dT \rho c J,$$

we obtain

$$q = \frac{dT}{dE} = -\frac{pT}{\rho cJ},$$ (V.20)

where ρ is the density of the crystal; c is the specific heat; J is the mechanical equivalent of heat. Using Eq. (V.20), we can write the equation for the electrocaloric effect in the form

$$\Delta T = q\Delta E = -\frac{pT}{\rho cJ}\Delta E.$$ (V.21)

Equation (V.21) shows that when p is positive and E has the same direction as **P**, the electrocaloric coefficient q is negative. In this case, an increase of the polarization P of a crystal, due to the application of the electric field, reduces the temperature of the crystal.

D. Pyroelectric Properties of Linear Dielectrics. Pyroelectric properties have been investigated most thoroughly for tourmaline crystals, which belong to the symmetry group 3·m. The pyroelectric polarization appears in tourmaline along a unique polar axis 3. The earliest investigations of the pyroelectric properties of tourmaline were qualitative: the method of charged powders (see §2, Chap. IV) was used to demonstrate the existence of the pyroelectric polarization. Quantitative measurements were later made of the total pyroelectric coefficient p_Z of tourmaline (the threefold symmetry axis was taken to be the Z axis of the crystallophysical system of coordinates); these crystals had various colors (Table 30).

Ackermann [10], Voigt [29], Röntgen [24], and other investigators studied pyroelectric properties of tourmaline, lithium sul-

TABLE 30. Total Pyroelectric Coefficient p_Z for
Tourmaline Crystals of Various Colors [10]

T, °C	p_Z for crystals of various colors (cgs esu)		
	yellow-green	rose-red	blue-green
—250	—0.08	—0.08	—0.04
+20	—1.28	—1.31	—1.06
+375	—1.86	—1.94	—1.52

fate, potassium tartrate, ammonium tartrate, and other crystals. These studies established, in particular, that the total pyroelectric coefficient p_m tends to vanish at absolute zero. These investigators paid special attention to the problem of the relationship between the primary and secondary pyroelectric effects. This relationship was approached from various points of view. One of the investigators (Röntgen) went so far as to assume that the whole pyroeffect in tourmaline crystals was of the secondary (false) type. The separation of the total pyroelectric effect into its components is difficult because in order to obtain a numerical value of the secondary pyroelectric coefficient (p"), it is necessary to know the piezoelectric coefficients, the elastic and thermal expansion coefficients, as well as the total pyroelectric coefficient p_m. Moreover, all these coefficients should be measured, for the sake of accuracy, using the same samples. It is assumed nowadays that although the primary (true) pyroelectric effect in linear pyroelectrics (such as tourmaline) is small, it is by no means negligible. Approximate estimates show that the primary coefficient p' represents about 10% of p_m.

Using the expression $p_m'' = e_{mn} \alpha_n$, we can estimate the secondary pyroelectric coefficient. Thus, using the room-temperature parameters of tourmaline $e_{31} = e_{32} = 3.09 \times 10^4$, $e_{33} = 9.6 \times 10^4$, $\alpha_1 = \alpha_2 = -3.6 \times 10^{-6}$, $\alpha_3 = -8.8 \times 10^{-6}$ cgs esu, we obtain $p_m'' = -0.95$ cgs esu. Assuming that $p' = 0.1 p''$, we find that the value of p_z for tourmaline is about -1.1 cgs esu, which is quite close to the values given in Table 30.

The following example gives some idea of the pyroelectric polarization of tourmaline. A tourmaline slab, cut at right-angles to the pyroelectric axis and 0.1 cm thick, heated uniformly by 10°C, acquires an electric charge of about 5×10^{-9} C/cm^2 and the potential difference between the electrodes enclosing the slab is 1200 V.

Since the piezoelectric effect can be considered as associated with the spontaneous polarization P_s of pyroelectric crystals, it would be interesting to know at least the approximate values of the magnitude of this effect. Such values can be obtained by direct measurements of the surface charge on a crystal freshly cleaved at right-angles to the pyroelectric axis. These measurements give P_s of 33 cgs esu for tourmaline, which corresponds to a surface charge density of about 0.01 μC/cm^2. However, this value cannot be regarded as reliable because the method used in the measurement of P is unsatisfactory.

More reliable values of P_s can be obtained by investigating the piezoelectric effect of pyroelectric crystals subjected to hydrostatic compression or expansion at a fixed temperature. In this case ($E = 0$, $\Delta T = 0$), the equation for the polarization [Eq. (V.9)] assumes the form

$$P_m = d_{mh} t_h.$$

Under hydrostatic compression $t_1 = t_2 = t_3 \equiv p_{hydr}$ (p_{hydr} is the hydrostatic pressure), $t_4 = t_5 = t_6 = 0$, $d_{mh} = d_{31} + d_{32} + d_{33} = d_{hydr}$ (here, the Z axis is denoted by the subscript 3 and is taken as the pyroelectric axis). This makes it possible to rewrite the above expression in the form

$$P_m = d_{hydr} p_{hydr} \qquad (V.22)$$

Table 31 lists the values of d_{hydr} found by direct measurements using hydrostatic expansion as well as the values calculated from d_{31}, d_{32}, and d_{33} of various crystals.

The values of d_{hydr} listed in Table 31 can be used to estimate P_s. Such estimates are based on the following considerations. When a crystal expands (due to a sudden reduction of the gas pressure in a chamber), the surface density of the spontaneous polarization charge changes on those faces of the crystal which are perpendicular to the pyroelectric axis Z (denoted by subscript 3). Including quantities of the first order of smallness, we find that the change is

TABLE 31. Piezoelectric Strain Coefficients, d_{hydr} [3]

Crystal	$d_{hydr} \cdot 10^8$, cgs esu	
	calculated	experimental
Tourmaline	8	12
Potassium tartrate	4	3
Lithium sulfate	39	42
Rhamnose	19	21

$$-\Delta P_3' = P_s (\Delta X + \Delta Y),$$

where ΔX and ΔY are the relative elongations of the crystal along the X and Y axes. On the other hand, the elongation of the sample along the Z axis increases the polarization by the amount

$$\Delta P_3'' = P_s \Delta Z.$$

Thus, the resultant polarization due to hydrostatic expansion is

$$\Delta P_3 := - P_3' + P_3'' = P_s (\Delta Z - \Delta X - \Delta Y). \qquad (V.23)$$

Using the generalized Hooke's law for crystals of class 2, which include rhamnose, potassium tartrate, lithium sulfate, and other pyroelectrics, we obtain

$$\begin{aligned}
\Delta X &= p_{\text{hydr}} \ (s_{11} + s_{12} + s_{13}), \\
\Delta Y &= p_{\text{hydr}} \ (s_{22} + s_{22} + s_{23}), \\
\Delta Z &= p_{\text{hydr}} \ (s_{33} + s_{23} + s_{13}).
\end{aligned} \qquad (V.24)$$

Employing Eq. (V.24), we can rewrite Eq. (V.23) in the form

$$\Delta P_3 \equiv P_3 = P_s p_{\text{hydr}} (s_{33} - s_{11} - s_{22} - 2s_{12}). \qquad (V.25)$$

On the other hand, since

$$P_3 = d_{\text{hydr}} p ,$$

we find that

$$P_s = \frac{d_{\text{hydr}}}{s_{33} - s_{11} - s_{22} - 2s_{12}}. \qquad (V.26)$$

The application of Eq. (V.26) to the experimental results gives $P_s \approx 86 \times 10^{-6}$ C/cm^2 for lithium sulfate and $P_s \approx 5.7 \times 10^{-6}$ C/cm^2 for potassium tartrate. A similar analysis yields $P_s = 17 \times 10^{-6}$ C/cm^2 for tourmaline, which is more than two orders of magnitude higher than the value of P_s obtained from measurements of the surface charge on a cleaved face. We shall show later that the spontaneous polarization of pyroelectrics is close to P_s of ferroelectrics. It is worth pointing out that the values of $P_s \sim 10^{-5}$ C/cm^2, obtained for linear pyroelectrics exhibiting weak polarizability, correspond to strong fields E_s of the order of $10^7 - 10^8$ V/cm. However, these fields are usually compensated by the external charge or by the conduction charge.

Equation (V.20) can be used to estimate the electrocaloric co-efficient:

$$q = - \frac{pT}{\rho c J}.$$

Applying this equation to tourmaline and assuming that $\rho = 3$ g/cm^3, c = 0.2 cal·g^{-1}·deg^{-1}, p = 1.3 cgs esu (Table 30), J = 4.18 × 10^7 ergs/cal, we find that q = 1.4 × 10^{-5} cgs esu at room temperature (T = 300°K). It follows from this value of q that a tourmaline slab, 0.1 cm thick, placed in a field of 1000 V, will be heated or cooled (depending on the direction of the field relative to P_s) by 5 × 10^{-5} deg if the slab is initially at room temperature.

§2. Pyroelectric Properties

of Ferroelectrics

A. Temperature Dependence of the Spontane-ous Polarization. Investigations of pyroelectric proper-ties of ferroelectrics consist primarily of studies of the tempera-ture dependence of the spontaneous polarization of such materials. This dependence is one of the most important characteristics of ferroelectrics and it is of intrinsic interest, apart from the py-roelectric properties.

The true value of the spontaneous polarization of a ferroelec-tric P_s can be found macroscopically only when all the domains are oriented along a selected direction. Usually, the value of P_s is de-termined by measuring the parameters of dielectric hysteresis loops.

Figure 111 shows schematically the Sawyer and Tower cir-cuit usually employed for observation of hysteresis loops on the screen of a cathode-ray oscillograph. A potential difference V (usually a low-frequency line voltage, 50-60 cps) is applied to a standard linear capacitor C_0 and a ferroelectric capacitor C_x con-nected in parallel. The circuit satisfies the condition $C_x \ll C_0$ and, therefore, we may assume that the whole applied voltage is concen-trated in the ferroelectric capacitor C_x, i.e., $V_x \approx V$. The same voltage is applied also to the horizontal deflecting plates of the oscillograph. A voltage V_0, taken from the standard capacitor C_0, is applied to the vertical plates. The latter voltage is a linear function of the polarization of the investigated capacitor C_x. Using the relationship

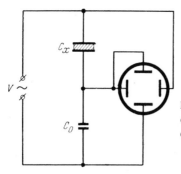

Fig. 111. Sawyer-Tower circuit for
oscillographic investigation of dielectric hysteresis loops.

$$C_x V_x = C_0 V_0 = Q,$$

where Q is the charge in each of the capacitors, and assuming that

$$P = \sigma,$$

$$Q = \sigma S,$$

where σ is the charge density, S is the capacitor area, and P is
the polarization, we find that

$$P = \frac{C_0}{S} V_0. \qquad\qquad (V.27)$$

It follows from Eq. (V.27) that the measurement of the polarization by means of this circuit reduces to the measurement of the
capacitor area and the value of V_0 proportional to the vertical de-
flection of the oscillograph beam.

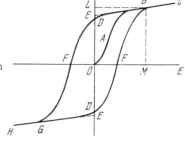

Fig. 112. Schematic representation
of a dielectric hysteresis loop.

The dependence of the polarization P on the electric field E, given in Fig. 112, shows schematically the usual hysteresis loop. Linear extrapolation of the polarization from the saturation region (BC) to zero field gives the spontaneous polarization P_s (intercept OE on the P axis). The total polarization of the ferroelectric (intercept OL) in the saturation field (intercept OM) consists of the spontaneous polarization P_s and of the induced polarization represented by the intercept EL. This extrapolation subtracts the induced polarization from the total value. Measurements of the hysteresis loop parameters at various temperatures yield the dependence

$$P_s = P_s(T).$$

We note also that the polarization, represented by the intercept OD in Fig. 112, is known as the remanent polarization and the field OF is the coercive force.

The temperature dependences of P_s, obtained by different workers on different samples of the same compounds, disagree quite strongly. A fairly large scatter of the values of P_s and various types of the dependence $P_s(T)$ are found not only for ceramic materials but also for single crystals. This is due to inhomogeneities and imperfections in crystals, as well as due to temperature gradients which cause different parts of a given crystal to undergo phase transitions at different times. An example of the differences in the reported data is given in Fig. 113, which shows the dependence $P_s(T)$ for barium titanate crystals with many

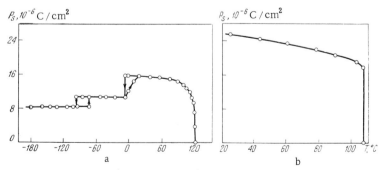

Fig. 113. Temperature dependence of the spontaneous polarization P_s of barium titanate crystals with many (a) and few (b) defects [19, 20].

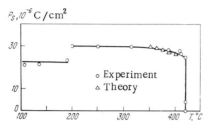

Fig. 114. Temperature dependence of the spontaneous polarization P_S of $KNbO_3$ crystals [28].

Fig. 115. Temperature dependence of the spontaneous polarization of methylammonium aluminum alum $(CH_3NH_3)Al(SO_4)_2$ along the crystallographic directions [100], [110], and [111] (curves 1, 2, 3, respectively) [18].

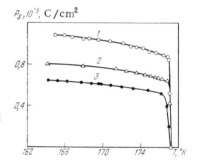

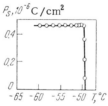

Fig. 116. Temperature dependence of the spontaneous polarization P_s of $(NH_4)_2SO_4$ [17].

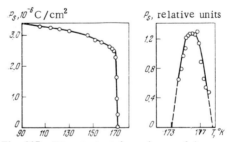

Fig. 117. Temperature dependence of the spontaneous polarization P_s of thiourea for two ferroelectric regions of this compound [14].

(a) and few (b) defects. We can clearly see that P_s of the crystal with more defects rises gradually when the temperature is reduced below the Curie point, while the polarization of the crystal with few defects jumps suddenly at the Curie point.

In general, the temperature dependences $P_s(T)$ of different compounds may be close to that shown in Fig. 113a or that given in Fig. 113b. However, the difference between the two dependences cannot be expained completely by imperfections in a crystal, the presence of a temperature gradient, etc. The nature of the dependence $P_s(T)$ is governed in the first instance by the nature of the change in the crystal structure, i.e., by the type of the phase transition.

The information now available makes it possible to establish clearly that the spontaneous polarization appears suddenly not only in barium titanate, but also in potassium niobate (Fig. 114), methylammonium aluminum alum (Fig. 115), ammonium sulfate (Fig. 116), and thiourea (Fig. 117, $-103°C$). The sudden appearance of the spontaneous polarization in these crystals does not exclude the possibility of a strong but smooth temperature dependence of the spontaneous polarization in the ferroelectric modification.

The spontaneous polarization of other crystals is known to increase quite smoothly. This has been demonstrated particularly clearly for Rochelle salt by measuring the rotation of the optical indicatrix of single domains (Fig. 97) during variation of temperature. Figure 118 shows the dependence $P_s(T)$ for Rochelle salt. The continuous rise of the polarization near the transition point is typical also of crystals of triglycine sulfate, triglycine fluoroberyllate, triglycine selenate (Fig. 119), ammonium fluoroberyllate (Fig. 120), sodium nitrite (Fig. 121), and other compounds.

Some crystals exhibit several ferroelectric phase transitions and their spontaneous polarization P_s can change suddenly at one transition temperature and gradually at another. An excellent example of such behavior is the $P_s(T)$ dependence for a crystal of $(NH_4)HSO_4$, shown in Fig. 122.

It is evident from Figs. 113–122 that the absolute values of the spontaneous polarization of different ferroelectrics lie within the range from 0.1 to 20–30 $\mu C/cm^2$.

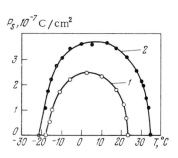

Fig. 118. Temperature dependence of the spontaneous polarization P_s of Rochelle salt: 1) ordinary Rochelle salt; 2) deuterated Rochelle salt [15].

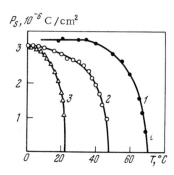

Fig. 119. Temperature dependence of the spontaneous polarization P_s of triglycine fluoroberyllate (1), triglycine sulfate (2), and triglycine selenate (3) [18].

Fig. 120. Temperature dependence of the spontaneous polarization P_s of ammonium fluoroberyllate $(NH_4)_2BeF_4$ [17].

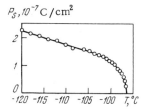

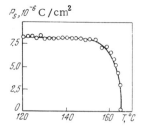

Fig. 121. Temperature dependence of the spontaneous polarization P_s of $NaNO_2$ [9].

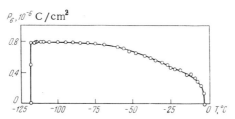

Fig. 122. Temperature dependence of the spontaneous polarization P_S of $(NH_4)HSO_4$ crystals along the [001] direction [22].

B. Spontaneous Strain and Thermal Expansion near Phase Transition Temperatures. The appearance of the spontaneous polarization in ferroelectrics is accompanied by spontaneous strain. A knowledge of this strain is essential for the understanding of pyroelectric properties of ferroelectrics near phase transition temperatures. The spontaneous strain at all three phase transitions of barium titanate can be seen from Fig. 31, which gives the temperature dependences of the lattice parameters, determined by x-ray diffraction in single crystals, and from Fig. 123, which gives the temperature dependence of the thermal expansion of a ceramic sample, determined by the dilatometric method.

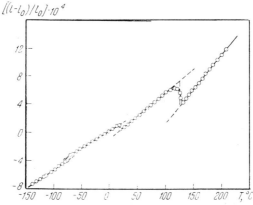

Fig. 123. Temperature dependence of the thermal expansion of polycrystalline $BaTiO_3$ [26].

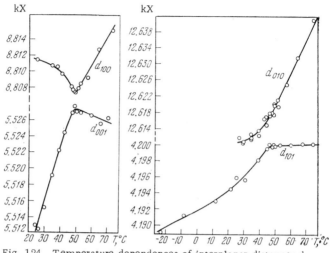

Fig. 124. Temperature dependences of interplanar distances d_{100}, d_{001}, d_{101}, and d_{010} of triglycine sulfate [1].

Information on the nature of distortions of the triglycine sulfate structure at its phase transition point can be obtained from Figs. 124 and 125. It is evident from Fig. 124 that the temperature dependences of the interplanar distances d_{100}, d_{001}, and d_{101} exhibit a kink near the phase transition point: below the transition point (49°C) the temperature dependences are nonlinear and above this point they are linear. The temperature dependence of d_{010}, which represents the deformation along the ferroelectric axis, is more gradual. The monoclinic angle β (triglycine sulfate is monoclinic in the paraelectric and ferroelectric modifications) also changes near the phase transition point ($\sim 49°C$): above the transition point the angle β is practically constant and equal to 105°38' but below this point it decreases gradually and becomes equal to 105°33' at 25°C.

The thermal expansion coefficients of triglycine sulfate, found from changes in the values of d and by an interferometric method (Fig. 125), have similar values near the phase transition point and they depend weakly on the temperature above the Curie point. However, all the thermal expansion coefficients α exhibit a sudden change at the Curie point (Fig. 125). The unit cell volume and the area of its base perpendicular to the b axis do not exhibit discontinuities at the phase transition point but change gradually.

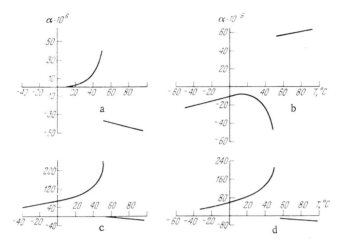

Fig. 125. Temperature dependences of the thermal expansion coefficients of triglycine sulfate along the axes, a, b, and c and at right-angles to the a axis (a, b, c, d, respectively) [13].

The characteristic features of the spontaneous deformation of a KH_2PO_4 crystal near its phase transition point can be seen in Figs. 126 and 127. At this transition (see Chap. IV) the tetragonal unit cell with the parameters $a_1' = a_2'$ (7.453 Å) and c transforms into an orthorhombic cell with the parameters a, b, and c. The values of a and b, given in Fig. 126, are the diagonals of the former tetragonal cell in the orthorhombic modification (the diagonal b becomes longer and the diagonal a becomes shorter).

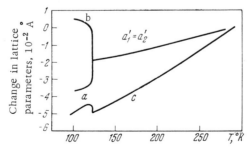

Fig. 126. Temperature dependences of the lattice constants of KH_2PO_4 (deviations from the room-temperature values) [23].

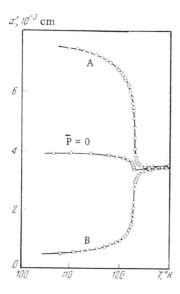

Fig. 127. Temperature dependence of the spontaneous deformation x' of KH_2PO_4: A) crystal polarized "upward" by a field of +1000 V/cm and expansion measured along the b axis (compare with Fig. 126); B) crystal polarized "downward" by a field of −1000 V/cm and compression measured along the a axis (compared with Fig. 126). Middle curve represents an unpolarized crystal [11].

The temperature dependence of the spontaneous shear r_{12} of KH_2PO_4, calculated using the data in Fig. 126, is shown in Fig. 128 together with the temperature dependence $P_s(T)$. It is evident from this figure that the temperature dependences of the spontaneous shear and spontaneous polarization are similar.

The spontaneous polarization of Rochelle salt is accompanied by a shear r_{23}. The temperature dependence of this shear in the range which includes both Curie points has been recorded by various methods (direct measurements of the shear in a sample, x-ray diffraction, converse piezoelectric effect, spontaneous electro-optical effect; see also Fig. 97). This temperature depen-

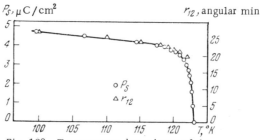

Fig. 128. Temperature dependence of the spontaneous polarization of KH_2PO_4 [11]. Triangles indicate spontaneous shear deduced from the data in Fig. 126.

dence is in qualitative agreement with the temperature dependence of the spontaneous polarization P_s. Ths absolute values of the maximum shear r_{23} have a considerable scatter and range from 8.7×10^{-4} (monoclinic angle 3') to 5.2×10^{-4} (monoclinic angle 1'48"). The differences may be due to the previous history of the samples employed and the different states of domains, depending primarily on the mechanical stresses in a crystal split into domains (see Chap. IV).

C. Thermal Effects at Phase Transitions. Changes in the spontaneous polarization at phase transitions in ferroelectrics, i.e., the appearance or disappearance of the spontaneous polarization, are accompanied by the evolution or absorption of heat ΔQ. Consequently, the specific heat has an anomaly in that range of temperatures in which the spontaneous polarization changes rapidly. These phenomena are related directly to the electrocaloric effect at phase transition points.

All ferroelectrics can be divided into two classes in accordance with the change in their entropy ΔS at the phase transition points. The entropy of crystals belonging to the first class is small, but it changes considerably: its values for the paraelectric and ferroelectric modifications may even have different orders of magnitude. Therefore, we may assume that a considerable contribution to the entropy of these crystals at the transition point is made by the entropy associated with the lattice vibrations. A typical ferroelectric exhibiting a large change in the entropy is barium titanate. The transition entropy of crystals of the second class is about 1 cal $\cdot$ mole$^{-1} \cdot$ deg^{-1} (irrespective of the Curie temperature). This shows clearly that the transition in such crystals is associated with ordering. Typical representatives of this class are ferroelectrics of the KH_2PO_4 group.

Measurements of the heats of transition carried out so far are insufficiently reliable because, in the majority of cases, they have been carried out on ceramic or multidomain samples.

Phase transitions of the first kind* are observed in $BaTiO_3$-type ferroelectrics at the Curie temperature and are accompanied

_____

* $BaTiO_3$ exhibits a phase transition of the first kind at 120°C, which is close to the critical Curie point, as confirmed by the sudden change in the lattice parameters, birefringence and spontaneous polarization, as well as by the thermal hysteresis of some properties near this point.

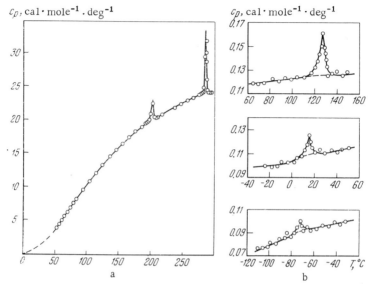

Fig. 129. Temperature dependence of the specific heat of BaTiO$_3$: a) according to Todd and Lorensen [27]; b) according to Shirane and Takeda [26].

by sudden changes in the lattice parameters, followed by more gradual changes (Fig. 31).

This change in the lattice parameters should be associated with a latent heat of transition as well as a continuous anomaly in the specific heat. However, the presence of domains, internal stresses, and imperfections in a crystal reduces the specific-heat anomaly to a more or less pronounced peak in the temperature dependence of c_p at the transition points (Fig. 129). This makes it difficult to separate the latent heat of transition from the general anomaly of the specific heat. Indirect measurements, based on the change in the temperature of a supercooled BaTiO$_3$ crystal caused by the appearance of the spontaneous polarization (this change amounts to 1°C), indicate that the latent heat of transition should be greater than 30 cal/mole. The values of the heats of transition ΔQ and of the changes in the entropy ΔS, found by different workers for BaTiO$_3$, KNbO$_3$, and PbTiO$_3$ from curves of the type shown in Fig. 129 and from the expressions

$$\Delta Q = \int \Delta c_p dT,$$
$$\Delta S = \int \frac{c_p}{T} dT,$$

TABLE 32. Heats of Transition ΔQ (cal/mole) and Changes in Entropy ΔS (cal$\cdot$mole$^{-1}\cdot$deg^{-1}) of BaTiO$_3$-Type Ferroelectrics [5]

Substance	Phase transition					
	from cubic to tetragonal		from tetragonal to orthorhombic		from orthorhombic to trigonal	
	ΔQ	ΔS	ΔQ	ΔS	ΔQ	ΔS
BaTiO$_3$	50 ∓ 5	0.125	22 ∓ 4	0.076	8 ∓ 2	0.04
	47	0.12	15.5	0.054	14.3	0.07
	47	0.12	16	0.058	12	0.06
			26	0.091		
KNbO$_3$	190 ∓ 5	0.27	85 ∓ 10	0.17	32 ∓ 5	0.14
	$134,5\mp5$	0.19				
PbTiO$_3$	1150	1.51				

are collected in Table 32. Cd$_2$Nb$_2$O$_7$, a ferroelectric with the oxygen-octahedral structure, exhibits a phase transition at $-90°C$; the heat of transition for this compound is estimated to be $\Delta Q = 18$ cal/mole and the change in the entropy is $\Delta S = 0.9$ cal$\cdot$mole$^{-1}\cdot$deg^{-1}.

The temperature dependence of the specific heat c_p of a triglycine sulfate crystal is shown in Fig. 130 in the range which includes the Curie point. The specific heat anomaly of this crystal extends over a fairly wide range of temperatures. However,

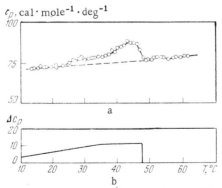

Fig. 130. Temperature dependences of the specific heat c_p (a) and of the change in the specific heat ΔC_p (b) of triglycine sulfate [16].

the shape of the curve is not typical of crystals exhibiting a phase transition of the second kind. The conclusion that triglycine sulfate undergoes a phase transition of the second kind follows from the temperature dependence of P_s (Fig. 119), the temperature dependences of the thermal expansion coefficients (Fig. 125), and from the gradual change of the volume of a crystal near the phase-transition point. The heat of transition ΔQ and the corresponding change in the entropy ΔS, found from Fig. 130, are 150 cal/mole and 0.48 cal $\cdot$ mole$^{-1} \cdot$ deg^{-1}, respectively.

The results of investigations of the thermal properties of KH_2PO_4-type ferroelectrics, carried out by various authors, are collected in Table 33, and Fig. 131 shows a typical temperature dependence of the specific heat. Since the spontaneous polarization of these crystals varies (although weakly) in a wide range of temperatures, it is difficult to determine the total heat of transition from curves of the type shown in Fig. 131. It is evident from Table 33 that the values of ΔS for ferroelectrics of this type are very similar, in spite of the considerable differences between their Curie temperatures (compare, for example, KH_2PO_4 and KD_2PO_4). This observation, as well as the order of magnitude of the entropy, indicate that phase transitions in these ferroelectrics are associated primarily with ordering processes.

Measurements of the specific heat of Rochelle salt in the range of temperatures including the two Curie points of this compound yield different values of the specific heat. However, the heats of transition are very small and can be measured with difficulty near the two Curie points. The change in the entropy ΔS is about -1.0 cal $\cdot$ mole$^{-1} \cdot$ deg^{-1} at the lower Curie point and is close to this value (but positive) at the upper Curie point.

TABLE 33. Heats of Transition ΔQ and Changes in Entropy ΔS of KH_2PO_4-type Ferroelectrics [18]

Substance	Curie temperature, °C	ΔQ, cal/mole	ΔS, cal $\cdot$ mole$^{-1} \cdot$ deg^{-1}	Substance	Curie temperature, °C	ΔQ, cal/mole	ΔS, cal $\cdot$ mole$^{-1} \cdot$ deg^{-1}
KH_2PO_4	-150	57 87 87	0.47 0.74 0.74	KD_2PO_4 KH_2AsO_4	-60 -176	100 84 84	0,47 0,87 0,90

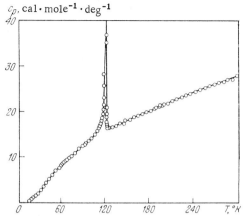

Fig. 131. Temperature dependence of the specific
heat of KH_2PO_4 at constant pressure [25].

D. Pyroelectric Phenomena. In subsections A–C
we have considered the temperature dependences of the spontaneous
polarization, spontaneous and thermal deformation, and the thermal effects in ferroelectrics, all of which will be used to discuss
the pyroelectric properties.

Barium titanate is not piezoelectric in the paraelectric modification and, therefore, the sudden appearance of a spontaneous
polarization at 120°C, accompanied by a spontaneous strain, must
be attributed to a spontaneous electrostriction. Applying one of
the equations for the electrostriction [Eq. (IX. 61b)]:

$$r_{ij} = Q_{ijmn}P_mP_n \qquad (V.28)$$

(Q_{ijmn} is the spontaneous electrostrictive coefficient; P_m and P_n
are the components of the polarization vector) of the cubic modification of $BaTiO_3$ (Table 62) yields the following relationship between the strain and polarization P_s along the Z axis (denoted by
the subscript 3):

$$\begin{aligned}
r_1 &= Q_{12}P_3^2, \\
r_2 &= Q_{12}P_3^2, \qquad (V.29) \\
r_3 &= Q_{11}P_3^2.
\end{aligned}$$

The spontaneous strains at the transition point, estimated
from the x-ray diffraction data (Fig. 31), are $r_1 = r_2 = -0.00159$, $r_3 =$

0.00366. Assuming that the change in the spontaneous polarization at the Curie point (Fig. 113b)* is 18×10^{-6} C/cm², we can find
the values of the spontaneous electrostrictive coefficients of BaTiO₃:

$$Q_{11} = \frac{r_3}{P_s^2} = 1.17 \cdot 10^{-12},$$

$$Q_{12} = \frac{r_1}{P_s^2} = -0.53 \cdot 10^{-12} \text{ cgs esu.}$$

The signs of these coefficients indicate that the electrostriction in
BaTiO₃ is positive: this compound expands along the direction of
the spontaneous polarization and contracts at right-angles to this
direction so that the unit cell volumes shows a net increase.

Considering the appearance of the spontaneous polarization
in the orthorhombic modification of BaTiO₃, which is directed along
the [110] axis of the original cubic cell, we can use the expression

$$r_6 = Q_{44} P_1 P_2 \tag{V.30}$$

to estimate the third electrostrictive coefficient Q_{44} of the cubic
modification. This estimate gives, for $r_6 \approx 0.0029$ and $P_s \approx 30 \times$
10^{-6} C/cm², the following value:

$$Q_{44} = 0.70 \cdot 10^{-12} \text{ cgs esu.}$$

The sudden change in the spontaneous polarization of BaTiO₃
at 120°C makes the values of the pyroelectric coefficients indeterminate at that temperature.

Cooling of BaTiO₃ after the appearance of the spontaneous
polarization in the tetragonal modification is accompanied by a further deformation of the lattice and by a change in the polarization.
A rough estimate of the relationship between the strain and po-

---

*The temperature of the transition from the cubic to tetragonal modification, shown in
Fig. 113b, is 107°C instead of 120°C, which is usually assumed for BaTiO₃. However,
Merz [19, 20] stresses specially that the results obtained for this anomalous crystal can
be used to describe barium titanate. A special investigation showed that the shift of
the Curie temperature of this crystal was due to special conditions during its growth.
In view of this, the results presented in Fig. 113 may be regarded as applying to a
transition in BaTiO₃ at 120°C.

larization shows that, in the temperature range 120-20°C, practically the whole of the polarization can be attributed to the converse piezoelectric effect which appears due to expansion of the
crystal along the polarization direction during cooling. This
means that the pyroelectric effect in this range of temperatures
is primarily of the secondary (false) type. The average value of
the total pyroelectric coefficient p_3 in the temperature range 120-
20°C is estimated to be (Fig. 113b):

$$p_3 = \frac{24 \cdot 10^3}{100} = 240 \text{ cgs esu.}$$

The available data are insufficient for obtaining a reliable value
of the primary (true) pyroelectric coefficient p' of $BaTiO_3$. The
quoted value of p_3 is the average for the whole temperature range
120-20°C. The coefficient p reaches its maximum value near the
Curie temperature (120°C) and has its lowest value near room
temperature.

The temperature dependence of the spontaneous polarization
of $BaTiO_3$ (Fig. 113a) shows that below room temperature this compound does not exhibit appreciable pyroelectric properties, with
the exception of the regions close to the phase-transition temperatures (near 50°C and −70°C).

Comparison of Figs. 119 and 124, which give the data for triglycine sulfate, shows that in the ferroelectric region (below 49°C)
this compound exhibits a negative electrostriction along the ferroelectric axis and a mixed electrostriction at right-angles to this
axis. The crystal as a whole has a negative volume electrostriction.

Triglycine sulfate, like barium titanate, does not have piezoelectric properties in the paraelectric modification. It follows that
its deformation, associated with the appearance of the polarization
at the Curie point, is of an electrostrictive nature. The nature of
the temperature dependence $P_s(T)$ and, in particular, the absence
of a polarization discontinuity at the Curie point, makes it difficult
to estimate the role of the piezoelectric polarization in the temperature dependence of the total spontaneous polarization. However, if it is assumed that only the spontaneous electrostriction is
observed in the temperature range 49-37°C, i.e., in the temperature range where P_s varies most rapidly (Fig. 119), the value of

the polarization at 37°C (6×10 cgs esu) and the relative strain along the Y axis (Fig. 124) in the same range of temperatures can be used to estimate the electrostrictive coefficient Q_{22} of triglycine sulfate: this coefficient is -15.0×10^{-12} cgs esu. This value is an order of magnitude higher than the corresponding coefficient of $BaTiO_3$. Using one of the equations relating the piezoelectric (g) and electrostrictive (Q) coefficients [see Eq. (IX.73)]:

$$g_{ijm} = 2Q_{ijmn}P_n, \qquad\qquad (V.31)$$

we can estimate the piezoelectric coefficient g_{22} of triglycine sulfate: this coefficient is -18×10^{-8} cgs esu at 37°C and -25.2×10^{-8} cgs esu at room temperature. Comparison of the deformation of a crystal (Fig. 124) with its spontaneous polarization yields the coefficients $g_{21} = -59.2 \times 10^{-8}$ cgs esu and $g_{23} = 15.2 \times 10^{-8}$ cgs esu at 37°C. These values of the coefficients g_{ik} of triglycine sulfate are in full agreement with the values reported by Sil'vestrova [8].

We can now draw some conclusions about the nature of the pyroelectric effect in triglycine sulfate. Assuming, as before, that the spontaneous strain at 49-37°C is not associated with the piezoelectric effect, we can estimate the average value of the primary pyroelectric coefficient p' in this range of temperatures:

$$p_2' = \frac{6 \cdot 10^3}{12} = 500 \text{ cgs esu.}$$

The average value of p_2' reaches its maximum (≈ 1000) near the transition temperature and passes through a minimum (≈ 200) at 37°C.

The total pyroelectric coefficient p_2 in the temperature range 22-37°C is estimated to be

$$p_2 = \frac{2.4 \cdot 10^3}{15} \cong 160 \text{ cgs esu.}$$

However, it is not yet possible to find the contributions of p_2' and p_2'' to this total coefficient.

The appearance of a spontaneous polarization along the Z axis of KH_2PO_4 expands the crystal along this direction (strain r_3) and produces a shear in the XY plane (strain r_3). Above the Curie temperature the polarization along the Z axis does not produce a piezoelectric strain along this axis (Table 46). It follows that the appearance of the spontaneous polarization is accompanied by a spontaneous electrostriction of the crystal along the Z axis. According to Table 62, the coefficient Q_{33} can be found from the relationship

$$r_3 = Q_{33} P_3^2. \tag{V.32}$$

Assuming (Fig. 128) that only the electrostrictive strain appears in the region of rapid change in the spontaneous polarization (123–121°K), the coefficient Q_{33} can be estimated from the above relationship: its value is 4.3×10^{-12} cgs esu. In the new (ferroelectric) modification the old direction of the Z axis becomes a unique polar axis and the piezoelectric coefficient g_{33} of this modification is no longer equal to zero. Using Eq. (V.31), we can estimate the coefficient g_{33} for the ferroelectric modification at 121°K: its value is 8×10^{-8} cgs esu.

The application of an electric field along the Z axis of KH_2PO_4 produces, above the Curie temperature, a piezoelectric shear in the XY plane, which can be estimated from the experimental data and represented by the coefficient $g_{36} = 5 \times 10^{-7}$ cgs esu. It is natural to expect the relationship between the spontaneous polarization P_3 and the spontaneous strain r_6 to be linear and piezoelectric in the ferroelectric region below the Curie point:

$$r_6 = g_{36} P_3. \tag{V.33}$$

Using the values of r_6 and P_3 in the temperature range 123–121°K (Figs. 126 and 128, respectively), we can estimate the piezoelectric coefficient g_{36}: its value is 5.5×10^{-7} cgs esu, which is in good agreement with the just quoted experimental value of g_{36} of the paraelectric modification. The linear relationship between P_s and r_6, obeyed in a wide range of temperatures, follows also directly from Fig. 128.

The strong piezoelectric coupling of the spontaneous strain and the spontaneous polarization of KH_2PO_4 indicates that the phenomena observed in this crystal below the Curie point are associated mainly with the secondary pyroelectric effect. The pyroelectric coefficient p_3 near the Curie point (123–121°K) is estimated to be

$$p_3 = \frac{10^4}{2} = 5000 \text{ egs esu,}$$

which indicates strong pyroelectric properties of this compound in the indicated range of temperatures. The coefficient p_3 of KH_2PO_4 below the transition point is about 100 cgs esu.

The spontaneous strain of Rochelle salt between its Curie points (−18°C to +24°C) is similar to the spontaneous strain of KH_2PO_4. The appearance of the polarization along the X axis gives rise to an electrostrictive strain r_1 along this axis ($g_{11} = 0$, as shown in Table 46) and to a piezoelectric shear in the YZ plane (strain r_4). The electrostrictive coefficients, found from direct measurements of thermal expansion [7], are

$$Q_{11} = -86.5 \cdot 10^{12},$$
$$Q_{12} = 17.3 \cdot 10^{-12},$$
$$Q_{13} = -24.2 \cdot 10^{-12} \text{ egs esu.}$$

The equation which describes the shear, associated with the appearance of the spontaneous polarization along the X axis, is of the form

$$r_4 = g_{14}P_1. \qquad\qquad (V.34)$$

Using the value $r_4 = 5.2 \times 10^{-4}$ (given earlier in this section) and assuming that P_1 is 770 cgs esu in the middle of the range between the Curie points (Fig. 118), we obtain a value of the coefficient g_{14} equal to 4.0×10^{-7} cgs esu. This value is very close to the experimental value of g_{14} of the paraelectric modification. This allows us to assume that the spontaneous strain of Rochelle salt between its Curie points is piezoelectric.

The piezoelectric nature of the spontaneous strain of Rochelle salt is associated mainly with the secondary pyroelectric effect observed when the temperature is varied. Near the Curie points the value of the total pyroelectric coefficient p_1 is estimated to be 150-200 cgs esu, but near the middle of the ferroelectric temperature range this coefficient is only 15-20 cgs esu. The results of an experimental investigation of the pyroelectric effect in Rochelle salt are given in Fig. 132a.

We shall now make some general comments about the pyroelectric effect in ferroelectric crystals. The change in the unit-cell parameters of a crystal due to variation in temperature is not necessarily associated with the electrostrictive and piezoelectric deformations; the deformation of the cell may occur inde-

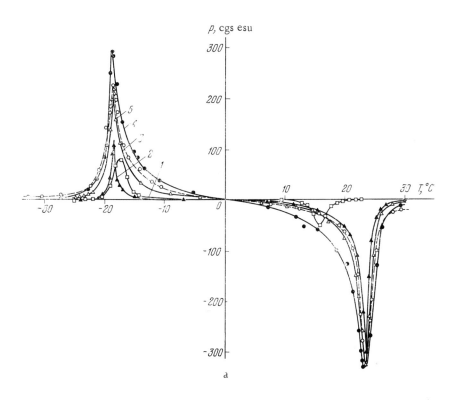

a

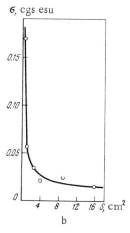

b

Fig. 132. Pyroelectric and piezoelectric properties of Rochelle salt: a) Temperature dependence of the pyroelectric effect obtained using the following loads (in gf/cm^2) to transform a crystal to the single-domain state: 0(1); 400(2); 880(3); 2280(4); 4100(5). b) Dependence of the specific piezoelectric charge σ, generated by hydrostatic expansion of X-cut samples, on the area of the samples [3].

pendently of any polarization (this may be the normal thermal deformation). An estimate of the contribution of the thermal deformation to the total deformation is, in general, difficult. However, qualitative considerations show that the thermal deformation (usually compression during cooling) reduces the spontaneous polarization when a crystal is heated. In the final analysis, the relationship between the thermal deformation, on the one hand, and the electrostrictive and piezoelectric deformations, on the other, determines the values and signs of the piezoelectric and electrostrictive coefficients. However, it is found that the normal thermal deformation of ferroelectrics is considerably weaker than the electrostrictive and piezoelectric deformations.

Assuming, in accordance with our definition, that the secondary pyroelectric effect is associated with the piezoelectric polarization, we are implying that the primary pyroelectric effect can be independent of deformation, or it may be associated with the electrostrictive deformation. If we assume that all the changes of the polarization in the primary pyroelectric effect are associated with electrostriction, we can estimate the relationship between the primary and secondary pyroelectric effects. According to the second expression in Eq. (IX.63b), this corresponds to a relationship between the first and second terms in the parentheses. The first of these terms describes the piezoelectric deformation and the second represents the electrostrictive deformation. Equation (IX.63b) shows that the electrostrictive deformation can be regarded as a correction to the piezoelectric effect. From this point of view, the primary pyroelectric effect associated with electrostriction can be regarded as a correction to the true secondary effect.

Using the values of g_{33} and Q_{33} given for KH_2PO_4 in the preceding paragraphs, we find that, in the temperature range 100-118°K ($\Delta P \approx 2.1 \times 10^3$ cgs esu), the piezoelectric strain is approximately eight times as large as the electrostrictive strain. Similar relationships are found also for other crystals in the ferroelectric state; this makes it possible to estimate roughly the contribution of the primary pyroelectric effect to the total effect of ferroelectrics outside the phase-transition region (such an estimate yields 10-20%).* The value of this contribution is in good

---

*However, it must be pointed out that the primary pyroelectric effect predominates near the phase-transition temperature of crystals which are not piezoelectric in the paraelectric modification (for example, triglycine sulfate, $BaTiO_3$).

agreement with the ratio of the primary and secondary pyroelectric effects in linear dielectrics. This is a consequence of the fact
that the electrostrictive coefficients and the spontaneous polarizations of both types of dielectric are similar.

Finally, we must note that the estimates of the spontaneous
piezoelectric effect, spontaneous electrostriction, and of the piezoelectric effect in ferroelectrics below the Curie point all apply
to individual domains or to a single-domain crystal. The presence
of a domain structure in crystals complicates these phenomena.
In particular, a crystal split into domains reverts, in its macrosymmetry, to the symmetry of the original paraelectric modification. This means that every ferroelectric split into domains is
nonpolar and does not exhibit macroscopic pyroelectric properties. If we wish to detect and investigate these properties, such a
crystal must be transformed partly or wholly to the single-domain
(unipolar) state. However, some crystals exhibit the unipolar
state even without application of external force (this is due to imperfections in such crystals). The degree of the "unipolarity"
depends strongly on the area of a sample: the "unipolarity" decreases when the area is increased. This can be seen clearly in
Fig. 132b, which shows the dependence of the specific piezoelectric charge (which represents the "unipolarity") on the area of
X-cut Rochelle salt samples subjected to hydrostatic expansion.

The pyroelectric coefficients of a single-domain ferroelectric crystal, like the pyroelectric coefficients of linear dielectrics, should tend to vanish on approach to absolute zero (this has
not yet been confirmed experimentally).

Piezoelectric and electrostrictive properties of crystals, associated with the presence of the domain structure, will be considered in the second volume of this book.

E. Electrocaloric Phenomena. The thermal phe-
nomena near the phase transition points of ferroelectrics may be
called the spontaneous electrocaloric effect. The magnitude of
this effect is given by Eq. (V.20).

Considering KH_2PO_4 and assuming that $p = 5000$ cgs esu, $T =
123°K$, $\rho = 2.34 \, g/cm^3$, $c = 0.1 \, cal \cdot g^{-1} \cdot deg^{-1}$, we find that $q = 0.06$
cgs esu. Assuming, for the same crystal, $\varepsilon_3 = 7 \times 10^4$ and $P_s =
10^4$ cgs esu at the Curie point, we find that the electric field at the
Curie point is approximately 1.7 cgs esu. This means that the

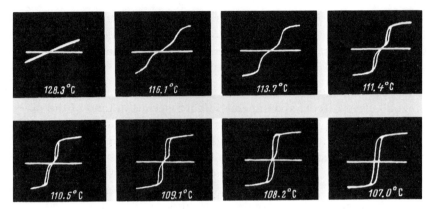

Fig. 133. Double hysteresis loops of a BaTiO₃ crystal above the Curie temperature (107°C) [20].

cooling of KH_2PO_4 due to the spontaneous electrocaloric effect (which is due to the appearance of the spontaneous polarization at the Curie point) is about 0.1°C ($\Delta T = q\Delta E$). A field of 10,000 V/cm near the Curie point can cool the crystal by about 2°C. This means that such a field can shift the Curie point by 2°C in the direction of higher temperatures.

The sudden change in the spontaneous polarization at the Curie point of $BaTiO_3$ prevents us from estimating the value of p at this point. However, it has been established experimentally that a crystal of $BaTiO_3$ kept at a temperature slightly above the Curie point can be switched to the ferroelectric state by the application of an electric field, as indicated by the appearance of double hystresis loops (Fig. 133). The field necessary to induce the ferroelectric state (represented by the length of the linear part of the curve from the center of the trace to the beginning of one of the loops) depends linearly on the difference between the actual temperature and the Curie point. The value of the coefficient q = dT/dE can be estimated from this linear dependence: it is equal to −0.45 cgs esu. Assuming that the appearance of the spontaneous polarization is entirely due to the lowering of the temperature by the electrocaloric effect (which appears as a shift of the Curie point in the direction of higher temperatures), we can estimate the primary pyroelectric coefficient p' of $BaTiO_3$. Assuming q = −0.45 cgs esu, ρ = 6.04 g/cm³, c = 0.16 cal·g⁻¹·deg⁻¹ for $BaTiO_3$ at the Curie temperature (380°K), we can use Eq. (V.20) to find p' = p =

46,000 cgs esu. The electrocaloric coefficient q = −0.45 cgs esu can be used to estimate the spontaneous electrocaloric effect in BaTiO$_3$. Assuming that the spontaneous polarization field in barium titanate crystals is approximately 2 cgs esu, we find that the change in the temperature of barium titanate at the Curie point due to the appearance of the spontaneous polarization is about 1°C (heating).

Electrocaloric properties (like pyroelectric properties) are most strongly pronounced in crystals of ferroelectrics which exhibit phase transitions of the first kind. Ferroelectric crystals which undergo phase transitions of the second kind (triglycine sulfate, Rochelle salt, etc.) have electrocaloric coefficients q whose values near the Curie point are more than one order of magnitude lower than the coefficient of BaTiO$_3$ (this is discussed in §3 of the present chapter).

Table 34 lists some coefficients associated with phase transitions of four ferroelectrics.

TABLE 34. Estimated Values of Some Coefficients Describing Properties of Ferroelectrics near Phase Transition Points

Property	Ferroelectrics			
	BaTiO$_3$	KH$_2$PO$_4$	Triglycine sulfate	Rochelle salt
Spontaneous polarization, μC/cm^2	$18 \cdot 10^{-6}$ (120° C) $26 \cdot 10^{-6}$ (20°C)	$4.66 \cdot 10^{-6}$ (100° K)	$2 \cdot 10^{-6}$ (37° C)	$0.23 \cdot 10^{-6}$ (5° C)
Pyroelectric effect, cgs esu	$p_3 = 240$ (20—120°C)	$p_3 = 5000$ (121—123° K)	$p_2 = 500$ (37—49° C)	$p_1 = 150$ (near Curie points)
Piezoelectric effect, cgs esu	—	$g_{33} = 8.0 \cdot 10^{-8}$ (121° K) $g_{36} = 5.5 \cdot 10^{-7}$ (121° K)	$g_{22} = -18.0 \cdot 10^{-8}$ $g_{21} = -59.2 \cdot 10^{-8}$ (37°C) $g_{23} = 15.2 \cdot 10^{-8}$	$g_{14} = 4.0 \cdot 10^{-7}$ (5° C)
Electrostriction, cgs esu	$Q_{11} = 1.17 \cdot 10^{-12}$ $Q_{12} = -0.53 \cdot 10^{-12}$ $Q_{44} = 0.70 \cdot 10^{-12}$	$Q_{33} = 4.3 \cdot 10^{-12}$ (121° K)	$Q_{22} = -15.0 \cdot 10^{-12}$ (37°C)	$Q_{11} = -8.5 \cdot 10^{-12}$ $Q_{12} = 17.3 \cdot 10^{-12}$ $Q_{13} = -24.2 \cdot 10^{-12}$

§3. Influence of Hydrostatic Compression on the Spontaneous Polarization of Crystals

From the point of view of crystal symmetry, we can consider pyroelectric phenomena to be the result of a scalar force in the form of heating. Hydrostatic compression or expansion is also a scalar force. We shall consider here only the influence of hydrostatic compression on the spontaneous polarization of crystals.

In §1 of the present chapter we have discussed some problems associated with the electric polarization of crystals of linear pyroelectrics under hydrostatic compression and we have calculated the spontaneous polarization for some of these crystals. Hydrostatic compression always alters the spontaneous polarization because of the direct piezoelectric effect. A calculation of the change in the spontaneous polarization, expressed in terms of the elastic (compliance) constants s, is given in §1.

We can easily show that, depending on the relationships between the values of the elastic constants s_{ij}, hydrostatic pressure can either increase or decrease the spontaneous polarization of linear pyroelectrics. The sign and magnitude of the change in the polarization can be found most simply from the sum of the piezoelectric coefficients (for example, the strain coefficients d_{ij}):

$$d_{31} + d_{32} + d_{33} = d_{\text{hydr}}$$

(the direction of the spontaneous polarization is assumed to be the c axis, denoted by a subscript 3). Using the actual values of the piezoelectric strain coefficients d with appropriate signs, we obtain the following result for tourmaline (see also Table 31): *

$$d_{\text{hydr}} = (+\,1.03 + 1.03 + 5.50)\cdot 10^{-8} = +\,7.56\cdot 10^{-8} \text{ cgs esu,}$$

---

*The values of the coefficients d_{ij} are taken from Mason's book [7]. Usually, the sign of one of these coefficients is given and the signs of the other coefficients are obtained analytically. In this case, the signs are selected so that an increase in the spontaneous polarization by an external force is represented by a positive sign and a decrease of the polarization is represented by a negative sign. Expansion of a crystal is taken to be a positive deformation and compression (including hydrostatic compression) is assumed to be a negative deformation.

for potassium tartrate $K_2C_4H_4O_6 \cdot \frac{1}{2}H_2O$

$$d_{hydr} = (-2.2 - 10.4 + 8.5) \cdot 10^{-8} = -4.1 \cdot 10^{-8} \text{ cgs esu,}$$

for ethylenediamine tartrate $C_6H_{14}N_2O_6$

$$d_{hydr} = (-34 + 33 - 20) \cdot 10^{-8} = -21 \cdot 10^{-8} \text{ cgs esu,}$$

and for lithium sulfate $(Li_2SO_4) \cdot H_2O$

$$d_{hydr} = (11.6 - 5.5 - 45.0) \cdot 10^{-8} = -38.9 \cdot 10^{-8} \text{ cgs esu.}$$

Thus, hydrostatic compression (strain or stress of negative sign) increases the spontaneous polarization of all these crystals, with the exception of tourmaline. In the case of tourmaline, the spontaneous polarization decreases with increasing hydrostatic pressure. A pressure of about 70,000 atm should destroy completely the spontaneous polarization of tourmaline. It must be pointed out that this estimate is based on the assumption that tourmaline does not undergo any phase transitions at high pressures and that its coefficient d_{hydr} is independent of the pressure.

Although quantitative changes in the spontaneous polarization induced by hydrostatic compression of linear pyroelectric crystals are of definite interest, a more important subject is the influence of hydrostatic pressure on the spontaneous polarization of ferroelectrics, which may shift the Curie point.

Qualitative information on the nature of the shift of the Curie point of ferroelectrics can be obtained by assuming that an increase in the polarization of a crystal (or a domain) in the low-temperature phase favors retention of this phase at higher temperatures, i.e., it tends to increase the Curie temperature. This is confirmed by experimental studies of the shift (increase) of the Curie point of ferroelectrics in external electric fields. For the same reason, a decrease in the polarization should lower the Curie temperature. Thus, the direction of the shift of the Curie point under hydrostatic pressure depends on whether the spontaneous polarization is increased or decreased by the pressure. If the ferroelectric modification of a crystal exists at temperatures higher than the paraelectric phase (consider, for example, the lower Curie point of Rochelle salt), the behavior should be reversed: an increase in the polarization should lower the Curie point and a decrease in the polarization should raise the Curie point. The application of an electric field lowers those transition temperatures which are similar to the lower Curie point of Rochelle salt. Using these considerations, we shall now discuss the shift of the phase transition temperatures of $BaTiO_3$, triglycine sulfate, and Rochelle salt when they are subjected to hydrostatic compression.

An increase in the spontaneous polarization of $BaTiO_3$, observed after cooling below the Curie temperature ($+120°C$), is accompanied by an expansion of this crystal along the c axis. Thus, a positive increase of the polarization along this direction corresponds to a positive deformation (elongation). This means that the piezoelectric coefficient g_{33} (or d_{33}) is positive. The other two coefficients which govern g_{hydr} (d_{hydr}), i.e., the coefficients $g_{31} = g_{32}$ ($d_{31} = d_{32}$), are negative because the experimental evidence shows that the coefficients g_{33} and g_{31} of $BaTiO_3$ have opposite signs. The absolute values of the piezoelectric coefficients at the Curie point can be found from Eq. (V.31):

$$g_{33} = 2Q_{33}P_s,$$

$$g_{13} = 2Q_{13}P_s.$$

For the cubic modification of $BaTiO_3$ we have $Q_{33} = Q_{11} = Q_{22} = 1.13 \times 10^{-12}$ cgs esu, $Q_{13} = Q_{12} = -0.53 \times 10^{-12}$ cgs esu and the spontaneous polarization at the Curie point is $P_s = 56 \times 10^3$ cgs esu (Fig. 113b). It follows that

$$g_{33} = 12.66 \cdot 10^{-8},$$

$$g_{13} = -5.94 \cdot 10^{-8} \text{ cgs esu},$$

and hence

$$g_{hydr} = (-5.94 - 5.94 + 12.66) \cdot 10^{-8} = 0.78 \cdot 10^{-9} \text{ cgs esu}.$$

The sign of g_{hydr} of the tetragonal modification of $BaTiO_3$ indicates that hydrostatic compression reduces the spontaneous polarization of barium titanate and, therefore, it lowers the Curie temperature.

It is a relatively easy matter to find the relationship between the shift of the Curie temperature and the applied pressure, i.e., to estimate the value of the coefficient $\gamma = dT_c/dp$. One of the ways of obtaining this relationship is to consider the shift of the Curie point caused by hydrostatic compression to be the result of the electrocaloric effect associated with the piezoelectric polarization. Since (§1 of the present chapter)

$$\frac{\Delta T_c}{\Delta E} = q \quad \text{and} \quad \Delta E = g_{\text{hydr}} \Delta p,$$

we obtain

$$\frac{\Delta T_c}{\Delta p_{\text{hydr}}} = q g_{\text{hydr}},$$

or in the differential form

$$\gamma = \frac{dT_c}{dp_{\text{hydr}}} = q g_{\text{hydr}}. \tag{V.35}$$

For BaTiO$_3$ $q = -0.45$ cgs esu and $g_{\text{hydr}} = 12.2 \times 10^{-9}$ cgs esu, and hence $\gamma = -5.5 \times 10^{-9}$ cgs esu, which is in good agreement with the experimental value $\gamma = -5.7 \times 10^{-9}$ egs esu.

The value of the coefficient γ for BaTiO$_3$ can be found also from the Clapeyron–Clausius equation [see Eq. (VI.12)]:

$$\frac{\Delta T_c}{\Delta p_{\text{hydr}}} = T_c \frac{\Delta V}{\Delta Q}, \tag{V.36}$$

where ΔV is the discontinuous change in volume at the transition point; ΔQ is the latent heat of transition. However, the use of this equation meets with some difficulties associated with the determination of the heat of transition. Moreover, it is difficult to determine accurately the change in volume at a phase transition. Nevertheless, the experimental values of the coefficient γ listed in Table 35 are in good agreement with the values calculated using Eq. (V.36). It is worth mentioning that the tetragonal-orthorhombic transition temperature of BaTiO$_3$ decreases (Table 35) only up to pressures of the order of 1500 atm. Above these pressures the coefficient γ changes its sign but its absolute value remains practically constant (up to pressures ≈ 3000 atm).

The appearance of the spontaneous polarization along the b axis of triglycine sulfate is accompanied by compression of the

TABLE 35. Coefficient $\gamma = \Delta T_c / \Delta p_{hydr}$ for $BaTiO_3$ at Various Phase Transitions [26]

Transition	Heat of transition ΔQ, cal/mole	Change in volume ΔV, $\mathring{A}^3$	$\gamma = \dfrac{\Delta T_c}{\Delta p_{hydr}}$, cgs esu	
			calc.	exper.
Cubic—tetragonal	50	—0.062	—6.7	—5.7
Tetragonal—orthorhombic	22	—0.014	—2.6	—2.9
Orthorhombic—trigonal	8	—0.006	2.0	—

crystal along this direction. This indicates that the sign of the piezoelectric coefficient g_{22} (d_{22}) of triglycine sulfate is negative.

Using the values of the coefficients g_{21}, g_{22}, and g_{23}, given earlier, we obtain

$$g_{hydr} = (-58.2 + 15.2 - 18) \cdot 10^{-8} = -61.0 \cdot 10^{-8} \text{ cgs esu.}$$

The sign of the coefficient g_{hydr} indicates that hydrostatic compression should shift the Curie temperature in the direction of higher temperatures, which is in agreement with the experimental data (Fig. 134).

Since the magnitude of the electrocaloric effect of triglycine sulfate is not known, it is not possible to calculate the shift of the Curie temperature (the coefficient γ) from Eq. (V.35). However, using the theory of phase transitions of the second kind, the Curie-temperature shift can be found from the Ehrenfest equation [see Eq. (VI.39)]:

$$\frac{dT_c}{dp} = \frac{\alpha - \alpha'}{c_p - c_p'} \frac{T_c}{\rho}, \tag{V.37}$$

Fig. 134. Dependence of the Curie temperature on hydrostatic pressure applied to triglycine sulfate [4].

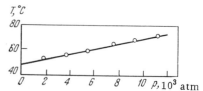

where α and α' are the volume thermal ·expansion coefficients above and below T_c (49°C); c_p and c_p' are the specific heats at constant pressure above and below T_c; ρ is the density of the crystal. Calculation of the volume expansion coefficients α and α', using the data in Fig. 125, evaluation of the change in the specific heat at $T_c = 322°K$ on the basis of Fig. 130, and the use of the value $\rho = 1.69$ g/cm^3, yields 4.3×10^{-9} cgs esu for the coefficient $\gamma = dT_c/dp$.

This value is in good agreement with the experimental value $\gamma = 3.8 \times 10^{-9}$ cgs esu (Fig. 134). Using this experimental value of γ and g_{hydr} given earlier, we can estimate the coefficient q near the Curie point from Eq. (V.35): its value is -0.012 cgs esu. This value of q for triglycine sulfate (which undergoes a phase transition of the second kind) is approximately 40 times smaller than the value of q for BaTiO$_3$ at 120°C (which undergoes a phase transition of the first kind). The shift of the Curie temperature under the action of electric fields and the electrocaloric effect of triglycine sulfate are also much smaller than for BaTiO$_3$.

Let us now consider the shift of the Curie points of Rochelle salt under the influence of hydrostatic pressure. We shall establish first the direction of the shifts from the sign of g_{hydr}. In order to determine the sign we must calculate the "monoclinic" piezoelectric coefficients of a crystal (or a domain) in the ferroelectric modification (symmetry class 2). In accordance with Eq. (V.31), the piezoelectric coefficients can be found from the relationships $g_{11} = 2Q_{11}\Delta P_s$; $g_{12} = 2Q_{12}\Delta P_s$; $g_{13} = 2Q_{13}\Delta P_s$.

Using the values of the coefficients Q_{11}, Q_{12}, and Q_{13} given earlier for the region of rising spontaneous polarization ($\Delta P > 0$) during cooling near the upper Curie point, we obtain $g_{11} = -9.94 \times 10^{-8}$, $g_{12} = 2.00 \times 10^{-8}$, $g_{13} = -2.78 \times 10^{-8}$, and $g_{hydr} = -6.36 \times 10^{-8}$ cgs esu. In the range of decreasing spontaneous polarization ($\Delta P < 0$) near the Curie point at -10°C, we have $g_{11} = 10.7 \times 10^{-8}$, $g_{12} = -2.14 \times 10^{-8}$, $g_{13} = 3.0 \times 10^{-8}$, and $g_{hydr} = 11.56 \times 10^{-8}$ cgs esu. Thus, the signs of the coefficients g_{hydr} show that hydrostatic compression ("negative" deformation) near the upper Curie point of Rochelle salt increases its spontaneous polarization and, therefore, shifts the upper Curie point in the direction of higher temperatures. Near the lower Curie point, hydrostatic compression reduces the spontaneous polarization of Rochelle salt. This also tends to shift the lower Curie point in the direction of higher temperatures. This is because a crystal kept at a temperature slightly higher than the lower Curie point may be transformed by pressure to the paraelectric modification since pressure can destroy the spontaneous polarization.

Experimental data confirm these qualitative conclusions. Figure 135 shows the results of investigations of the linear shift of the two Curie points of Rochelle salt in the direction of higher temperatures. The coefficients γ for the upper and lower Curie points, found from the experimental data, are 10.4×10^{-9} and 3.65×10^{-9} cgs esu, respectively. A more rapid rise of the temperature of the upper Curie point tends to expand the ferroelectric range of temperatures with increasing pressure.

Using Eq. (V.35) we can estimate the electrocaloric coefficient q near the upper and lower Curie points of Rochelle salt. Calculations for $+16°C$ and $-10°C$ yield values of q which are -0.16 and $+0.032$ cgs esu, respectively. It follows that the electrocaloric effect near the upper Curie point results in the cooling of a crystal on the application of an electric field (which means that the field shifts the upper Curie point in the direction of higher temperatures). The application of an electric field near the lower Curie point heats a crystal, which is equivalent to a shift of this Curie point in the direction of lower temperatures. Thus, hydrostatic pressure and an electric field have the same effect on the upper Curie point: they shift it in the direction of higher temperatures. However, at the lower Curie point the effect of hydrostatic pressure is opposite to that of an electric field: the pressure shifts the Curie point in the direction of higher temperatures and the field tends to lower the Curie point.

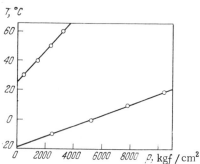

Fig. 135. Dependences of the upper and lower Curie points on hydrostatic pressure applied to Rochelle salt [12].

We must stress that the electrocaloric effect in Rochelle salt is basically different from the corresponding effect in barium titanate. The electrocaloric coefficient q of barium titanate increases suddenly at the Curie point from zero to some finite value (this corresponds to a phase transition of the first kind). The coefficient q of Rochelle salt is also equal to zero at the Curie point, but it increases gradually with increasing polarization (a phase transition of the second kind). The electrocaloric coefficient of Rochelle salt reaches its maximum in the middle of the ferroelectric range of temperatures and at this point it is approximately equal to 0.22 egs esu.

Hydrostatic compression of crystals of guanidine aluminum sulfate, which does not exhibit a ferroelectric phase transition, increases their spontaneous polarization. At 5000 atm, P_s is equal to the polarization observed at $-110°C$ at atmospheric pressure. Calculations show that the change in P_s is proportional, at least to within an order of magnitude, to the change in the specific volume, irrespective of whether it is caused by hydrostatic compression or by cooling. However, the coefficient of proportionality is found to be 20–25 times higher than that which would be obtained from a simple change in the number of dipoles per unit volume. This observation indicates that hydrostatic compression alters the magnitudes of elementary dipoles and not only their number per 1 cm^3. This behavior of dipoles in guanidine aluminum sulfate is associated with a strong anisotropy of the rigidity of this crystal. The crystal is deformed much more easily along the polar axis than at right-angles to this axis.

References

1. Z. I. Ezhkova, G. S. Zhdanov, and M. M. Umanskii, Kristallografiya, 4:249 (1959).
2. I. S. Zheludev and V. V. Gladkii, Kristallografiya, 11:415 (1966).
3. I. S. Zheludev and M. M. Tagieva, Kristallografiya, 7:589 (1962).
4. I. S. Zheludev, N. A. Tikhomirova, and V. M. Fridkin, Kristallografiya, 7:795 (1962).
5. W. Känzig, "Ferroelectrics and antiferroelectrics," Solid State Phys., 4:1 (1957).
6. W. G. Cady, Piezoelectricity, McGraw-Hill, New York (1946).
7. W. P. Mason, Piezoelectric Crystals and Their Application to Ultrasonics, Van Nostrand, New York (1950).
8. I. M. Sil'vestrova, Dissertation [in Russian], Institut Kristallografii AN SSSR, Moscow (1963).

9. A. S. Sonin, I. S. Zheludev, and G. F. Dobrzhanskii, Izv. Akad. Nauk SSSR, Ser. Fiz., 24:1209 (1960).

10. W. Ackermann, Ann. Physik, 46:197 (1915).

11. V. Von Arx and W. Bantle, Helv. Phys. Acta, 17:298 (1944).

12. D. Bancroft, Phys. Rev., 53:587 (1938).

13. S. Ganesan, Acta Cryst., 15:81 (1962).

14. G. J. Goldsmith and J. G. White, J. Chem. Phys., 31:1175 (1959).

15. J. Hablützel, Helv. Phys. Acta, 12:489 (1939).

16. S. Hoshino, T. Mitsui, F. Jona, and R. Pepinsky, Phys. Rev., 107:1255 (1957).

17. S. Hoshino, K. Vedam, Y. Okaya, and R. Pepinsky, Phys. Rev., 112:405 (1958).

18. F. Jona and G. Shirane, Ferroelectric Crystals, Pergamon Press, Oxford (1962).

19. W. J. Merz, Phys. Rev., 76:1221 (1949).

20. W. J. Merz, Phys. Rev., 91:513 (1953).

21. D. Meyerhofer, Phys. Rev., 112:413 (1958).

22. R. Pepinsky, K. Vedam, S. Hoshino, and Y. Okaya, Phys. Rev., 111:1508 (1958).

23. M. De Quervain, Helv. Phys. Acta, 17:509 (1944).

24. W. C. Röntgen, Ann. Physik, 45:737 (1914).

25. C. C. Stephenson and J. G. Hooley, J. Am. Chem. Soc., 66:1397 (1944).

26. G. Shirane and A. Takeda, J. Phys. Soc. Japan, 7:5 (1952).

27. S. S. Todd and R. E. Lorensen, J. Am. Chem. Soc., 74:2043 (1952).

28. S. Triebwasser, Phys. Rev., 101:993 (1956).

29. W. Voigt, Lehrbuch der Kristallphysik, Teubner, Leipzig (1910); 2nd ed. (1928).

30. B. Zwicker and P. Scherrer, Helv. Phys. Acta, 17:346 (1944).

31. K. N. Baranskii, L. A. Gribov, and V. P. Prikhod'ko, Kristallografiya, 1:368 (1956).

32. O. G. Blokh and I. S. Zheludev, Kristallografiya, 5:390 (1960).

33. I. S. Zheludev and O. G. Blokh, Kristallografiya, 3:639 (1958).

34. I. S. Zheludev and A. A. Fotchenkov, Kristallografiya, 3:308 (1958).

35. J. F. Nye, Physical Properties of Crystals, Clarendon Press, Oxford (1957).

36. B. A. Strukov, Kristallografiya, 6:635 (1961).

37. S. Nomura, Y. Asao, and S. Sawada, J. Phys. Soc. Japan, 16:917 (1961).

Chapter VI

Theory of Spontaneous Polarization

Introduction

In the preceding chapter we have described linear pyroelectrics, assuming simply that they exhibit spontaneous polarization. We have attributed this polarization to a transformation of the crystal structure from a nonpolar paraelectric form to a polar modification. Since ferroelectrics (more precisely, ferroelectric domains) belong to the polar symmetry classes of crystals, they can be regarded as a subgroup of pyroelectric materials. The formal similarity of the symmetry of ferroelectric domains and linear pyroelectrics as well as the similar absolute values of the spontaneous polarization of these two types of crystal do not exclude the possibility of a basic difference: before the appearance of the spontaneous polarization the antiparallel directions in ferroelectrics are equivalent, but in pyroelectrics they are not. Consequently, ferroelectrics split into domains, but linear pyroelectrics do not. This means that the spontaneous polarization of linear pyroelectrics cannot be rotated by an electric field, but the corresponding polarization of ferroelectrics can, and such rotation gives rise to the well-known dielectric hysteresis. It is important to note that there are no ferroelectric phase transitions in pyroelectrics and that their spontaneous polarization can exist throughout the range of existence of the crystalline state.

These properties of linear pyroelectrics are usually explained by assuming that the states with opposite orientations of the spontaneous polarization are separated by very high potential barriers. The energies of these barriers correspond to tempera-

tures of $\sim 10^4$ deg. This means, in particular, that linear pyroelectrics can be regarded as ferroelectrics with Curie point at
very high temperatures, exceeding the temperatures of the upper
limit of the existence of these crystals. However, such a point of
view is unsatisfactory because it does not explain why ferroelectric crystals split into domains below the Curie temperature, but
linear pyroelectrics do not.

This difficulty can be overcome by assuming that the spontaneous polarization directions in pyroelectrics are polar before
the appearance of the polarization. This assumption automatical-
ly ensures that the spontaneous polarization has the same direction throughout a linear pyroelectric crystal. On the other hand,
the directions along which the spontaneous polarization appears in
ferroelectrics are not polar in the paraelectric modification. We
have stressed in Chap. II that there are no ferroelectrics which
cannot exhibit the antiparallel orientation of domains. This sug-
gests that the spontaneous polarization in hypothetical high-temperature nonpolar phases of pyroelectrics appears (in contrast to
ferroelectrics) along polar directions.

This approach to the symmetry of pyroelectrics allow us to
use Tables 7-11 to separate pyroelectric from ferroelectric transitions. Examples of pyroelectric transitions are represented by
the appearance of the spontaneous polarization along a threefold
axis in the cubic class $3/\overline{4}$, which transforms these crystals to the
group $3 \cdot m$, or the appearance of the spontaneous polarization along
a twofold axis in the symmetry classes $3:2$, $m \cdot 3:m$, which transforms them to the group 2, etc. Linear pyroelectrics can belong
only to six point groups of symmetry $3 \cdot m$, $2 \cdot m$, m, 3, 2, and 1, but
not to the other four pyroelectric groups $6 \cdot m$, $4 \cdot m$, 6, and 4. A
similar analysis can be carried out quite easily for the space symmetry groups of crystals, using Tables 13-17. It must be pointed
out that there has as yet been no report of pyroelectrics belonging
to the symmetry groups $6 \cdot m$, $4 \cdot m$, 6, and 4.

It is very desirable to find, at least qualitatively, why the
spontaneous polarization states of some crystals are thermodyna-
mically stable. This is best done using simple models. We shall
assume that the crystal lattice consists of point electric dipoles of
moment p (the formation and stability of such a lattice may be due
to dipole or any other forces, but we shall not be interested in this

aspect). In this model the concept of an effective electric field F
has an exact meaning: this is the field acting on each dipole. If
the average macroscopic field E and the polarization P are parallel (for example, if they are directed along an axis of symmetry
of the lattice), it follows that

$$F = E + fP,$$

where f is the Lorentz factor (for a cubic lattice $f = 4\pi/3$). The
polarization of such a "crystal" in an external electric field can
be considered in the same way as the polarization of a gas of dipole molecules or as the magnetization of the spin gas in ferromagnets. A simple extension of the Weiss theory of ferromagnetism [16] shows that, under thermodynamic equilibrium conditions, a "crystal" of this type has a finite spontaneous polarization P (in the absence of an external electric field E) in the temperature range from T = 0°K to the Curie point T_c, given by

$$T_c = \frac{fpP_\infty}{3kT},$$

where P_∞ is the saturation polarization, i.e., the polarization at
T = 0°K; k = 1.38 × 10^{-16} erg/°K is the Boltzmann constant. Above
the Curie temperature (T > T_c), P_s = 0. If we assume that $f \sim 1$,
p = 10^{-18} cgs esu, and $P_\infty \sim 10^6$-10^5 cgs esu (these values are
close to empirical data),* we find that $T_c \sim 10^2$-10^3°K.

Thus, our discussion shows that the spontaneous polarization
may exist (in the model chosen, it must exist) due to the difference between the effective and average macroscopic fields. It is
important to note that, in contrast to ferromagnetism, the Curie
temperature in the ferroelectric case is found to be $T_c \sim 10^2$-
10^3°K, which is in approximate agreement with actually observed
Curie temperatures. In other words, the classical electrostatic
interaction, corresponding to $f \sim 1$, can be responsible for spontaneous polarization up to temperatures $T_c \sim 10^3$°K. In the Weiss
theory of ferromagnetism it is necessary to assume that $f \sim 10^3$-
10^4, which cannot be due to the magnetic interaction.

---

*For a cubic lattice of point dipoles $f = 4\pi/3$. The moment of a polar molecule, or
the dipole moment per unit cell in a pyroelectric crystal, is usually of the order of
10^{-18} cgs esu. The saturation polarization is P_∞ = pN, where N is the number of dipoles of moment p per unit volume, i.e., if N $\sim 10^{23}$ cm^{-3}, $P_\infty \sim 10^5$ cgs esu.

Since the existence of spontaneous electric polarization in crystals can be explained using classical representations, it follows that, in the majority of cases, the classical approach to ferroelectricity is quite sufficient. An important justification for this approach is the observation that elementary electric dipoles (similar to the spin magnetic moments of electrons) do not exist in nature. This does not mean that the problem of spontaneous polarization is simple and that quantum effects (for example, those associated with the interaction of particles) can be neglected in developing a theory of the spontaneous polarization.

There is as yet no single theory of the spontaneous polarization which can account for all the observed phenomena. Nevertheless, important theoretical results are available and the most important of these will be presented in the following sections.

§1. Spontaneous Polarization
of Linear Pyroelectrics

Before the first detailed investigations of the properties of pyroelectric crystals, the concept of spontaneous polarization has been considered in a hypothetical form. The hypothesis of such polarization was first put forward by Kelvin, who suggested the existence of permanently polarized molecules in crystals. In 1921, Larmor developed a theory of the pyroelectric effect without invoking the existence of the spontaneous polarization.

Boguslavskii [4] was the first to develop a theory of the pyroelectric state, which was essentially a theory of the spontaneous polarization and its temperature dependence. Boguslavskii considered a linear chain consisting of alternating positive and negative particles (Fig. 136). Such a chain has an electric moment. If the distances between particles designated by numbers $(2n - 1)$, $2n$, and $(2n + 1)$ are l and l', respectively, the electric charge of each particle is e, and the number of particles in such a chain is 2N, the electric moment of the whole chain is Nel, and the moment per unit length is

$$P_0 = \frac{el}{l + l'} \, . \tag{VI.1}$$

When the distances between the particles change by Δl and $\Delta l'$ the

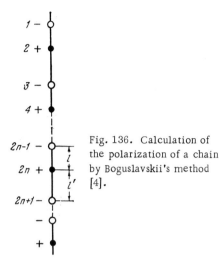

Fig. 136. Calculation of the polarization of a chain by Boguslavskii's method [4].

electric moment changes by the amount

$$P - P_0 = \frac{e\,(l'\Delta l - l\Delta l')}{(l + l')^2}.$$ (VI.2)

Next, Boguslavskii found the temperature dependences of Δl and $\Delta l'$. He assumed that when an i-th particle was displaced (because of thermal motion) by a distance u_i, it was acted upon only by the forces due to neighboring particles and the potentials of these forces (expanded as a series) could be represented in the form

$$\frac{a'}{2}\,(u_{2n+1} - u_{2n})^2 - \frac{b'}{3}\,(u_{2n+1} - u_{2n})^3.$$

and

$$\frac{a}{2}\,(u_{2n} - u_{2n-1})^2 - \frac{b}{3}\,(u_{2n} - u_{2n-1})^3$$

The potential energy of the whole chain is equal to the sum

$$V_i = \sum \left\{ \frac{a}{2}\,(u_{2n} - u_{2n-1})^2 - \frac{b}{3}\,(u_{2n} - u_{2n-1})^3 + \right.$$

$$\left. + \frac{a'}{2}\,(u_{2n+1} - u_{2n})^2 - \frac{b}{3}\,(u_{2n+1} - u_{2n})^3 \right\}.$$ (VI.3)

The average values of $\overline{\Delta l}$ and $\overline{\Delta l'}$ ($\Delta l = u_{2n} - u_{2n-1}$, $\Delta l' = u_{2n+1} - u_{2n}$) can be found using the Gibbs statistical formula:

$$\overline{\Delta l} = \frac{\int \cdots \int \Delta l\,(u)\,e^{-\Phi/kT}\,du\,d\Phi}{\int \cdots \int e^{-\Phi/kT}\,du\,d\Phi} \,,$$

where $\Phi = V_i + T$; $T = \Sigma(q_{2n-1}^2/2m + q_{2n}^2/2m')$ is the kinetic energy of the chain; $q_{2n-1} = mu_{2n-1}$, $q_{2n} = m'\dot{u}_{2n}$; m and m' are respectly, the masses of the negative and positive particles.

We shall not repeat the rest of Boguslavskii's treatment, but we shall give the final expressions for Δl and $\Delta l'$ obtained in the second approximation:

$$\overline{\Delta l} = \frac{bkT}{a^2} \,,$$

(VI.4)

$$\overline{\Delta l'} = \frac{b'kT}{a'^2} \,.$$

Substituting $\overline{\Delta l}$ and $\overline{\Delta l'}$ in Eq. (VI.2), we obtain

$$P - P_0 = \frac{e\left(\dfrac{l'b}{a^2} - \dfrac{lb'}{a'^2}\right)}{(l + l')^2}\,kT.$$

(VI.5)

These calculations apply to the case when the external mechanical and electrical forces are equal to zero. Therefore, the temperature dependence of the spontaneous polarization given by Eq. (VI.5) applies to the total pyroelectric effect (Chap. V). Boguslavskii also carried out a calculation for a clamped chain, i.e., when the length of the chain is fixed. In this case, the temperature dependence of the spontaneous polarization is given by the formula

$$P = P_0 = \frac{\dfrac{b}{a} - \dfrac{b'}{a'}}{a + a'} \cdot \frac{4ekT}{(l + l')^3} \,,$$

(VI.6)

which corresponds to the primary (true) and not to the total pyroelectric effect.

A linear temperature dependence of the spontaneous polarization P can be obtained in a somewhat different manner, not using the chain model. Let us assume that a displacement x of a particle whose electric charge is e corresponds to a change of the electric moment by an amount ex. The change in the electric moment per unit volume of a crystal is then $\Delta P = Ne\bar{x}$, where N is the number of charged particles per unit volume and $\bar{x}$ is the average displacement of a particle. We can easily see that, in this case, the model of a pyroelectric crystal exhibiting spontaneous polarization is an array of electric dipoles. If the potential corresponding to the restoring forces is expanded as a series in powers of x

$$V = ax^2 + bx^3 + cx^4 + \ldots,$$

it is found that the average displacement can be calculated from the statistical formula

$$\bar{x} = \frac{\int\limits_{-\infty}^{+\infty} xe^{-\Phi(x)/kT}\,dx}{\int\limits_{-\infty}^{+\infty} e^{-\Phi(x)/kT}\,dx},$$

where $\Phi(x) = -eEx + ax^2 + bx^3 + cx^4$. The second approximation, in which the fourth-order term is ignored (c = 0) yields the expression

$$\bar{x} = \frac{eE}{2a} - \frac{3b}{2a}\left(\frac{kT}{2a} + \frac{(eF)^2}{4a^2}\right). \tag{VI.7}$$

In this formula

$$F = E + \frac{4\pi}{3}P \tag{VI.8}$$

is the internal electric field acting on a charged particle.

If the external field is E = 0, we can use Eqs. (VI.7) and (VI.8) [neglecting the term with E^2 in Eq. (VI.7)] to obtain the following expression for the spontaneous polarization:

$$P = \frac{3NebkT}{\dfrac{2\pi Ne^2}{3a} - 1}. \tag{VI.9}$$

The question whether Eq. (VI.9) represents the primary or secondary pyroelectric effect has no meaning since no assumptions about deformation of a crsytal have been made in the model employed. If we assume that when $\bar{x}$ changes, the thickness of a crystal changes by the same amount, we find that we are dealing with the total pyroelectric effect; if the unit-cell parameters are not affected and there are no mechanical stresses, we are dealing only with the primary effect.

This classical theory of the spontaneous polarization and of its temperature dependence is purely qualitative and cannot be used to explain the available experimental data, particularly the behavior of pyroelectrics at low temperatures. Accurate measurements of the derivative of the spontaneous polarization with respect to the temperature (the pyroelectric constant p), carried out by Ackermann [29] for several crystals in a wide range of temperatures show that the temperature dependence of p resembles the temperature dependence of the specific heat (Fig. 137). Therefore, it seems natural to develop a quantum theory of pyroelectricity using the model of independent Einstein oscillators. Such an elementary quantum theory was developed by Boguslavskii [4].

An important point in the quantum and classical theories of pyroelectricity is the introduction of a term depending on x^3 in the expansion of the potential energy in powers of the displacement x of an oscillating particle. This term is responsible for the pyroelectric effect and for the thermal expansion. Thus, the model on which Boguslavskii's quantum theory is based is an array of independent anharmonic oscillators, which is different from the mod-

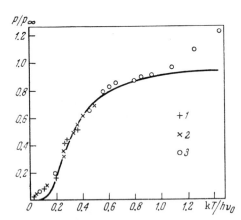

Fig. 137. Temperature dependence of the relative pyroelectric coefficient p/p_∞ [29]: 1) sodium lithium sulfate; 2) lithium selenate; 3) yellow-green tourmaline.

el of harmonic oscillators in the elementary theory of the specific heat developed by Einstein. The quantum nature of the theory is expressed by the condition

$$\iint dx dq = zh, \qquad z = 0, 1, 2\ldots, \qquad (VI.10)$$

where $q = m dx/dt$ and m is the mass of an oscillating particle. Integration in Eq. (VI.10) is carried out over an area bounded by the curve

$$E = \frac{a}{2} x^2 + \frac{b}{3} x^3 + \frac{1}{2m} q^2.$$

Since the oscillators are anharmonic the average displacement from the equilibrium position $\tilde{x}$ has a definite nonzero value and it depends on the energy E_z:

$$\tilde{x}_z = \left| \frac{\frac{d}{dE} \iint x\, dx\, dq}{\frac{d}{dE} \iint dx\, dq} \right|_{E=E_z} . \qquad (VI.11)$$

Evaluation of Eq. (VI.11) yields the following simple relationship:

$$\tilde{x}_z = - \frac{b E_x}{a^2} . \qquad (VI.12)$$

If a particle carriers a charge e, the electric moment is

$$p = - \frac{eb E_z}{a^2} . \qquad (VI.13)$$

According to the Gibbs statistical formula, the number of oscillators whose energy is E_z is

$$n = \frac{e^{-E_z/kT}}{\sum\limits_{0}^{\infty} e^{-E_z/kT}} , \qquad (VI.14)$$

and, therefore, the total electric moment per unit volume is given by the expression

$$P - P_0 = - \frac{ebN}{a^2} \cdot \frac{\sum\limits_{0}^{\infty} E_z e^{-E_z/kT}}{\sum\limits_{0}^{\infty} e^{-E_z/kT}} , \qquad (VI.15)$$

where N is the number of oscillators per unit volume.

The discrete values of the energy are found from Eq. (VI.10), whose solution is of the form

$$E_z = zh\nu \left(1 - \frac{15}{32} \cdot \frac{zh\nu b^2}{a^3} + \ldots \right), \tag{VI.16}$$

where $\nu = (1/2\pi)(a/m)^{1/2}$ is the frequency of the anharmonic oscillator. Substituting in Eq. (VI.15) the values of E_z from Eq. (VI.16) and assuming that $b = 0$ (the first approximation), we finally find the spontaneous electric moment

$$P - P_0 = -\frac{eNb}{a^2} \cdot \frac{h\nu}{e^{h\nu/kT} - 1} \tag{VI.17}$$

and the pyroelectric coefficient

$$p = p_\infty \frac{(h\nu/kT)\, e^{h\nu/kT}}{(e^{h\nu/kT} - 1)^2}, \tag{VI.18}$$

where

$$p_\infty = \frac{ebN}{a^2}.$$

Boguslavskii compared the conclusions of his quantum theory with the experimental data of Ackermann and obtained a very good agreement between the theoretical and experimental pyroelectric coefficients p in the temperature range 150-400°K. Below 150°K and above 400°K the theoretically calculated values of p did not agree with the experimental data, and it was found that the differences were greater for those crystals whose oscillator frequencies ν were higher. Comparison of the theoretical and experimental results indicated that the theory diverged from the experiment at low temperatures near the characteristic (Debye) temperature $\theta = h\nu/k$. The degree of approximation obtainable using Eq. (VI.18) can be seen from Fig. 137, in which the continuous curve is theoretical and the points represent measured values of p for yellow-green tourmaline.

From the theory of the specific heat it is known that the discrepancy between the experimental data and Einstein's formula disappears when the model of independent oscillators, all having the same fixed oscillation frequency ν, is replaced by a model of coupled vibrators. In this case, a single frequency ν is replaced by a spectrum of frequencies which can be regarded as continuous for a crystal because it is a system with a large number of degrees of freedom. The Debye formula for this model is in good agreement with the experimental data and predicts the T^4 law for the temperature dependence of the lattice energy. However, attempts to apply this formula to the pyroelectric effect at low temperatures have not been successful. The pyroelectric coefficients calculated using the Debye formula decrease more rapidly with decreasing temperature than do the coefficients found experimentally.

The Ackermann data are plainly insufficient to determine the temperature dependence of the spontaneous polarization (or of the pyroelectric constant) at low temperatures. Experimental data obtained in a narrow range of temperatures, close to the temperature of liquid helium, are essential. However, even Ackermann's results show that at very low temperatures the spontaneous polarization should decrease quadratically with decreasing temperature. Using this assumption, Boguslavskii modified Eq. (VI.17) by introducing a coefficient depending on the frequency ν:

$$P_\nu = \varphi(\nu)\, \frac{h\nu}{e^{h\nu/kT} - 1}\; ; \qquad (VI.19)$$

The coefficient $\varphi(\nu)$ was selected so as to obtain the required polarization law. Assuming that $\varphi(\nu) = f/\nu^2$, where f is a constant, and integrating over all possible frequencies ν, Boguslavskii obtained the following dependence for the total polarization

$$P = \frac{3Nfk^2T^2}{h\nu_{max}^3}\;, \qquad (VI.20)$$

which reflected − as expected − the true temperature dependence of the spontaneous polarization at low temperatures. It must be pointed out that, as in the classical dipole model of a pyroelectric crystal [see Eq. (VI.9)], the quantum theory is not based on any assumptions about thermal deformation of a crystal as a whole. Therefore, in this quantum theory of the spontaneous polarization the question of whether the pyroelectric effect is primary or secondary has no meaning.

The derivation of Eq. (VI.20) is not based on a rigorous theory but uses an artificial device in order to obtain an expression which fits the experimental data. This deficiency is avoided in the temperature dependence of the spontaneous polarization derived by Born using the dynamic theory of crystal lattices. This dependence and its derivation are given in Born's original papers [34, 35], which deal with the pyroelectric effect in crystals. We shall mention only that Born's dependence gives the same quadratic law for the spontaneous polarization at low temperatures as the Boguslavskii formula (VI.20).

§ 2. Thermodynamic Theory of the Spontaneous Polarization of Ferroelectrics

A thermodynamic theory of ferroelectricity, including a theory of the spontaneous polarization of ferroelectrics, was developed mainly by Ginzburg [7, 8] and Devonshire [38, 39].

In order to describe the processes associated with the spontaneous polarization, it is convenient to consider the free energy of a crystal G as a function of the temperature T, mechanical stresses t, and the polarization P. The differential form of this function is

$$dG = - SdT + r_i dt_i + E_m dP_m, \qquad (VI.21)$$

where S is the entropy; r_i are the components of the strain tensor; E_m are the components of the electric-field vector. For a stress-free crystal (t = 0), the function G can be expanded in powers of the polarization with temperature-dependent coefficients.

A. Crystals Which Have Only One Spontaneous Polarization Axis. In crystals with only one spontaneous polarization axis (Rochelle salt, triglycine sulfate, KH_2PO_4, and many others) we can have only two orientations of P_s: $+P_s$ and $-P_s$. Since these two directions are equivalent, an expansion of the free energy G(P, t) for t = 0 contains only terms with even powers of the polarization[†]:

$$G = G_0 + \frac{1}{2} \alpha^* P_s^2 + \frac{1}{4} \beta P_s^4 + \frac{1}{6} \gamma P_s^6 + \ldots \qquad (VI.22)$$

[†] To distinguish it from the polarizability α, the first coefficient of the expansion of the thermodynamic potential is denoted by $\alpha *$.

In this case, the electric field is given by the expression

$$E = \frac{\partial G}{\partial P_s} = \alpha^* P_s + \beta P_s^3 + \gamma P_s^5 + \dots \tag{VI.23}$$

The curve representing the dependence of G on the polarization depends strongly on the number, signs, and values of the coefficients in the expansion (VI.22). If the signs of all the terms in the expansion are positive (α^*, β, γ, ... > 0), this curve has one minimum at the origin of the coordinates, where $P_s = 0$ (Fig. 138A). In this case, the paraelectric state is stable over the whole range of P.

If only one of the coefficients in the expansion is negative, we find that in the absence of an external field (E = 0) the expansion (VI.23) has, in addition to $P_s = 0$, other solutions for which $P_s \neq 0$, and which represent a spontaneously polarized crystal. Analysis of the free energy of the state of spontaneous polarization can show whether this state is stable.

The free energy extrema, defined by the equation $\partial G/\partial P_s = 0$, give the first solution $P_s = 0$, which corresponds to an extremum at the origin of the coordinates. The other extrema can be found from the equation

$$\alpha^* + \beta P_s^2 + \gamma P_s^4 + \dots = 0. \tag{VI.24}$$

Let us analyze this equation in detail. Assuming first that $\gamma = 0$, $\alpha^* + \beta P_s^2 = 0$, we obtain the spontaneous polarization in the form

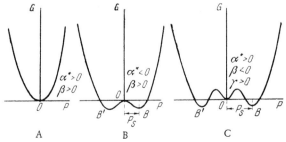

Fig. 138. Dependence of the free energy G on the polarization in the paraelectric (A) and ferroelectric phases (B, C). Cases b and c represent transitions of the second and first kind, respectively.

$$P_s^2 = -\frac{\alpha^*}{\beta} . \qquad (VI.25)$$

The solution for P_s in the above relationship has a physical meaning only if α^* and β have opposite signs. A graphical representation of the dependence G on the polarization, corresponding to
the case $\alpha^* < 0$, $\beta > 0$, is given in Fig. 138B. In this case, the
free energy has a maximum at the origin as well as two symmetrical minima B and B'. It follows that the spontaneous polarization state is stable.

Comparison of Figs. 138A and 138B shows that continuous variation of α^* from positive to negative values alters a stable paraelectric state ($\alpha^* > 0$) to a stable ferroelectric state ($\alpha^* < 0$);
at the transition temperature between these states, T_c, we have
$(\alpha^*)T_c = 0$. In this case, the spontaneous polarization P_s is also
a continuous function of the temperature (Fig. 139a), and it vanishes
at the transition temperature T_c. If we assume that the coefficient
α^* is a linear function of the temperature:

$$\alpha^* = \frac{T - T_c}{C^*} , \qquad (VI.26)$$

(C^* is a constant), we find that Eq. (VI.25) yields a parabolic temperature dependence of the spontaneous polarization (if β = const):

$$P_s^2 = k\,(T_c - T), \qquad (VI.27)$$

where k is some constant. The energy of a crystal varies continuously through the transition point and the transition does not require latent heat but is accompanied by a specific heat discontinuity, typical of phase transitions of the second kind.

Let us now go back to Eq. (VI.24). If other coefficients (but
not α^*) in this equation are negative (for example, if $\beta < 0$, $\gamma > 0$),

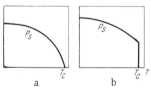

Fig. 139. Schematic curves representing temperature dependences
of the spontaneous polarization in
the case of phase transitions of the
second (a) and first (b) kinds.

the curve representing G is more complex. The presence of a minimum at the origin of the coordinates ($\alpha > 0$) is compatible with the existence of the spontaneous polarization $P_s \neq 0$ only when there are other minima satisfying the condition $G_{P_{s=0}} \geq G_{P_{s \neq 0}}$. This condition means that [see Eq. (VI.22)]

$$\frac{1}{2}\alpha^* P_s^2 + \frac{1}{4}\beta P_s^4 + \frac{1}{6}\gamma P_s^6 = 0. \qquad (VI.28)$$

Equations (VI.24) and (VI.28) should be compatible and, therefore, we must satisfy the relationships

$$P_s^2 = -\frac{3}{4}\frac{\beta_0}{\gamma_0}, \qquad (VI.29)$$

$$\alpha_0^* \gamma_0 = \frac{3}{16}\beta_0^2, \qquad (VI.30)$$

which represent the state of a crystal at the transition temperature (the values at the transition temperature are indicated by the subscripts 0 of the coefficients α^*, β, and γ). It follows from these two relationships and from the condition $\alpha^* > 0$ that β and γ should have opposite signs. The dependence of the free energy on the polarization near T_C (but below it) is shown graphically in Fig. 138C ($\alpha^* > 0, \beta < 0, \gamma > 0$). It is evident from Fig. 138C that the G(P) curve now has three minima: one at the origin of the coordinates at $P_s = 0$ and two other minima corresponding to $P_s \neq 0$ (we shall call these minima B and B'). If the relationship between the depths of these minima depends on the temperature, and if the potential barriers are not high, a transition from the paraelectric to the ferroelectric state is possible. In contrast to the preceding case (Fig. 139b), the spontaneous polarization and the energy of the crystal change suddenly at the transition point. The latent heat of transition is finite, which is typical of phase transitions of the first kind.

According to Eq. (VI.21) the entropy of the system is given by the expression

$$S = -\left(\frac{\partial G}{\partial T}\right)_{P,t},$$

which, together with Eq. (VI.22), yields

$$S = S_0 - \frac{1}{2} P^2 \frac{\partial \alpha^*}{\partial T} - \frac{1}{4} P^4 \frac{\partial \beta}{\partial T} - \cdots, \tag{VI.31}$$

where S_0 is the entropy at zero polarization. Thus, in the case when only the first term in Eq. (VI.31) is important, the change in the entropy (the entropy of the transition) can be written in the form

$$\Delta S = S - S_0 \cong - \frac{1}{2} P^2 \frac{\partial \alpha^*}{\partial T} . \tag{VI.32}$$

Using Eq. (VI.26), we can transform Eq. (VI.32) to the form

$$\Delta S = - \frac{1}{2C^*} P_s^2. \tag{VI.33}$$

It follows from the last expression that a sudden change in P_s is accompanied by a sudden change in S, indicating the presence of a latent heat of transition ΔQ (a phase transition of the first kind), given by the relationship

$$\Delta Q = \frac{T_c}{2C^*} P_s^2 . \tag{VI.34}$$

In the case of transitions of the second kind, in which the slope of P^2 changes suddenly, we observe a specific heat discontinuity at the transition point.

So far, we have considered the free energy of the system, ignoring mechanical stresses and electric fields (t = 0, E = 0). We shall take into account the influence of stresses and fields on the temperature of the system, i.e., on the position of the transition temperature. For transitions of the first kind, the free energy of the polar or ferroelectric phase (denoted by the subscript f) is equal to the free energy of the paraelectric phase (denoted by the subscript p) at the transition point ($G_f = G_p$). Hence, it follows from Eq. (VI.21) that

$$0 = dG_f - dG_p = -(S_f - S_p)dT + (r_{if} - r_{ip})dt_i + \tag{VI.35}$$

$$+ (P_{mf} - P_{mp})dE_m,$$

where T is the temperature of the transition corresponding to a stress t and a field E_m . Assuming that the field E is constant and that the stress is in the form of hydrostatic pressure p, we obtain the equation

$$\frac{dT}{dp} = \frac{\Delta V}{S_f - S_p} \qquad (VI.36)$$

(ΔV is the change in the volume at the transition point), which is the well-known Clapeyron — Clausius equation [see Eq. (V.35)].

Assuming that the stresses in Eq. (VI.35) are constant, we obtain the expression

$$\frac{dT}{dE_m} = \frac{P_{mf} - P_{mp}}{S_f - S_p}, \qquad (VI.37)$$

which can be used to calculate the change in the transition temperature under the influence of an electric field. In particular, using the change in the entropy at the transition, given by Eq. (VI.33), we can rewrite Eq. (VI.37) in the form

$$q = \frac{dT}{dE} = \frac{\Delta P}{\Delta S} = -\frac{2C^*}{P_s} . \qquad (VI.38)$$

In transitions of the second kind, the entropy of the two phases is the same. Equating S_f and S_p, we obtain Ehrenfest's equation (V.37) for hydrostatic compression:

$$\frac{dT}{dp} = \frac{T(\Delta_{if} - \Delta_{ip})}{c_f - c_p}, \qquad (VI.39)$$

where c_f and c_p are the specific heats of the ferroelectric and paraelectric phases at constant pressure; Δ_{if} and Δ_{ip} are the volume expansion coefficients.

Some of these thermodynamic relationships can be checked easily against published experimental data. In the case of ferroelectrics which undergo a phase transition of the first kind, the value of T_c in an expression of the Eq. (VI.26) type should be replaced (because of thermal hysteresis) by a temperature T_c' which represents the true transition temperature and which differs by several degrees from T_c. (For example, in the case of $BaTiO_3$

TABLE 36. Experimental Check of the Relationship
$\Delta Q = T_c P_s^2 / 2C *$ for Some Ferroelectrics [12]

Substance	$T_c/C^\bullet$	P, 10^3, cgs esu	$T_c/2C^\bullet \cdot P_s^2 \cdot 10^6$, ergs/cm^3	ΔQ, 10^6, ergs/cm^2
KH_2PO_4	0.475	13.9	45.9	41.2; 62.7
KD_2PO_4	0.614	13.9; 27	58.5; 220	71.4
KH_2AsO_4	0.43; 0.36	15.1; 15.1	49; 41	55.8
PbH_2PO_4	0.55; 0.44	16.8; 16.8	77; 62	No data
Rochelle salt	1.67	0.74	0.46	No reliable data

$T_c^l - T_c = 11°C$.) The value of the coefficient α_0^*, which corresponds to the transition temperature in such cases, is found from
the relationship

$$\alpha_0^* = \frac{(T_c' - T_c)}{C^*} .$$ (VI.40)

Equation (VI.34) gives satisfactory results for Rochelle salt
and for KH_2PO_4-type ferroelectrics, as listed in Table 36. Equation (VI.38) for $BaTiO_3$ ($\Delta P = 54 \times 10^3$ cgs esu, $\Delta S = 0.12$ cal ·
mole^{-1}·deg^{-1}) gives $q = dT/dE = -0.53$ cgs esu, which is close
to the value $q = -0.45$ cgs esu cited in Chap. V. Equation (VI.36)
describes satisfactorily the experimentally established shift of
the Curie point of $BaTiO_3$ under hydrostatic pressure, as discussed
in Chap. V (Table 35). The validity of Ehrenfest's relationship for
the shift of the Curie point has also been demonstrated in Chap. V
for triglycine sulfate (which undergoes a phase-transition of the
second kind).

B. Free Energy of Rochelle Salt. In some cases,
the experimental data can be used to find the function $\alpha *(T)$ and
the overall nature of the free energy G throughout the ferroelectric range of temperatures. In particular, the two Curie points of
Rochelle salt indicate that the function $\alpha *(T)$ should be an inverted
dome-shaped curve, which intersects the abscissa at the Curie
points. Retaining terms of up to P^4 in Eq. (VI.22), we obtain

$$\alpha^* = -\beta P_s^2.$$ (VI.41)

Moreover, if we assume that β is independent of temperature ($\beta =$
const), it follows from the above expression that to find the dependence $\alpha^* = \alpha *(T)$, i.e., to interpolate the function G, we must

know the dependence $P_s = P_s(T)$. This latter dependence is well known (Fig. 118).

Deviations of the system from the symmetrical (nonferroelec-tric) state due to the appearance of or change in the spontaneous polarization in Rochelle salt can be described in several ways. Us-ing the expansion of the free energy in the form of Eq. (VI.22), we can describe deviations not only by the polarization but also by the shear strain of the unit cell r_{23} or by the angle of rotation of the optical indicatrix of a domain about the a axis because of the spon-taneous electro-optical effect. As shown in Chap. V, these param-eters are proportional to P_s. In particular, the use of the tempera-ture dependence of the angle of rotation of the optical indicatrix (Fig. 97) yields, when combined with a relationship similar to Eq. (VL.41), an expression for $\alpha^* = \alpha^*(T)$. The results of plotting of the change in the free energy $(G-G_0)$ as a function of the tempera-ture and of the monoclinic angle $\eta = \alpha^0 \pi / 180$:

$$G - G_0 = \alpha^* \eta^2 + \beta^* \eta^4 \qquad (VI.42)$$

are shown in Fig. 140.

The coefficient β^*, estimated from the specific heat discon-tinuity at the upper Curie point (5 cal/mole), is 5×10^7 cal/mole. According to Fig. 97, the maximum value of the monoclinic angle is $\eta_{max} = \alpha^0 \pi / 180 = 1.4 \times 10^{-2}$. Hence, it follows that the maxi-mum change in the free energy, due to deviation of the system from the symmetrical state, is $\Delta G = \beta^* \eta_{max}^4 = 2$ cal/mole. The thermodynamic potential surface, shown in Fig. 140a, can be rep-resented by a set of contour lines corresponding to constant values of ΔG. Curves outside the ferroelectric range of temperatures are found by extrapolation. Figure 140b shows a model of the sur-face representing the free energy. In the nonferroelectric range of temperatures the surface has troughs which reach down to the plane $\eta = 0$. The Curie transition points correspond to saddle points between which there is a depression with two hollows. The presence of a ridge joining the Curie points indicates the instabili-ty of the orthorhombic modification of Rochelle salt in the ferro-electric range of temperatures and the necessary splitting of a sample into monoclinic domains corresponding to potential wells lying on both sides of the $\eta = 0$ plane. We can go over from one parameter (η) to another (P_s or r_{23}) simply by changing one of the scales in the model.

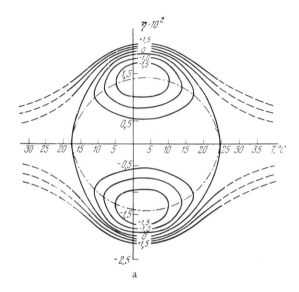

a

b

Fig. 140. Three-dimensional representation of the thermodynamic potential of Rochelle salt: a) map of the surface with values along the outer lines given in cal/mole (the chain curve shows the experimental dependence of the monoclinic parameter η); b) three-dimensional model: each step represents 0.5 cal/mole [11].

C. Free Energy of a Cubic Ferroelectric [27a, 27b, 27c]. A cubic crystal has many ferroelectric axes. Thus, a crystal of symmetry class $\bar{6}/4$ has three equivalent fourfold rotation axes, four sixfold rotation-reflection axes, six twofold rotation axes, etc. The appearance of the polarization along any one of these systems of axes can be represented by the components P_x, P_y, P_z, obtained by resolving the polarization vector P_s along the axes of an orthogonal system of coordinates. We shall assume that the X, Y, Z axes of this system coincide with the fourfold axes of a crystal (if there are no fourfold axes the coordinate axes are taken along the twofold axes). This makes it possible to write the free energy of a cubic crystal in the form

$$G = G_0 + \frac{1}{2}\alpha^*(P_x^2 + P_y^2 + P_z^2) + \frac{1}{4}\beta_1(P_x^4 + P_y^4 + P_z^4)$$
$$+ \frac{1}{2}\beta_2(P_y^2 P_z^2 + P_z^2 P_x^2 + P_x^2 P_y^2) + \frac{1}{6}\gamma_1(P_x^6 + P_y^6 + P_z^6)$$
$$+ \frac{1}{2}\gamma_2[P_x^4(P_y^2 + P_z^2) + P_y^4(P_z^2 + P_x^2) + P_z^4(P_x^2 + P_y^2)] + \frac{1}{2}\gamma_3 P_x^2 P_y^2 P_z^2 + \ldots$$
$$\text{(VI.43)}$$

The minima of the free energy G can be found (in the absence of an external electric field E) from the following relationships:

$$E_x = \frac{\partial G}{\partial P_x} = 0; \quad E_y = \frac{\partial G}{\partial P_y} = 0; \quad E_z = \frac{\partial G}{\partial P_z} = 0. \quad \text{(VI.44)}$$

The solution of the system (VI.44) shows that these minima occur primarily in the paraelectric cubic phase (phase I) for which $P_x = P_y = P_z = 0$. This phase is stable when $\alpha^* > 0$. As demonstrated in subsection A, when this condition is not satisfied, we obtain the ferroelectric uniaxial tetragonal phase (phase II). In this case, the relationship $\alpha^* + \beta_1 P_z^2 = 0$ should be observed in the case of a transition of the second kind; if the transition is of the first kind, we should obtain the following relationships

$$\alpha^* = \frac{3}{16}\frac{\beta_1^2}{\gamma_1} \quad \text{and} \quad 3\beta_1 + 4\gamma_1 P_z^2 = 0.$$

A minimum of G is obtained also for the ferroelectric tetragonal phase II for which we find that $P_x = P_y = 0$ and $P_z = P$, if P is related to α^*, β_1, and γ_1 by the expression

$$\alpha^* + \beta_1 P^2 + \gamma_1 P^4 = 0.$$

When the tetragonal modification is transformed to the cubic phase by heating, it is found that phase II is stable $(\partial^2 G / \partial P_z^2 > 0)$ as long as the following relationship is satisfied:

$$\beta_1 + 2\gamma_1 P^2 > 0. \tag{VI.45}$$

When the tetragonal modification transforms to the orthorhombic phase (phase III, which will be discussed later), the tetragonal phase remains stable as long as the following relationship is obeyed:

$$\beta_2 + \gamma_2 P^2 > 0. \tag{VI.46}$$

A minimum of G is observed also for the ferroelectric ortho-rhombic phase III, for which $P_x = P_y = P_z \neq 0$, $P_z = 0$ with the additional condition that P is related to α^*, β, and γ by the expression

$$\left(\beta_1 + \frac{1}{2}\beta_2\right) P^2 + \left(\gamma_1 + \frac{3}{4}\gamma_2\right) P^4 + \alpha^* = 0.$$

The orthorhombic phase is stable when

$$\left(\beta_1 + \frac{1}{2}\beta_2\right) + 2\left(\gamma_1 + \frac{3}{4}\gamma_2\right) P^2 > 0,$$

which indicates that when a crystal is heated, the transition from the orthorhombic to the tetragonal modification does not take place until the condition

$$\beta_2 + \gamma_2 P^2 < 0 \tag{VI.47}$$

is violated, and the transition from the orthorhombic to the trigonal or rhombohedral phase (phase IV, to be discussed later) takes place only after violation of the condition

$$2\beta_2 + (\gamma_3 - \gamma_2) P^2 > 0. \tag{VI.48}$$

The ferroelectric trigonal phase IV also has a minimum of G; this phase is characterized by $P_x = P_y = P_z = P$ and, moreover, P is related to α^*, β, and γ by the expression

$$\left(\beta_1 + \frac{2}{3}\beta_2\right) + 2\left(\gamma_1 + \frac{2}{3}\gamma_2 + \frac{1}{9}\gamma_3\right) P^2 + \alpha^* = 0.$$

The trigonal phase is stable when

$$\left(\beta_1 + \frac{2}{3}\beta_2\right) + 2\left(\gamma_1 + \frac{2}{3}\gamma_2 + \frac{1}{9}\gamma_3\right)P^2 > 0,$$

which shows that when this phase is heated, the transition to the orthorhombic modification takes place after violation of the condition

$$3\beta_2 + \gamma_3 P^2 < 0. \tag{VI.49}$$

The relationships represented by Eqs. (VI-45)-(VI.49), which give the conditions for the transformation of a crystal from one modification to another and take into account the available data about the transition, can be used to determine the signs of the coefficients α^*, β, and γ in each specific case and to determine the temperature dependences of these coefficients. In the case of barium titanate, we obtain the following information: $\beta_1(T)$ decreases monotonically with increasing temperature but $\beta_2(T)$ increases monotonically; the coefficients γ_1, γ_2, and γ_3 are independent of temperature and it is assumed that the coefficients γ_1 and γ_2 are positive but the coefficient γ_3 is negative. When these conditions are satisfied, we obtain the sequence of transitions in $BaTiO_3$ which is observed experimentally.

The actual values of the transition temperatures, as well as the dependences of the permittivity on the temperature and spontaneous polarization, yield numerical values of some of the coefficients α^*, β, and γ of $BaTiO_3$. At the temperature of the transition from the cubic to the tetragonal modification the known coefficients have the following values: $\alpha_0^* = 1.02 \times 10^{-2}$ cgs esu, $\beta_{10} = -10.8 \times 10^{-13}$ cgs esu, $\gamma_{10} = 2.28 \times 10^{-22}$ cgs esu.

The dependence of the change in the free energy ΔG of the polarization is plotted in Fig. 141 for an unstressed crystal investigated at various temperatures. It is evident from this figure that a phase transition should occur at 391°K, which is in agreement with the experimental data.

Assuming a linear temperature dependence of the coefficient α^*, as given by Eq. (VI.26), and making no other assumptions, we can obtain the sequence of phase transitions which is actually observed for $BaTiO_3$. We can also calculate the temperature depen-

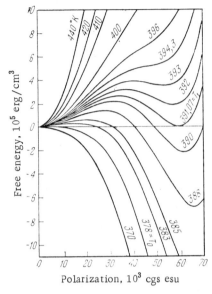

Fig. 141. Dependence of the free energy on the polarization of a BaTiO$_3$ crystal near the point of transition from the tetragonal to the cubic phase.

dences of the dielectric, piezoelectric, and elastic parameters of this compound in all its phases. A clear illustration of the success of the thermodynamic theory of BaTiO$_3$ is provided by Fig. 142, which gives the theoretically calculated temperature dependences of the unit-cell parameters of various modifications. This dependence is close to the experimental data (Fig. 31).

Some of the coefficients of the expansion of Eq. (VI.22) will be considered in Chap. VII in connection with the temperature dependence of the polarizability of ferroelectrics.

We shall now make some general comments on the thermodynamic theory of the spontaneous polarization of ferroelectrics.

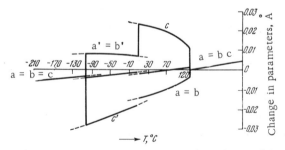

Fig. 142. Theoretical temperature dependence of the unit-cell parameters of various modifications of barium titanate.

First of all, we note that the expansion (VI.22) is, generally speaking, a direct extension of the general theory of phase transitions of the second kind to ferroelectric phenomena or, more exactly, to phenomena associated with the appearance of or change in the spontaneous polarization. The characteristic features of this theory are responsible for the fact that only the terms with the even powers of P_s (P_s^2, P_s^4, P_s^6) are used in the expansion. However, there is no real justification for neglecting other terms in this expansion when describing phase transitions resulting in the appearance of spontaneous polarization. In particular, there is no reason to neglect the third-order invariants consisting of the components P_x, P_y, and P_z for cubic crystals and of the components P_x and P_y for uniaxial crystals.

The symmetry of some of the crystals allows the existence of such invariants. This is true of polar-neutral crystals (Chap. I, §5), with symmetries of the type $3/\bar{4}$, $\bar{4}\cdot m$, $m\cdot3{:}m$, $4{:}2$, etc. The presence of these invariants shows that the appearance of the polarization along the polar directions of such crystals may be accompanied by some anomalies. These anomalies include the splitting of a crystal into layers, dependences of the $P_s \propto (T_c - T)$ type along some directions [instead of the dependences $P_s^2 \propto (T_c - T)$, where T_c is the Curie temperature], etc.

In some polar-neutral crystals (for example, crystals of the class $6{:}2$) splitting into layers parallel to the basal plane can occur even when the spontaneous polarization appears along a nonpolar direction which lies in the basal plane.

However, it is not yet possible to conclude that such transitions in polar-neutral crystals are ferroelectric, i.e., that they are accompanied by splitting into domains, dielectric hysteresis, etc. It is more likely that such transitions represent the appearance of polarization in linear pyroelectrics (as discussed in the Introduction to the present chapter), in antiferroelectrics, or in ferrielectrics.*

---

* In polar-neutral crystals of intermediate symmetry a spontaneous polarization along the principal axis means that there are no third-order invariants in the expansion of Eq. (VI.22). In such cases the phase transition is ferroelectric. An example of this type is the appearance of spontaneous polarization along the Z axis in KH_2PO_4 (the symmetry of the paraelectric modification of this crystal is $\bar{4}\cdot m$). The characteristic features of this class of crystals are observed when the polarization appears along one of the polar directions. The Z axis of such crystals is not polar.

There is no reason to assume that the spontaneous polarization can always be used as a parameter for expanding the free energy [see Eq. (VI.22)] of all phase transitions accompanied by the appearance of spontaneous polarization. In fact, spontaneous polarization cannot be used as such a parameter when the transition is not due to but simply accompanied by the appearance of spontaneous polarization. This can occur in some crystals on the appearance of magnetization due to the magnetoelectric effect or, in other crystals, when the transition is due to the appearance of optical activity. From the point of view of crystal symmetry, such transitions are accompanied by a change of symmetry in which the new symmetry group is not the highest common subgroup of the symmetry group of the crystal and of the symmetry group of the spontaneous polarization vector (polar vector). The new group is simply one of the common subgroups of these two symmetry groups but not the highest subgroup. A hypothetical example of this type is a change of the crystal symmetry $\bar{6}/2$ due to the appearance of optical activity along a twofold axis, accompanied by the appearance of a spontaneous polarization P_s along the same axis. Usually, the appearance of P_s along this axis gives rise to the symmetry transformation $\bar{6}/2 \rightarrow 2 \cdot m$ (Table 7). The very limited knowledge of such transitions prevents us from drawing conclusions about their nature and especially whether such transitions can give rise to ferroelectric properties.

In transitions involving a change in the number of unit cells in ferroelectrics the value of P_s again cannot be used as the parameter in an expansion of Eq. (VI.22). A transition of this type, involving doubling of the lattice parameter a, does indeed occur in $(NH_4)_2BeF_4$ at $-93°C$. A theoretical analysis of this transition shows that the parameter representing the deviation of the crystal from its symmetrical (paraelectric) state is η (in the case of Rochelle salt this parameter is the monoclinic angle α^0) which is not proportional to P_s but is related to it by the expression $|P_s| \propto \eta^2$.

Ginzburg [9] recently used the results of experimental investigations of ferroelectrics to discuss the characteristic features of the ferroelectric phase transitions on the basis of a general theory of phase transitions of the second kind. The characteristic features of the phase transitions were attributed by Ginzburg to a relationship between the volume and correlation energies. According to Ginzburg, the correlation energy of a solid is of the or-

der of the volume free energy when the "asymmetry" parameter
of the system (the parameter in terms of which the free energy is
expanded) changes appreciably over distances of the order of the
lattice constant. This explains the specific-heat anomalies of or-
derable alloys or $\alpha \rightleftharpoons \beta$ transitions in quartz extending over temperature intervals amounting to tens of degrees; this is in agree-
ment with the theory in which a transition is described by an expansion of the free energy of the type given by Eq. (VI.22).

The correlation energy of ferroelectrics is introduced by an
additional term δ (grad P)^2 in the expansion (VI.22). This term
disappears, by definition, from the expansion for the spatially uniform case. An estimate of the term δ (grad P)^2, obtained by Ginzburg, shows that, in the case of long wavelength phonons, the correlation energy of ferroelectrics is small compared with the volume energy. The volume energy of ferroelectrics is itself small
in the sense that the spontaneous polarization is very weak compared with the polarization which would be obtained as a result of a
shift of ions through a distance equal to the lattice constant (in
BaTiO$_3$ the shift corresponding to the ferroelectric polarization is
only 3% of the lattice constant).

Ginzburg analyzed the behavior of the function G, represented
by the expansion (VI.22), near the transition temperature and found
that this expansion described well a phase transition in a ferroelectric only if $(\Delta P)^2 \ll P^2$, which means that fluctuations must be
relatively small. Phase transitions in many ferroelectrics are
thus described successfully by the expansion (VI.22) because in
such ferroelectrics the fluctuations are suppressed and the volume energy near the Curie temperature is small.

§3. Molecular Models and the Spontaneous

Polarization of Ferroelectrics

We have discussed in Chaps. II and III some aspects of the
relationship between the structure and spontaneous polarization.
In spite of the fact that an analytic treatment of this relationship
is, in general, very complex and the results obtained in this way
are not always significant, it is worthwhile to consider the most
important investigations of this relationship between the structure
and polarization.

A. Electronic Polarization and its Role in Spontaneous Polarization. Before we consider electronic polarization in ferroelectric crystals, we must find whether the internal fields in crystals are capable of producing spontaneous polarization and of inducing a phase transition to the polarized state simply because of electronic polarizability. We shall ignore the motion of nuclei and shall assume that the nuclei of polarizable ions or atoms form a rigid nonpolar lattice. This lattice can be regarded as consisting of sublattices so that ions which are crystallographically equivalent in the paraelectric modification are also equivalent in the ferroelectric modification. For example, if the polarization is directed along the [001] axis in BaTiO$_3$, it is necessary to distinguish the sublattice of the O$_I$ oxygen ions from the sublattice of the O$_{II}$ ions (Fig. 29). For other directions of P$_s$, we must consider other sublattices.

To simplify the problem, the fluctuating electric moments of ions in a given sublattice are replaced by fixed moments having some average value. This is physically equivalent to neglecting the correlation between the nearest neighbors (this cannot be done, for example, in polar liquids).

In the simplest structures (having the centrosymmetric configuration in the paraelectric modification, for example, BaTiO$_3$) the electric moments of different sublattices may be assumed to be directed along the same axis.

When these assumptions are made, we can determine the local field F acting on the ions in the i-th sublattice:

$$F_i = E + \sum_j f_{ij} P_j, \qquad (VI.50)$$

where P$_j$ is the polarization of the j-th sublattice; E is the average macroscopic (external) field; f_{ij} is the Lorentz factor. For an isotropic medium and a simple cubic lattice the expression (VI.50) transforms into the Lorentz equation

$$F = E + \frac{4\pi}{3} P, \qquad (VI.51)$$

in which the field $4\pi P/3$ is known as the internal Lorentz field. The matrix of the Lorentz factors is usually calculated on the assumption that polarized ions act on each other as if they were point dipoles. This assumption is fully justified in the case when electron orbits of different ions do not overlap.

If ions of the i-th type have an electronic polarizability η_i, the electric moment of the ions of this type p_i is described by

$$p_i = \eta_i F_i,$$

and the polarization P_i is given by

$$P_t = N n_i \eta_i F_i, \tag{VI.52}$$

where N is the number of unit cells per 1 cm^3 and n_i is the number of ions of the i-th type in one unit cell.

Using Eqs. (VI.51) and (VI.52), we obtain the relationship

$$\frac{\varepsilon - 1}{\varepsilon + 2} = \frac{4\pi}{3} N \sum_i n_i \eta_i \tag{VI.53}$$

(ε is the permittivity), which is the special case of the Clausius – Mosotti formula in which only the electronic polarizability of ions is included. Experiments show that the properties of the majority of cubic ionic crystals obey Eq. (VI.53) if ε is taken to be the optical value of the permittivity, found from the relationship $\varepsilon_\infty = n^2$, where n is the refractive index. This shows that the assumptions made in a description of the electronic polarization of some crystals are indeed justified.

In order to estimate whether the electronic polarization is sufficiently strong to induce a transition from an unpolarized to a polarized state, we must take into account the fact that the spontaneous polarization can appear when the energy of the interaction between dipoles (these dipoles are induced by the effective field F) exceeds the energy required to distort the electron shells, i.e., to produce the necessary dipole moment.

If a simple cubic lattice consists of ions of one type only, the energy of electrons belonging to a polarized ion can be written in the form

$$\frac{p^2}{2\eta} + a_4 p^4 + a_6 p^6 + \ldots,$$

where p is the dipole moment and η is the electronic polarizability. Hence, it follows that the energy per 1 cm^3 of a crystal, associated with the distortion of the electron shells, is given by

$$A_{el} = \frac{P^2}{2N\eta} + a_4 P^4 + a_6 P^6 + \ldots \qquad \text{(VI.54)}$$

On the other hand, the energy of the electrostatic interaction of point dipoles in the presence of an electric field is

$$A_{dip} = -\frac{4\pi}{6} P^2. \qquad \text{(VI.55)}$$

The minus sign in the last expression indicates that the polarized state is energetically more favorable than the unpolarized state; in view of this, the electrostatic interaction is sometimes called the dominant interaction of a ferroelectric transition.

The sum of the energies (VI.54) and (VI.55) is

$$A = \frac{1}{2}\left(\frac{1}{N\eta} - \frac{4\pi}{3}\right) P^2 + a_4 P^4 + a_6 P^6 + \ldots \qquad \text{(VI.56)}$$

It follows that the polarized state becomes stable when the polarizability exceeds the critical value, i.e., when

$$\eta \geqslant \frac{3}{4\pi N}, \qquad \text{(VI.57)}$$

which corresponds to the so-called $4\pi/3$ catastrophe.

As a rule, the condition (VI.57) is not satisfied in crystals and there is no spontaneous polarization. However, the matrix of the Lorentz factors f_{ij} of some cubic crystals has, along some directions, coefficients which exceed considerably the value $4\pi/3$. If the relationship (VI.57) is satisfied under these conditions, the spontaneous polarization can appear in a crystal even at lower values of η.

The electronic polarizability η of the Ti^{4+} ions in $BaTiO_3$ is 0.19×10^{-24} cm^3. Calculations show that the spontaneous polarization (the $4\pi/3$ catastrophe) can appear along the [001] direction in cubic $BaTiO_3$ only if the polarizability of Ti^{4+} exceeds the value just quoted by $\eta' = 5.97 \times 10^{-24}$ cm^3. The specific electronic polarization of $BaTiO_3$

$$\frac{4\pi}{3} N \sum n_i \eta_i,$$

calculated from Eq. (VI.53) using the values $n = \sqrt{\varepsilon} = 2.4$, η (Ba) = 1.95×10^{-24} cm^3, η (O) $= 2.4 \times 10^{-24}$ cm^3, and η (Ti) $= 0.19 \times 10^{-24}$ cm^3, amounts to 0.61. It follows that the remainder of the polarization $(1 - 0.61 = 0.39)$ should be due to the ionic polarizability.

However, we can show that the difference between the coefficients of the matrix f_{ij} and the Lorentz value $4\pi/3$ of the tetragonal modification requires a smaller (but finite) correction η' than that given above.

A calculation of the matrix of the coefficients f_{ij} for some structures (including the tetragonal modification of BaTiO$_3$) was carried out by Skanavi [19], Slater [61], and others.

Calculations for the tetragonal modification of BaTiO$_3$ are carried out as follows. First of all, we write down the expressions for the effective field at each lattice site in the form of a sum consisting of the average macroscopic (external) field and of the polarization due to ions of several types. The external field is assumed to be directed parallel to [001], which is taken to be the Z axis. Sublattices of Ba, Ti, O$_I$, and O$_{II}$ atoms are considered (Fig. 29).

The sublattice polarizations are given by the following system of equations

$$F(\text{Ba}) = \frac{P(\text{Ba})}{N \cdot n(\text{Ba}) \cdot \eta(\text{Ba})} = E + f_{11} \cdot P(\text{Ba}) + f_{12} \cdot P(\text{Ti}) + f_{13} \cdot P(\text{O}_I)$$

$$+ f_{14} \cdot P(\text{O}_{II}),$$

$$F(\text{Ti}) = \frac{P(\text{Ti})}{N \cdot n(\text{Ti}) \cdot \eta(\text{Ti})} = E + f_{21} \cdot P(\text{Ba}) + f_{22} \cdot P(\text{Ti}) + f_{23} \cdot P(\text{O}_I)$$

$$+ f_{24} \cdot P(\text{O}_{II}),$$

$$F(\text{O}_I) = \frac{P(\text{O}_I)}{N \cdot n(\text{O}_I) \cdot \eta(\text{O}_I)} = E + f_{31} \cdot P(\text{Ba}) + f_{32} \cdot P(\text{Ti}) \qquad \text{(VI.58)}$$

$$+ f_{33} \cdot P(\text{O}_I) + f_{34} \cdot P(\text{O}_{II}),$$

$$F(\text{O}_{II}) = \frac{P(\text{O}_{II})}{N \cdot n(\text{O}_{II}) \cdot \eta(\text{O}_{II})} = E + f_{41} \cdot P(\text{Ba}) + f_{42} \cdot P(\text{Ti})$$

$$+ f_{43} \cdot P(\text{O}_I) + f_{44} \cdot P(_{II}).$$

The coefficients of the various values of P for all these equations are sums over the dipole distributions in the sublattices. In the case considered here, the coefficients f_{ij} are given by the following expressions:

$$f_{11} = f_{22} = f_{33} = f_{21} = f_{12} = \frac{4\pi}{3},$$

$$f_{13} = f_{31} = \frac{4\pi}{3} - 8.668,$$

$$f_{34} = f_{43} = f_{14} = f_{41} = \frac{4\pi}{3} + 4.334,$$

$$f_{23} = f_{32} = \frac{4\pi}{3} + 30.080,$$

$$f_{24} = f_{42} = \frac{4\pi}{4} - 15.040,$$

$$f_{44} = \frac{4\pi}{3} - 4.334.$$

It follows from these expressions that the strongest interaction is that between the Ti and O_I ions. The coefficients describing this interaction $(f_{23} = f_{32} = 4\pi/3 + 30.080)$ are approximately 8.2 times larger than the usual value of $4\pi/3$, which is why the electric field rises considerably in the region of the central ion in the perovskite structure.

We can find the state of the system with $P \neq 0$ in the absence of an external field ($E = 0$), i.e., the spontaneous polarization ("polarization catastrophe") state, by postulating that the determinant of the four equations in (VI.58) vanishes. If we also assume that the polarizabilities $\eta(O_I) = \eta(O_{II})$ and $\eta(Ba)$ have the values given in the expressions just cited and that the polarizability of the titanium ions can be represented in the form

$$\eta(Ti) = 0.19 \cdot 10^{-24} \, cm^3 + \eta'(Ti),$$

we find that the relevant determinant vanishes when

$$\eta' = 0.95 \cdot 10^{-24} \, cm^3$$

This value of η' shows that the contribution of the ionic polarizability is

$$\frac{4\pi}{3} N \cdot n(Ti) \cdot \eta'(Ti) = 0.062. \qquad (VI.59)$$

Comparison of this value with 0.39, obtained for cubic $BaTiO_3$, shows that the displacement of the titanium ion from the center of the oxygen octahedron (in the tetragonal modification) increases strongly the contribution of the electronic polarization mainly because of an increase of the polarization due to the O_I ions. The fields of the O_I ions interact with the Ti ions, forming chains of dipoles oriented along the same direction and giving rise to the spontaneous polarization of barium titanate.*

According to Slater's calculations, the contribution of the titanium ions to the total polarization is 37% (31% due to the displacement of ions and 6% to the electronic polarization), whereas the contribution of the O_I ions may reach 59%.

Equation (VI.59) shows that, no matter how small the ionic polarization in $BaTiO_3$, the electronic polarization is by itself insufficient to produce the spontaneous polarization. In other words, the electronic polarizability of single ions cannot explain the ferroelectric phase transition of $BaTiO_3$ from the cubic to the tetragonal modification.

This analysis of the electronic and ionic polarization of $BaTiO_3$ should be regarded as approximate. Thus, the results of calculations depend strongly on the polarizability of the oxygen ions which differs considerably from one compound to another. Slater's calculations ignore the reduction in the effective fields due to the overlap of the electron shells of the ions. Moreover, the effective fields are calculated by Slater for fixed ion positions. Furthermore, there is no justification for attributing the whole ionic polarization to Ti, since the contribution of such polarization is governed by the selection of the system of coordinates which is arbitrary (in the case considered the origin of the coordinates is assumed to be at the center of the oxygen octahedron). We must also mention a strong displacement of the titanium ion from the center of the octahedron (Chap. II). In this connection, it should be stressed that the most important conclusion is not that the ionic polarizability is associated only with the titanium ions but that the interaction is strongest between the Ti and O_I ions and that this interaction may give rise to the spontaneous polarization.

---

*To be consistent, we should say that ions are displaced as a result of a change in the tetragonal internal field due to the electronic polarization. The opposite point of view (a change in the internal field as a result of ion displacements) will be discussed later. These two points of view are not contradictory and give the same final results.

A similar calculation for $LiTaO_3$ has been carried out on the assumption that this ferroelectric has the structure of ilmenite and not that of pseudoilmenite. These calculations show that the spontaneous polarization can appear only in the presence of an additional polarizability of metal ions amounting to about half the electronic polarizability. In the case of the hexagonal (nonferroelectric) modification of $BaTiO_3$ the additional polarizability of the Ti ions, necessary for the appearance of the spontaneous polarization, should be 1.6×10^{-24} cm^3, which is approximately twice as large as the corresponding value for the ferroelectric (tetragonal) modification.

If it is assumed that the conditions for the $4\pi/3$ catastrophe are satisfied in some crystal, the phase-transition temperature can be obtained only if the temperature dependence of the polarizability η is known for at least one of the ions. The simplest assumption is that the temperature dependence of η is weak (linear) or that η varies as $1/T$. The first of these assumptions makes it possible to describe, in principle, the 120°C transition in $BaTiO_3$ and the second assumption accounts for transitions in Rochelle salt and in KH_2PO_4.

Jaynes and Wigner [45, 46] suggested an electron theory for calculating the temperature dependence of the polarizability of $BaTiO_3$. The fact that $BaTiO_3$ is not a purely ionic crystal and that oxygen-octahedral compounds have anomalously large refractive indices (which do not agree with the electronic polarizabilities of ions in these compounds) is used by Jaynes and Wigner as proof that the state of electrons in a crystal plays an important role. In contrast to the method just discussed (electronic polarizabilities of single ions), Jaynes and Wigner considered the electronic state of the TiO_6 octahedron as a whole. Each octahedron is regarded as a system with an internal electron quantum state which is independent of the states of neighboring unit cells. Thus, Jaynes and Wigner assume a strong exchange-type interaction between elements in the oxygen octahedron, which determines the nature of the chemical bonding. In the absence of an electric field the ground state of this electron configuration is cubic and symmetrical and does not have a dipole moment.

Jaynes and Wigner next assume that the interaction between neighboring octahedra should be considerable if they are in states with approximately equal energies but opposite particles (according to this theory, the octahedra interact only via the effective Lorentz field without participation of short-range forces). This interaction perturbs the ground state of the octahedron and distorts the initial (cubic and symmetrical) wave function of this state. The wave function of the octahedron then becomes a linear combination of the original (cubic and symmetrical) functions, which now has a finite dipole moment.

The initially degenerate energy level of the ground state is split by this perturbation in such a way that the energy of the perturbed state is less (by about 4kT) than the energy of the ground state. This governs the stability of the state with a finite dipole moment. The calculated energy spectrum of the system can be used to allow for the influence of the temperature by statistical means. Next, the free energy and polarization are determined using partition functions.

Not all the assumptions of this electron theory are really acceptable. In particular, the attribution of great importance to the state of electrons underestimates the role of the well-established displacements of ions in polarized structures. These displacements are used by Jaynes and Wigner to conclude (in order to obtain agreement with the experimental data) that the electronic polarization of the octahedra represents only half the total spontaneous polarization. The other half is attributed to the displacements of ions and the displacements of electron shells of the Ba ions.

Moreover, the theory of Jaynes and Wigner includes four parameters which can be easily selected so as to obtain agreement with a phenomenological description of a "clamped" crystal. One of these parameters is the difference between the energies of the perturbed and unperturbed states (close to 4kT), which has already been mentioned. This corresponds to infrared absorption in the region of 10 μ, which has yet to be discovered experimentally.

In spite of these deficiencies, the theory of Jaynes and Wigner is of considerable interest because the problem of the quantum states of octahedra in oxygen-octahedral ferroelectrics is very important in the determination of the nature of bonds between various ions. An important result of their theory is the proof that the spontaneous polarization may, in principle, be solely due to electron effects.

A theoretical model of ABO_3-type ferroelectrics, which also considers electron states of a crystal, has recently been put forward by Khozyainov [26].

In contrast to Jaynes and Wigner, Khozyainov does not consider the oxygen octahedron but the complex AB lattice formed by two simple cubic sublattices A and B. An analysis of such a lattice shows that, in the presence of a resonance-excited level in B, the AB lattice has the properties of the bcc structure. The first Brillouin zone of such a lattice is a dodecahedron, consisting of two half-zones between which there is a cubic discontinuity surface. The lattices of the oxygen ions do not have resonance levels and, therefore, they can be regarded as a background which determines the shape of the potential wells at the A and B sites.

Khozyainov introduces also a correlation interaction between electrons which is effective only in a narrow energy "layer" near the Fermi surface; this layer is nearly cubic for a certain population of the zone. Considering the correlated pairs of electrons with nonzero total momentum and showing that the effective correlation region in the phase space is increased by a tetragonal distortion of a crystal, Khozyainov concludes that the polarized state of a crystal is energetically more favorable.

Other ferroelectric modifications of ABO_3-type compounds can be considered in a similar manner, and it is found that the criterion for the validity of this model is well supported by the experimental data on ferroelectrics.

We shall end this brief review of the main theories of the spontaneous polarization of ferroelectrics (based on electronic polarizabilities and electron states) by pointing out the empirical criterion of the existence of polarized states in perovskite-type structures, suggested by Matthias [53] as well as by Smolenskii and Kozhevnikova [21]. According to these authors, the electron configuration of a metal ion located at the center of an oxygen octahedron should be similar to the electron configuration of an inert gas atom. This hypothesis has been considered in more detail at the end of Chap. II.

B. Polarization Due to Mutual Displacements of Ionic Sublattices. The mutual displacement of ionic sublattices, associated with the appearance of the spontaneous polazization (Chaps. II and III), can easily give rise to a dipole structure and thus contribute appreciably to the spontaneous polarization. This is sometimes known as the ionic polarization contribution. Since the displacement of sublattices is generally mutual, we cannot speak of the ionic polarization of a given sublattice; the ionic polarization attributed to any given sublattice (defined as the product of the charge and the displacement) depends on the selected coordinates, whereas the total ionic polarization is independent of the selected coordinates.

The electron theories of spontaneous polarization, discussed earlier in the present chapter, are based on the assumption that the electron shells of atoms (or ions) are deformed spontaneously, and this gives rise to an elastic displacement of ions from their equilibrium positions. The supporters of the theory of ion displacements proceed in the opposite way: they assume that the displacements of ions are the cause and the electron dipole moments, appearing under the action of the internal fields, are the effect of the displacement of ions.

A calculation of the spontaneous polarization based on the displacements of ions requires a knowledge of these displacements (which we shall regard as static) and of the ion charges. Unfortunately, such a calculation can be carried out only for relatively simple structures, for which the values of the interval fields can be calculated.

Some authors have calculated the contribution of the ionic component to the total polarization of barium titanate and other ferroelectrics and antiferroelectrics with the oxygen-octahedral type of structure. A typical calculation of this type is given in the preceding subsection for $BaTiO_3$, taking into account only the displacements of the Ti ions. Thorough calculations of this type have been carried out for a large number of compounds (using computers) by G. S. Zhdanov and his colleagues [6].

The starting point in the calculations of Zhdanov et al. is the known or assumed model of the crystal structure. The lattice is assumed to consist of point charges (equal to the effective charges of ions)* to which we must add the point electron dipole moments

---

*If a crystal is not purely ionic, the degree of its "ionicity" can be described by the effective charge defined as the fraction of the charge pertaining to the ionic contribution to bonds.

(induced by the internal fields), whose magnitudes and directions are not known and must be determined. The values of the effective charges and the electronic polarizabilities are assumed to be known and the charges as well as the dipoles are assumed to be located at the actual displaced positions of ions in the lattice.

Zhdanov et al. calculated the fields in barium, lead, calcium, and cadmium titanates, as well as in sodium tantalate, lead zirconate, and in ABO_3 model crystals. The purpose of these calculations was to determine the influence of the polarizability, charges, and radii of ions on the distributions of the fields. The field gradients ΔE were calculated by Zhdanov et al. for $BaTiO_3$ and for ABO_3 crystals based on barium titanate; this has made it possible to study the influence of various parameters of the cations A and B on the field gradients at the positions of the ions.

Using the known charges and displacements of ions, the ionic contribution to the spontaneous polarization can be determined using the relationship

$$P_{ion} = e_i^{eff} \delta z_i, \qquad (VI.60)$$

where e_i^{eff} is the effective charge of an i-th ion and δz_i is the displacement of this ion.

The calculations of Zhdanov and his colleagues show that the sum of the ionic and electronic polarizations agrees with the experimentally determined spontaneous polarization if the effective charges is taken to be equal to half the purely ionic charge. This means that, in the case of $BaTiO_3$, the electronic contribution to the polarization is 30% and the ionic contribution is 70%. According to Slater, the ionic charge of titanium in $BaTiO_3$ is equal to the elementary electronic charge.

Analysis of the calculations of the ionic polarization shows that the ion-displacement model can be used quite satisfactorily in calculations of the spontaneous polarization of ferroelectrics of the oxygen–octahedral type. However, it must be stressed that because of the arbitrary nature of the selection of the effective ionic charge and the scarcity of data on the electronic polarizabilities of ions we can obtain (in the majority of cases) only qualitative information on the internal fields and on the various contributions to the polarization.

C. Models of Ferroelectrics Which Take into Account the Influence of Lattice Vibrations on the Polarization of Ions. "Polarizability" of Ions. Since isotopic substitution alters the temperatures of phase transitions and the values of the spontaneous polarization of ferroelectrics, it follows that lattice vibrations play an important role in the processes associated with the appearance of spontaneous electric polarization.

We shall consider first the fundamentals of two theories which take into account the lattice vibrations: the theory of local minima (or "jumping" ions) due to Mason and Matthias [52] and the theory of anharmonic oscillators due to Ginzburg [7, 8], Devonshire [38], and Slater [61] (see the review of Smolenskii and Isupov [20]).

These authors have made many assumptions and approximations in their calculations. A crystal is regarded as an assembly of point ions which are vibrating, in the absence of spontaneous polarization, independently of one another. They have considered a system of anharmonically vibrating ions since the phenomenon of ferroelectricity cannot be explained by assuming that ions vibrate harmonically, i.e., that they are held at their equilibrium positions by elastic restoring forces.

The potential energy U of an anharmonically vibrating ion can be represented in the form:

$$U = \frac{c}{2} x^2 + \frac{b}{4} x^4. \tag{VI.61}$$

For the sake of simplicity, we shall assume that ions are displaced only along one axis (X). The quantity x in Eq. (VI.61) denotes the displacement of an ion relative to the center of a unit cell, and b, c are coefficients (b is always positive, but c may be positive or negative). If $c > 0$, we are dealing with the usual case of an anharmonically vibrating ion whose elasticity coefficient is c and the anharmonicity coefficient is b. If $c < 0$, the potential energy minimum does not lie at $x = 0$ but at $x = \pm (-c/b)^{1/2} = \pm (|c|/b)^{1/2}$. This can be proved easily by finding the derivative dU/dx from Eq. (VI.61) and by equating this derivative to zero. This gives the potential-energy minimum ($d^2U/dx^2 > 0$). Thus, ions within a unit cell have several equilibrium positions corre-

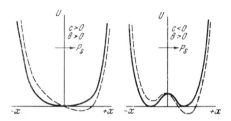

Fig. 143. Dependence of the potential energy U of an ion on its displacement x. The continuous curves correspond to Ps = 0 and the dashed curves correspond to $P_s \neq 0$.

sponding to the potential-energy minima. Since ions have a definite thermal energy, they can jump from one equilibrium position to another (hence, the term "jumping" ions). The dependence of the potential energy U of an ion on its displacement x is shown in Fig. 143.

So far, we have considered the displacements of ions at temperatures higher than the Curie point. We shall now deal with the displacements in the ferroelectric region. Several ions participating in the thermal motion can simultaneously be displaced in the same direction. This produces an internal field due to the displacements of these ions and of their electron shells. At the Curie point, the thermal motion is not very strong and the resultant internal field retains ions in their displaced positions. The slightest lowering of the temperature strongly increases the number of ions displaced along a given direction. This gives rise to the spontaneous polarization P_s.

In the presence of an internal field E' = $f P_s$ the potential of an ion is of the following form:

$$U = \frac{c}{2} x^2 + \frac{b}{4} x^4 - qE'x, \qquad (VI.62)$$

where q is the ion charge. The term −qE'x represents the change in the potential energy of the ion due to the appearance of the internal field. The force acting on a charge q, which is in an electric field E', is, of course, qE'. The work done by this force in displacing the charge through a distance x is qE'x. Consequently, the energy of the ion decreases by the same amount because the work is done at the expense of the energy of the system. The dependence of the potential energy of an ion on its displacement in the presence of the spontaneous polarization is also shown in Fig. 143.

We can use Eq. (VI.62) to find the displacement x of an ion corresponding to the potential-energy minimum in the ferroelectric region:

$$\frac{dU}{dx} = cx + bx^3 - qE',$$

$$cs + bs^3 - qE' = 0. \tag{VI.63}$$

We shall now transform Eq. (VI.63). We have shown that the internal field is $E' = f P_s$. The spontaneous polarization P_s is equal to the sum of the moments of the electric dipoles $p = qs$, resulting from the displacement of ions of charge q, i.e., $P_s = pN = qsN$, where N is the number of ions per 1 cm^3. It is assumed that only one ion species is displaced in a crystal and the displacement of the electron shells of the ions can be ignored. If the displacements of the electron shells are included, the spontaneous polarization is still proportional to the displacement of the ions, but the coefficient of proportionality is different. Thus, $E' = f qNs$ and

$$cs + bs^3 - fq^2Ns = 0. \tag{VI.64}$$

Hence,

$$s = 0 \quad \text{or} \quad s = \pm \sqrt{\frac{fq^2N - c}{b}}. \tag{VI.65}$$

Equation (VI.64) has a nonzero solution only when the radicand of Eq. (VI.65) is positive, and since b is always positive, it follows that a solution is obtained when

$$fq^2N > c. \tag{VI.66}$$

It follows from Eq. (VI.64) that, when $f q^2N > c$, a stable solution cannot be obtained for the displacement s of harmonically vibrating ions (b = 0).

Multiplying both sides of Eq. (VI.66) by s and using $f q^2Ns = f qpN = qf P_s = qE'$, we obtain the following inequality:

$$qE' > cs. \qquad\qquad (VI.67)$$

The condition (VI.67) is similar to the condition (VI.57), which postulates the "$4\pi/3$ catastrophe" in the theory of internal fields.
The right-hand side of the inequality (VI.67) is numerically equal
to the elastic restoring force, which appears when ions are displaced, and the left-hand side represents the force due to an internal field, i.e., the force due to the interaction of the dipoles
formed as a result of the displacement of ions.

Thus, the spontaneous polarization appears in those crystals
in which the dipole−dipole interaction force exceeds the elastic
force. If the ions in a crystal have several potential energy minima within one unit cell, the inequality (VI.67) is always satisfied, even when the internal field is weak, because $c < 0$ (naturally, in this case, we cannot speak of the elastic force and of the
elasticity coefficient).

In those cases when $c > 0$, the internal field must be strong
and the elasticity coefficient small. We have already mentioned
that a strong internal field may appear in a crystal when large
oxygen ions alternate, along some directions, with small multiply
charged cations. These conditions are satisfied in crystals with
the perovskite structure, in rhenium trioxide, in pyrochlore, and
in some other crystals. The elasticity coefficient is governed by
the unit-cell size and by the dimensions of ions; it depends on the
nature of the chemical bonds in crystals. In the great majority of
ferroelectrics of the oxygen-octahedral type a small cation (Ti^{4+},
Zr^{4+}, Nb^{5+}, Ta^{5+}, and W^{6+}) is surrounded by six oxygen ions.

The model of anharmonic oscillations has been developed
further by other workers, particularly by Smolenskii, Kozlovskii,
and Pasynkov. Thus, the condition for the appearance of the spontaneous polarization in a ferroelectric, given by Eq. (VI.67), has
been established by Smolenskii and Kozlovskii [22]. In the derivation of this condition, Smolenskii and Kozlovskii assumed that, in
the absence of the spontaneous polarization, the anharmonic vibrations of ions are independent and completely random. Actually, the
vibrations of ions in crystals are correlated and, therefore, Kozlovskii [14] has considered the opposite limiting case of a rigid
lattice of ions responsible for the polarization (ferroelectrically
active ions of Chap. II).

Kozlovskii [15] later investigated the dynamics of ionic lattices of ferroelectric crystals, including the correlation of the motion of ions, and considered the case corresponding to the theory of local minima and uncorrelated displacements as well as the case corresponding to the rigid displacement of a ferroelectrically active (Chap. II) lattice as a whole. In particular, Kozlovskii showed that the spontaneous polarization can appear also when the conditions for the displacement of a single ion are unfavorable. This happens because of the collective effect in which the displacement of a single ion causes displacements of its neighbors. Kozlovskii has suggested that all ferroelectrics can be divided into weakly and strongly correlated. The weakly correlated ferroelectrics should exhibit phase transitions of the second kind and the strongly correlated substances should exhibit phase transitions of the first kind. The application of Kozlovskii's theory to $BaTiO_3$ has made it possible to estimate the spontaneous polarization of a crystal in the tetragonal modification: the polarization is 26×10^{-6} C/cm^2, which is in agreement with the experimental value.

Considering the case of two sublattices capable of displacement, Kozlovskii concludes that if both are nonferroelectric, a crystal is not ferroelectric if the interaction between them is weak ("rigid" lattices) but if the interaction is strong, a ferroelectric transition of the second kind may be observed. In the case of two ferroelectrically active lattices, we can have two phase transitions of the first kind in the case of weak interaction and one transition of the second kind in the case of strong interaction. The case of diatomic ferroelectrically active molecules, in which correlation exists within the molecules but not between them, is regarded by Kozlovskii as corresponding to the phase transitions in Rochelle salt and its analogs. The different relationships between the elastic and effective-field forces in such crystals may give rise to different combinations of transitions, such as two transitions of the second kind, as observed experimentally for Rochelle salt.

Since it is difficult to find which of the sublattices of a ferroelectric crystal is active in the ferroelectric sense, it is necessary to take into account the anharmonicity of vibrations of all the ions. In this connection, we must mention that the "ferroelectric activity" of the titanium sublattice in $BaTiO_3$ is questioned by some workers. According to these workers, the strongly anharmonic vibrations are those of the oxygen and associated barium ions. In particular, Syrkin [24] investigated the potential relief of the titanium ions in $BaTiO_3$. He calculated the coefficients in the expansion of the potential energy of an ion in terms of small displacements, using elementary interaction laws and making no assumptions about the nature of the potential relief. Syrkin showed that only the oxygen ions have several local potential energy minima in a unit cell. The position of the titanium ion is stable (at the center of the unit cell). According to Syrkin, the position of Ba is even more stable. We must point out, however, that Syrkin's calculations are based on the assumption that barium titanate is purely ionic (it is very difficult to make allowance for the covalent binding).

Pasynkov [18] considered the theory of the appearance of spontaneous polarization on the assumption that all the ions in the lattice of a crystal are vibrating anharmonically. In particular, Pasynkov shows that a system of ferroelectrically active sublattices has a single transition point corresponding to the disappearance of the spontaneous displacements of these sublattices (relative to the symmetrical positions). However, difficulties are encountered when Pasynkov's general conclusions are applied to specific ferroelectrics.

Takagi [66] considered the problem of the spontaneous polarization of $BaTiO_3$ within the framework of the theory of anharmonic vibrations of lattices, assuming that different sublattices vibrate independently. He calculated the free energy of a crystal as the sum of the electrostatic energy of ions, the electron energy (including the dipole moment and the electron polarizability), the elastic energy due to displacements of the sublattices from their equilibrium positions, and the energy of lattice vibrations. An important specific result of Takagi's theory is the conclusion that the ferroelectric state of $BaTiO_3$ is slightly more favorable than the antiferroelectric state. A deficiency in Takagi's theory is that $BaTiO_3$ is considered as a purely ionic crystal, i.e., that the partial overlap of the electron shells of ions is ignored.

Pirenne [57] and Gibbs [43] used the concept of a dipole qs in a rectangular potential well to describe ferroelectrics which are not of the oxygen-octahedral type. This approximation is justified for an ion lighter than its neighbors (for example, for a hydrogen ion).

In the case of KH_2PO_4, the hydrogen ions in hydrogen bonds are described quantum-mechanically as particles in rectangular potential wells. This explains the strong isotopic effect in KH_2PO_4. The "polarizability" of ions is assumed to be the average value of the moment qs, per unit internal field. In order to obtain agreement with the phenomenological results, this "polarizability" of an oscillator is approximated by an expression inversely proportional to the temperature. The values of the energy levels of hydrogen, calculated using this approximation, are not in agreement with the experimental data.

In order to explain the phenomenological properties of Rochelle salt, it must be assumed that at first the "polarizability" increases with increasing temperature, then it passes through a maximum, and finally decreases again. It can be shown that an array of oscillators in a rectangular potential well can behave in this way if the bottom of the well is inclined in one direction in one half of the well and in another direction in the other half. The symmetry of KH_2PO_4 is in agreement with this model. Below a certain temperature the polarizability of such an array decreases with decreasing temperature because of the tendency to antipolarization (antiferroelectric properties). At higher temperatures the polarizability decreases with increasing temperature because of the occupation of higher and higher levels, which are polarized less strongly. However, according to this model, the high- and low-temperature paraelectric modifications should be structurally different, which has not been confirmed experimentally.

D. Spontaneous Polarization of Ferroelectrics Resulting from Structure Ordering. The dielectric properties of oxygen-octahedral ferroelectrics can be explained if one of the polarizabilities η has a weak linear temperature dependence (Chap. VII). This explains why the anharmonic oscillator models can be applied successfully to such ferroelectrics. The difficulties encountered in dealing with the properties of Rochelle salt KH_2PO_4, triglycine sulfate, and similar ferroelectrics indicate that the temperature dependence of the polarizability η should be different. It is known that above the Curie point (above the upper Curie point in the case of Rochelle salt) the macroscopic polarizability α of such ferroelectrics is inversely proportional to temperature. This indicates that a Langevin-type theory (see Introduction to the present chapter) can be used to describe the spontaneous polarization of ferroelectrics.

Such a theory is based on the assumption of the existence of permanent dipoles which may be oriented by an internal field. In polar liquids these dipoles are polar molecules. However, polar molecules capable of orientation cannot be identified in the lattice of a crystal. The equivalent of a polar molecule in a crystal may be an ion (of charge q), which can occupy two or more equilibrium positions. An example of such an ion is the hydrogen ion in the O–H...O bonds (Fig. 48) in triglycine sulfate, which can occupy two stable equilibrium positions at distances s from the center of the bond. This ion can be regarded as a pseudodipole p = qs, which can be oriented in two ways. An activation energy is required for transition from one equilibrium position to the other. The average value of the energy of such a pseudodipole, per unit internal field, obeys the law 1/T, and the orientation of pseudodipoles below the Curie temperature is determined by the ordering of ions. An increase in the spontaneous polarization of a crystal is then described by a function which depends on the total number and distribution of equilibrium positions of an ion forming a dipole.

This approach to the nature of the spontaneous polarization of Rochelle salt has been used by Kurchatov [16] as well as Mason [51b]. Their theory is based on a system of hydrogen bonds, determined by x-ray diffraction [31], and on the assumption of Ubbelohde and Woodward [68], that the hydrogen bond between the oxygen atoms (1) and (10) (Fig. 58) is responsible for the spontaneous polarization of Rochelle salt. However, we have mentioned in Chap. III that, according to recent information, it is more likely that the spontaneous polarization of Rochelle salt is due to the hydroxyl group $(OH)_5$ and the water molecule H_2O (8) (Fig. 58). However, this applies only to that part of the theory of Kurchatov and Mason which deals with calculations of the dipole moment and the barrier energy separating two equilibrium positions of a pseudodipole. According to Mason, a dipole has different energies in antiparallel positions, which corresponds to (for a unit cell containing four pairwise asymmetrical bonds 1-10) asymmetrical potential barriers, shown in Fig. 144. In the low-temperature paraelectric modification the pairs of dipoles are oriented antiparallel along the [100] axis, in the high-temperature paraelectric phase they are completely disordered, and in the ferroelectric range between the Curie temperatures they are oriented parallel (a similar explanation of the two Curie points of Rochelle salt has been given earlier by Fowler [42]).

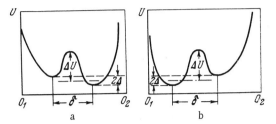

Fig. 144. Probable distribution of the potential along
a hydrogen bond in Rochelle salt in the case of non-
equivalence of particles in the bond: a, b) opposite
(antiparallel) distributions of nonequivalent particles
along the bond.

Using this model, Mason developed a theory based on the expression for the free energy in the form G = U−TS. Let us assume that 2N is the total number of dipoles per unit volume, that
$N(1 + n_1)/2$ is the number of dipoles corresponding to one potential
barrier (for example, that shown in Fig. 144a), and that $N(1 + n_2)/2$
is the number of dipoles oriented along the positive direction of the
a axis ([100]), which corresponds to the potential barrier of Fig.
144b. The polarization P can then be written in the form

$$P = Np(n_1 + n_2), \tag{VI.68}$$

where p is the dipole moment. If 2Δ is the difference between the
dipole energies for the two opposite orientations and f is the internal-field coefficient (used to express the energy of the interaction of the dipoles in the form $-fp^2/2$), the internal energy of a
crystal can be written

$$U = \frac{1}{2}fN^2p^2(n_1 + n_2)^2 + \Delta(2 + n_2 - n_1)N. \tag{VI.69}$$

Assuming that the energy S is only of the configurational type, the
expression for the free energy G can be written in terms of $(n_1 + n_2)$
and two constants α and β, given by the expressions

$$\alpha = \frac{fNp^2}{kT}, \qquad \beta = \frac{\Delta}{kT}. \tag{VI.70}$$

Having found the free-energy minimum, Mason obtains a non-
zero solution for $(n_1 + n_2)$ when the constants α and β satisfy certain conditions. When these conditions are satisfied, a crystal

should exhibit spontaneous polarization. Nevertheless, in order to calculate the two Curie temperatures, Mason is forced to assume that the dipole moment p depends on the temperature. However, this assumption makes it difficult to explain the presence of two Curie points of Rochelle salt at high pressures and constant volume.

Devonshire [40] has attempted to eliminate this deficiency of Mason's theory by assuming that the two positions of the hydrogen atom have different statistical weights. This corresponds to the assumption that the entropy S has not only a configurational term but also a term associated with vibrations, because − according to the classical representations − the hydrogen atom should have different vibration frequencies at its two equilibrium positions. Using this slight modification of Mason's theory, Devonshire has been able to explain the presence of two Curie points at constant volume. Nevertheless, Devonshire's theory cannot explain satisfactorily the broadening of the ferroelectric range of temperatures with increasing hydrostatic pressure.

Mitsui [54] describes the spontaneous polarization of Rochelle salt and isomorphous crystals using basically the model of Mason and Devonshire. He approaches more rigorously the calculation of internal fields by the use of two parameters (b and c) for the description of the interaction of dipoles (instead of a single parameter f employed by Mason and Devonshire). Mitsui's theory explains the behavior of Rochelle salt under hydrostatic pressure, but it remains qualitative because it does not give full information on the coefficients in the expansion of the free energy. Nevertheless, a suitable selection of the coefficients b and c gives good agreement between the calculated and experimental properties of several substances.

The mechanism of ordering of hydrogen ions in hydrogen bonds is the basis of a theory of KH_2PO_4 developed by Slater [60]. We have mentioned earlier that the structure of KH_2PO_4 consists of PO_4 tetrahedral groups, bound to neighboring groups of the hydrogen bonds $O-H...O$. Hydrogen ions have two equilibrium positions in each bond and these positions are located symmetrically with respect to the bond center (Fig. 56). According to Slater, the possible positions of the hydrogen ions obey the following rules: 1) each bond has only one hydrogen ion; 2) there are only two (out of four possible) hydrogen ions near each PO_4 group.

This means that the structure consists of H_2PO_4 groups (and, of course, K) and that the presence of molecular groups of the H_3PO_4 and $(HPO_4)^{2-}$ type is so unlikely that they can be ignored altogether. We can easily see that two hydrogen ions can be bound to the four oxygen ions of a PO_4 group in six ways. Because of the tetragonal symmetry, these six configurations are not equivalent. If the two hydrogen ions are closer to the two "upper" oxygen ions, the resultant H_2PO_4 group can then be regarded as a dipole oriented along the $-c$ axis. When the hydrogen ions are closer to the "lower" oxygen ions, this dipole is oriented along the $+c$ axis. These configurations are assumed to be energetically equivalent and are normalized to zero energy. The cases when one hydrogen ion is closer to the "upper" oxygen ion and the other hydrogen ion is closer to the "lower" oxygen correspond to dipoles oriented at right-angles to the c axis (there are four such configurations). These configurations are also energetically equivalent and associated with the energy parameter ε. In other words, it is assumed that the energy of a crystal in the absence of an external electric field is governed by the number of dipoles which are oriented perpendicular to the c axis, multiplied by the constant quantity ε. The electrostatic interaction is ignored. In the presence of an external field E, applied along the $+c$ axis, the energy of a crystal decreases:

$$U = N_0\varepsilon - (N_+ - N_-)pE, \qquad (VI.71)$$

where p is the dipole moment; N_0, N_+, and N_- are, respectively, the numbers of the H_2PO_4 dipoles oriented at right-angles to the c axis, along the $+c$ direction, and along the $-c$ direction; $N_0 + N_+ + N_- = N$ is the total number of the dipoles. Thus, the problem reduces to finding the function $W(N_+, N_-, N_0)$, which governs the order-disorder processes for each of the orientations. The solution of the problem gives an expression for the entropy of the system in the form $S = k \ln W(N_+, N_-, N_0)$, where k is the Boltzmann constant. Using thermodynamic relationships, we can now obtain the dielectric and thermal properties of potassium dihydrogen phosphate.

The free energy is written in the form $G(N_+, N_-, N_0) = U - TS$. The condition for a free-energy minimum makes it possible to eliminate N_0 and to express the free energy as a function of the variables $x = (N_+ - N_-)/N$. Figure 145 shows graphically the function $G(x)$ for the case $E = 0$; $x = \pm 1$ corresponds to the case of a

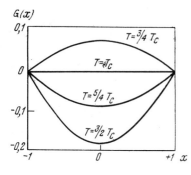

Fig. 145. Dependence of the free energy of KH_2PO_4 on the relative polarization at various temperatures (Slater's theory [60]).

completely polarized crystal and x = 0 represents an unpolarized crystal. The unpolarized state is stable at temperatures $T > T_c$ and the polarized state is stable at $T < T_c$. At the transition temperature T_c, a crystal transforms from the unpolarized to the totally polarized state.

Thus, analysis of the function W predicts directly the possibility of a phase transition whose temperature is given by the relationship

$$kT_c = \frac{\varepsilon}{\ln 2}. \qquad (VI.72)$$

The change in the entropy at the transition is $\Delta S = (R \ln 2)/2 = 0.69$ cal·mole^{-1}·deg^{-1}. The theory predicts also a further increase of the entropy above the transition temperature in a wide range of temperatures so that the total change in the entropy is estimated to be 0.805 cal·mole^{-1}·deg^{-1}. This change is in good agreement with the experimental data. A suitable selection of the coefficients p and ε gives good agreement between the calculated values of the spontaneous polarization (corresponding to saturation) and of the Curie temperature with the experimental data.

The nature of the phase transition which follows from Slater's theory is very special. It is a very unusual transition since every intermediate state between the totally polarized and totally unpolarized states is as stable as the initial and final stage. This transition is similar to a phase transition of the first kind in the sense that the polarization and energy change suddenly and the change indicates a latent heat of transition. On the other hand, the transition is analogous to a transition of the second kind because the changes are homogeneous so that each quantity varies continuously with time. We can regard Slater's transition as the limiting case of a phase transition of the second kind.

We have reported earlier that KH_2PO_4 undergoes a normal phase transition of the second kind and that this transition stretches over a finite (although narrow) range of temperatures. Slater has explained this departure from his theory by the presence of local inhomogeneities and stresses in a crystal, which give rise to different transition temperatures in different parts of a crystal. However, this assumption does not dispose of all the contradictions between Slater's theory and the experimental data on the phase transition in potassium dihydrogen phosphate. It can be shown that allowance for the piezoelectric effect does not help either. Only a weakening of Slater's conditions (1 and 2) can give rise to a phase transition of the second kind [67, 64a, 64b].

A serious deficiency in Slater's theory is its failure to explain the isotopic effect, i.e., the considerable increase of T_c when hydrogen is replaced by deuterium (the Curie point rises from 123°K to 213°K). Senko [59] has shown that the isotopic effect can be explained within the framework of Slater's theory by including the dipole–dipole interaction, but this variant of Slater's theory disagrees with the experimental data in other respects (temperature dependence of the spontaneous polarization and the value of the change in the entropy).

Attempts have also been made to consider the appearance of the spontaneous polarization as the structure ordering in ferroelectrics of the oxygen-octahedral type. We can mention here the theory of local minima due to Mason and Matthias [52].

Mason and Matthias assume that each titanium ion has six equilibrium positions in a unit cell and these positions correspond to local minima of the potential energy. Mason and Matthias conclude that because of this multiplicity of equilibrium positions the titanium –oxygen bond is partly covalent and the equilibrium position of the titanium ion is not at the center of an octahedron but slightly closer to one of the oxygen ions. Because of thermal motion the ions "jump" from one equilibrium position to another. At sufficiently high temperatures $(T > T_c)$, the thermal motion causes the average position of the titanium ion to coincide with the center of the octahedron. This cannot happen at $T < T_c$ because the energy of the thermal motion is insufficiently large and, therefore, the titanium ion is displaced toward one of the oxygen ions.

The dipole polarization P_d, due to the asymmetrical distribution of ions over the potential wells, is given by

$$P_d = Np \frac{\sinh(pF/kT)}{2 \cosh(pF/kT)}, \qquad (VI.73)$$

where F is the effective field; N is the number of unit cells per unit volume; p is the dipole moment of a unit cell. It is assumed that the effective field is

$$F = E + fP = \frac{E + fP_d}{1 - f\gamma}, \qquad (VI.74)$$

where f is the internal-field coefficient and γ is the polarizability due to all mechanisms, with the exception of the displacement of the titanium ion. This theory is semi-empirical because the coefficient f is not calculated but found from the experimental data.

The maximum value of the spontaneous polarization at low temperatures is found from the relationship

$$\frac{P_s^2}{Nk\theta} = \frac{3}{f(1 - f\gamma)}, \qquad (VI.75)$$

where θ is the reduced Curie temperature.

The value of $f(1 - f\gamma)$, estimated from the experimental data for $BaTiO_3$, is 0.032, which should be compared with 0.39 found from Eq. (VI.75) for $P_s = 26 \times 10^{-6}$ C/cm^2, N = 1.56×10^{22} cm^{-3}, $\theta = 380°K$; this shows that the theory disagrees strongly with the experimental data.

The Mason–Matthias theory also fails to yield reasonable values of the change in the entropy of the ferroelectric transition. A change in the state of the titanium ion (from six equiprobable positions to one) should change the entropy by k ln 6 = 1.79 relative units (per unit cell), which is 90 times larger than the experimental value. In addition to the simplicity of the phase-transition mechanism, which is discussed in the theory of spontaneous polarization of the oxygen-octahedral type of ferroelectrics, the Mason–Matthias theory has other deficiencies. In particular, nuclear resonance investigations of $KNbO_3$ have demonstrated that the position of the niobium ion at the center of the octahedron is the equilibrium position above the Curie point (Chap. II). This makes the model of "jumping" ions unacceptable in the theory of spontaneous polarization of the oxygen-octahedral type of ferroelectrics.

Klyachkin [13] treated the transitions giving rise to spontaneous polarization as the effects of statistical ordering in the space of ionic displacements. Klyachkin uses the statistical method of N. N. Bogolyubov [2]. His theory applies to ferroelectrics with the oxygen-octahedral type of structure. The states above and below the transition temperature are regarded as differing in the nature of their stability: the cubic structure should be observed in the region $T > T_c$ and the tetragonal structure should be found at temperatures $T < T_c$.

Klyachkin assumes that, in the cubic structure, ions vibrate harmonically (or anharmonically) at the cubic lattice sites in a potential field of cubic symmetry. This structure has a definite vibrational spectrum, quite different from that of the tetragonal structure. In the phase transition region, $T \sim T_c$, the structure is unstable. This permits displacements of individual ions from their equilibrium positions. At $T \sim T_c$ the equilibrium positions, relative to which vibrations take place, do not have the regular structure of the cubic or tetragonal lattice.

Using this model, Klyachkin considered the process of statistical ordering of ion displacements and the appearance of a new structure below the Curie point. According to his theory, the ordered state of $BaTiO_3$-type ferroelectrics corresponds to the tetragonal ordering of the equilibrium positions of the vibrating ions. In contrast to the averaging methods used for the Langevin dipole gas, Klyachkin carried out averaging not only over the directions but also over the dipole magnitudes.

The physical properties of a crystal were considered by Klyachkin using the potential energy of an ion in its displaced position. It is assumed that only one (out of five) $BaTiO_3$ sublattice is ordered. The dynamic criterion obtained by Klyachkin for the appearance of the spontaneous polarization is

$$c_\alpha^{kk} > c_\alpha^k, \qquad c_\gamma^k > 0, \qquad\qquad \text{(VI.76)}$$

where c_α^{kk} are the elastic moduli of the polarized modification of a sublattice of type k; c_α^k are the elastic moduli of the same sublattice, associated with the effects of interaction with all the other sublattices.

The results yielded by Klyachkin's theory are mainly of a qualitative nature. Klyachkin is unable to describe correctly the properties of $BaTiO_3$ using a single displaced sublattice. Nevertheless, Klyachkin's theory is free of some of the deficiencies of the theory of anharmonic oscillators which is based on the conventional representation of the ordering of ions.

§4. Ferroelectric Phase Transitions

in the Light of the Dynamic

Theory of Lattices

A. Elements of the Theory of Vibrations of the Crystal Lattice.* For the sake of simplicity, we shall consider first a chain consisting of particles of two different masses m_1 and m_2. We shall number these particles from 1 to 2N. Let us assume that the odd-numbered particles are of mass m_1 and the even-numbered are of mass m_2. We shall take the distance between neighboring particles to be $a/2$. Such a chain can be treated as a one-dimensional crystal with a basis. The equations of motion of the particles are of the form

$$m_1\ddot{u}_{2l+1} = -M\left[(u_{2l+1}-u_{2l})-(u_{2l+2}-u_{2l+1})\right],$$
$$m_2\ddot{n}_{2l} = -M\left[(u_{2l}-u_{2l-1})-(u_{2l+1}-u_{2l})\right],$$

(VI.77)

where u_{2l}, u_{2l+1}, u_{2l-1} are displacements of the particles from their equilibrium positions; M is the quasielastic force constant. These equations can also be written in the form

$$m_1\ddot{u}_{2l+1} = -2M\left(u_{2l+1}-\frac{u_{2l+2}+u_{2l}}{2}\right),$$
$$m_2\ddot{u}_{2l} = -2M\left(u_{2l}-\frac{u_{2l+1}+u_{2l-1}}{2}\right).$$

(VI.78)

*The theory of free vibrations of the crystal lattice was developed mainly by Born and his colleagues [34, 35].

We shall seek the solutions of these equations in the form of harmonic vibrations, forming traveling waves. Because of the difference between their masses, the amplitudes of vibrations of the two kinds of particles are different. The traveling waves along the X axis are written in the form

$$u_{2l+1} = Ae^{2\pi i(qx_{2l+2j}-vt)},$$

$$u_{2l} = Be^{2\pi i(qx_{2l}-vt)} . \tag{VI.79}$$

Here, q is the wave number ($q = 2\pi/\lambda$, where λ is the wavelength); v is the frequency ($\omega = 2\pi v$, where ω is the angular frequency); $x_{2l} = 2l$ a and $x_{2l+1} = x_{2l} + a/2$ are the coordinates of the equilibrium positions of the particles; A and B are, respectively, the amplitudes of the vibrations of particles of masses m_1 and m_2 (we shall assume that $m_2 > m_1$). The displacements of neighboring particles are related by the following expressions:

$$\left.\begin{array}{l} u_{2l} = u_{2l-1}\dfrac{B}{A}\,e^{-\pi iqa}, \\[2mm] u_{2l+2} = u_{2l+1}\dfrac{B}{A}\,e^{\pi iqa}, \\[2mm] u_{2l+1} = u_{2l}\dfrac{A}{B}\,e^{\pm\pi iqa}. \end{array}\right\} \tag{VI.80}$$

Double differentiation of Eq. (VI.79) yields

$$\ddot{u}_{2l} = -4\pi^2 v^2 u_{2l}. \tag{VI.81}$$

Substituting the values of the displacements u and the accelerations ü from Eq. (VI.79) into the equations of motion (VI.78), we obtain a relationship between the amplitudes of the vibrations of the particles:

$$\left.\begin{array}{l} (2\pi^2 m_1 v^2 - M)\,A + M\cos(\pi qa)\,B = 0, \\[2mm] M\cos(\pi qa)\,A + (2\pi^2 m_2 v^2 - M)\,B = 0. \end{array}\right\} \tag{VI.82}$$

Equations (VI.82) are compatible when

$$\begin{vmatrix} 2\pi^2 m_1 v^2 - M & M\cos(\pi qa) \\[2mm] M\cos(\pi qa) & 2\pi^2 m_2 v^2 - M \end{vmatrix} = 0. \tag{VI.83}$$

Writing out this determininant in full, we obtain the following equation for the frequency of the vibrations of the chain:

$$4\pi^4 v^4 - \frac{M(m_1 + m_2)}{m_1 m_2} 2\pi^2 v^2 + \frac{M^2}{m_1 m_2} \sin^2(\pi q a) = 0. \qquad (VI.84)$$

Solving this equation for $\omega = 2\pi v$, we obtain the dispersion relationship, which is the relationship between the angular frequency and the wave number q:

$$\omega^2 = \frac{M(m_1 + m_2)}{m_1 m_2} \pm \frac{M}{m_1 m_2} \sqrt{(m_1 + m_2)^2 - 4m_1 m_2 \sin^2(\pi q a)}. \qquad (VI.85)$$

Substituting the frequency of the vibrations into either of the expressions in Eq. (VI.82), we find the ratio of the amplitudes of the vibrations of particles of different masses:

$$\frac{B}{A} = -\frac{m_1 - m_2 \pm \sqrt{m_1^2 + m_2^2 + 2m_1 m_2 \cos(2\pi q a)}}{2M \cos(2\pi q a)}. \qquad (VI.86)$$

It is evident from Eq. (VI.85) that for every one value of the wave number q, we have two frequencies ω_+ and ω_- whose absolute values are different and which are obtained by choosing the plus or minus sign in front of the radical in Eq. (VI.85). The extreme values of q, which ranges from 0 to 1/2 a, correspond to the frequencies ω_+ and ω_-:

q	ω_-	ω_+
0	0	$\omega_1 + \omega_2$
$\dfrac{1}{2a}$	$\omega_1 = \dfrac{M}{\pi m_2}$	$\omega_2 = \dfrac{M}{\pi m_1}$

The two solutions obtained from Eq. (VI.85) correspond to two frequency modes or branches: the acoustical mode $\omega_- = \omega_-(q)$ and the optical mode $\omega_+ = \omega_+(q)$. When the wave number is reduced (the wavelength is increased) the frequency of the acoustical mode vibrations decreases to zero whereas the frequency of the optical mode increases and reaches a maximum. This is due to the different nature of the vibrations of neighboring particles. In the acoustical mode the neighboring particles vibrate in phase and the long wavelengths correspond to displacements of whole unit cells (Fig. 146a). In the optical mode the neighboring particles vibrate in antiphase. In this case, the long wavelengths correspond to vibrations within unit cells (Fig. 146b). These vibrations may

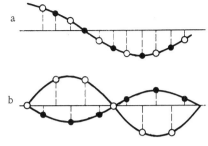

Fig. 146. Phases of vibrations of particles in the acoustical (a) and optical (b) waves.

be considered as relative vibrations of two translation lattices, consisting of particles of different kinds. It follows from Eq. (VI.86) that at q = 0 we have

$$\left(\frac{B}{A}\right)_- = 0, \qquad \left(\frac{B}{A}\right)_+ = \frac{m_1}{m_2}, \qquad (VI.87)$$

which is in agreement with the nature of the vibrations of the chain just described. In the acoustical mode the particles vibrate in phase and the vibrations are of the same amplitude for both types of particle. In the optical mode the particles vibrate in antiphase and the amplitude of the vibrations is inversely proportional to the particle mass. In the limit of very high values of the wave number q_{max}, we have

$$\left(\frac{B}{A}\right)_- = 0, \qquad \left(\frac{B}{A}\right)_+ = -\frac{m_2 - m_1}{m_1}. \qquad (VI.88)$$

In this case, the heavier particles remain at rest in the acoustical mode.

The existence of two different modes or branches in the vibration spectra of crystals is supported by the results obtained from the scattering of cold neutrons.

The theory of vibrations of a one-dimensional chain can be generalized to the case of three dimensions. In the case of a diatomic crystal (containing two atomic species) we have six branches of the function $\omega = \omega(q)$. Three of these are the acoustical modes and the other three are optical. A graphical representation of these modes is given in Fig. 147.

B. Lattice Dynamics and Ferroelectric Phase Transitions in Cubic Diatomic Crystals. Ginzburg

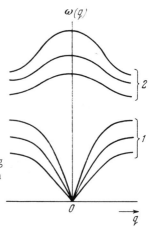

Fig. 147. Acoustical (1) and optical
(2) modes of the vibration spectrum
of a three-dimensional diatomic crystal. The dependences on q are actually three-dimensional. The curves
given here are the functions $\omega(q)$ along
straight lines passing through the origin
of coordinates.

[8, 9], Anderson [1], and Cochran [36] applied the basic theory of
crystal lattice dynamics to the dielectric properties of crystals,
particularly to ferroelectric and antiferroelectric phase transitions. The basic idea of this approach is to prove that, under certain conditions, at least one normal vibration mode can become
unstable. From this point of view, a ferroelectric transition is
the result of such an instability, which alters the structure of a
crystal and, therefore, gives rise to spontaneous polarization. After the transition the crystal again becomes stable.

Following Cochran [36], we shall consider, in principle, the
possibility of the appearance of an instability of the transverse
optical vibration mode in a cubic crystal. We shall apply our analysis specifically to NaCl- and CsCl-type structures. The dynamic
theory of crystal lattices shows that a crystal is stable with respect to small deformations if all its normal vibration modes have
real frequencies. The problem of finding the normal vibration
modes in terms of the force constants of the structures considered is simplified considerably if the wave vector q coincides with
one of the axes of symmetry, i.e., if it is parallel to one of the
[100], [110], or [111] directions. The case of q parallel along the
[100] direction is particularly simple. In this case, the displacements of the particles can coincide either with the [100] axis (the
longitudinal mode) or with the [010] or [001] axes (the transverse
modes). All the atoms in the (100) planes move in phase. The
quasielastic force constants for such vibrations represent the

coupling between the neighboring planes of atoms, and the problem
becomes similar to that of a linear chain considered in the preceding subsection. Three systems of equations similar to Eq.
(VI.77) give rise to a sixth-order determinant, which yields three
equations (each of the second order). One of these equations gives
the dispersion relationship for the longitudinal mode and the other two (identical) equations give the solutions for the two transverse modes. The problem can be simplified still further by assuming that $q = 0$. As in the preceding subsection, all the atoms
of a given species are in the same position in any one of these
modes and the only quasielastic force constant is that representing
the coupling between the two sublattices of Na (or Cs) and Cl atoms.

We shall now show that the frequency of normal vibrations
(the transverse optical mode, TO) can vanish. We shall employ
the shell model of a crystal, according to which each ion consists
of a core coupled by an anisotropic quasielastic force constant to
a shell formed by its outer electrons. We shall assume, for simplicity, that only the negative ions are polarized and that non-
Coulomb forces ("overlap" forces and covalent bonds) can act between the shells but not between the cores of the negative ions.
In this model we have three sublattices: 1) positive ions; 2) cores
of negative ions; 3) shells of negative ions. Their equations of
motion are of the form

$$\left. \begin{array}{l} m_1 \ddot{u}_1 = R_0 (v_2 - u_1) + \dfrac{4\pi}{3} PZe, \\[2mm] m_2 \ddot{u}_2 = k (v_2 - u_2) + \dfrac{4\pi}{3} PXe, \\[2mm] 0 = k (u_2 - v_2) + R_0 (u_1 - v_2) + \dfrac{4\pi}{3} PYe. \end{array} \right\} \qquad \text{(VI.89)}$$

Here, u_1, u_2, and v_2 are, respectively, the displacements of the
positive ions and of the cores and shells of the negative ions from
their respective equilibrium positions; Ze, Xe, and Ye are the
corresponding charges; e is the electronic charge; $X + Y + Z = 0$.
Apart from the Coulomb forces (associated with the polarization
P), we shall consider short-range forces described by the constants R_0 and k. The third equation of motion in the system (VI.89)
represents the case when the shells occupy the equilibrium positions corresponding to the instantaneous configurations of the
cores. The wave vector q can be regarded as directed along the
[100] axis and atoms are displaced along the [001] direction.

Assuming that $u_1 = \mathcal{U}_1 e^{-i\omega t}$ (similar expressions apply to u_2 and v_2) as well as $P = \mathcal{P}e^{-i\omega t}$, and substituting these expressions in the system (VI.89), we find that the third equation can be transformed into

$$\mathcal{P}\left\{1 - \frac{4\pi (Ye)^2}{2v (k + R_0)}\right\} = \frac{Z'e}{v} (\mathcal{U}_1 - \mathcal{U}_2). \qquad (VI.90)$$

In this equation $Z' = Z + YR_0/k + R_0 < Z$; v is the volume of one unit cell.

We shall now find the expression for the electronic polarizability of a crystal η_e. If the effective field acting in a dielectric is $E = \mathcal{E}_e e^{-ipt}$, where p is such a frequency at which the cores can be considered to be at rest, the condition for equilibrium of any shell assumes the form

$$\mathcal{E}Ye = (k + R_0) V_2,$$

and the polarization is given by the expression

$$\mathcal{P} = \frac{YeV_2}{v} ,$$

which shows that the electronic polarizability in the shell model is given by the relationship

$$\eta_e = \frac{Pv}{\varepsilon} = \frac{(Ye)^2}{k + R_0} . \qquad (VI.91)$$

It is known that, according to the Clausius–Mosotti equation, the expression for the high-frequency permittivity ε_e [see Eq. (VI.53)] is of the form

$$\frac{\varepsilon_e - 1}{\varepsilon_e + 2} = \frac{4\pi}{3v} \eta_e. \qquad (VI.92)$$

Using Eq. (VI.92), we can rewrite Eq. (VI.90) in the form

$$\mathcal{P} = \frac{Z'e (\varepsilon_e + 2) (\mathcal{U}_1 - \mathcal{U}_2)}{3v} . \qquad (VI.93)$$

Finally, using the expressions for $\mathcal{U}_1, \mathcal{U}_2$, and $\mathcal{P}$, and substituting Eq. (VI.93) into Eq. (VI.89), we obtain

$$\mu\omega_T^2 = R_0' - \frac{4\pi (\varepsilon_e + 2) (Z'e)^2}{9v}. \tag{VI.94}$$

We have used the following notation in the above equation:

$$\mu = \frac{m_1 m_2}{m_1 + m_2}; \qquad R_0' = \frac{kR_0}{k + R_0} < R_0.$$

The subscript T of ω indicates that we are considering the transverse optical mode.

The frequency of the longitudinal optical mode, corresponding to q = 0, can be found similarly, taking into account the macroscopic field $(-4\pi P)$ as well as the correction to the Lorentz field $4\pi P/3$. The final result is

$$\mu\omega_L^2 = R_0' + \frac{8\pi (\varepsilon_e + 2) (Z'e)^2}{9v\varepsilon_e}. \tag{VI.95}$$

It follows from Eq. (VI.94) that the frequency of the transverse optical (TO) mode in the type of crystal considered may indeed vanish when

$$R_0' = \frac{4\pi (\varepsilon_e + 2) (Z'e)^2}{9v}. \tag{VI.96}$$

We can show that the condition (VI.96) is equivalent to the "polarization catastrophe" (§ 2 in the present chapter) if we recall that the ionic polarizability α_i is given by the relationship

$$\alpha_i = \frac{(Z'e)^2}{R_0'}, \tag{VI.97}$$

and the quantity $(\varepsilon_e + 2)\alpha_i/3$ is equal to the total static polarizability $\alpha_s = \alpha_e + \alpha_i$. In this case, the condition (VI.57) becomes

$$\frac{4\pi}{3v} (\alpha_e + \alpha_i) = 1. \tag{VI.98}$$

Using the well-known relationship between the frequencies ω_T and ω_L and the permittivities [5, 25]

$$\frac{\omega_L^2}{\omega_T^2} = \frac{\varepsilon_s}{\varepsilon_e}, \tag{VI.99}$$

we can see that ω_T vanishes when the static permittivity becomes infinite: $\varepsilon_s = \infty$. This is a consequence of a ferroelectric phase transition resulting from the instability of the TO mode.

Going back to Eq. (VI.96), we note that in real diatomic alkali halide crystals the left- and right-hand sides of this equation are of the same order of magnitude, but R_0' is about twice as large as the right-hand side. This is why alkali halide crystals do not exhibit ferroelectric phase transitions.

The possibility of the instability of the TO mode in NaCl- or CsCl-type crystals does not mean that such a crystal is unstable with respect to other modes, even when the short-range forces act solely between the nearest neighbors. An analysis shows that inclusion of the interaction of the second-nearest neighbors makes the probability of the lattice instability more likely. However, in principle, when $q = 0$ (or when it is close to zero) we can have all the usual values of ω for all the modes, with the exception of the TO mode.

Taking the force constant R_0' to be about half the actual value for alkali halide crystals and using the actual polarizability and other parameters of NaCl, we can calculate the dispersion relationships for all the vibration modes. The results of such a calculation are presented in Fig. 148.

It is evident from Fig. 148 that most of the modes behave in a relatively normal manner but ω_T is close to zero near $q = 0$. Even a slight increase of R_0', compared with that used in this calculation, would increase ω_T and reduce ε_s to finite values.

So far, we have considered only the harmonic vibrations of the lattice. An allowance for the anharmonicity makes the parameters such as R_0' temperature-dependent. The inclusion of the anharmonicity makes it possible to find, in particular, the conditions for a phase transition, to determine the dependence $\varepsilon = \varepsilon(T)$, to find the transition temperature, etc.

If the crystal structure does not vary exponentially with time, a phase transition to a different modification should be accompanied by an increase of the frequency ω_T. This occurs when the short-range forces between the lattice atoms are not purely harmonic and isotropic. Considering the free energy of the crystal as a function of the displacement u and restricting our discussion to the displacements of the particles along the X axis, we can write

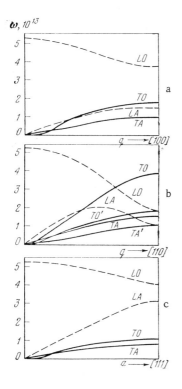

Fig. 148. Dependence of the frequency on the wave vector q oriented along: a) [100]; b) [110]; and c) [111] directions, respectively. The parameters governing $\omega(q)$ are selected so that the TO frequencies are zero at q = 0.

the restoring elastic force in the form

$$F_{\text{elast}} = R'u + Bu^3 + B'u^5.$$

The displacing Coulomb force, considered as a function of u, is of the form

$$F_{\text{Coul}} = \frac{4\pi \, (\varepsilon_e + 2) \, (Z'e)^2 u}{9v}.$$

These two forces are shown graphically in Fig. 149. The curvature of the dependence of the elastic force on u is exaggerated and the coefficient B is assumed to be negative. According to Eq. (VI.94), the value of ω_T^2 is proportional to the difference of the slopes of the two curves at the origin of the coordinates in Fig. 149, whereas ε_s is inversely proportional to the difference of these slopes. When the temperature is lowered, the slope of the curve representing the Coulomb force increases until the two curves intersect at some value u_{trans} . Near the value of u_{trans} we

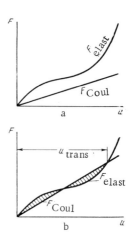

Fig. 149. Dependence of the elastic restoring force F_{elast} and of the
displacing Coulomb force F_{Coul} on
the displacement u above the transition temperature (a) and at the
transition temperature (b), as given
by Cochran [36].

can have stable but anharmonic vibrations of the two lattices. This
case corresponds to a phase transition to the tetragonal modification accompanied by the appearance of spontaneous polarization.
However, this transition does not take place until the free energies
of both phases become equal. This equality is represented graphically by the equality of the areas of the dashed regions in Fig.
149b. Above T_c (transition temperature) the crystal is stable, between T_c and θ (reduced Curie temperature) it is metastable, and
below θ it is unstable. Because of this instability the crystal transforms to the tetragonal modification.

We note that a similar treatment of a phase transition has already been given in the phenomenological discussion of the models of anharmonic oscillators (§3 in the present chapter), but here
the interpretation of the transition is somewhat different. We must
point out that Cochran has been able to relate the macroscopic parameters α^*, β, and γ [used in an expansion of the (VI.22) type]
to the atomic parameters. We have mentioned that, by selecting
the macroscopic parameters in a suitable manner, we can pre-
dict the three consecutive phase transitions for $BaTiO_3$ which give
spontaneous polarization directed along the [100], [110], and [111]
axes, respectively. Having found the relationship between the ma-
cro- and microparameters, Cochran ahows that a suitable selection of the parameters yields dielectric properties of a diatomic
crystal which are in good agreement with the properties of barium
titanate.

The instability of a particular vibration mode in a crystal can also explain transitions accompanied by the appearance of the polarization along the [110] and [111] directions. In the first case, the quantities $(R_0')_x$ and $(R_0')_y$ increase continuously, $(\varepsilon_s)_x$ decreases continuously, and the corresponding transverse optical frequency increases with decreasing temperature and increasing u_2. However, this frequency has a tendency to saturation and its temperature dependence is similar to the temperature dependence of the spontaneous polarization $P_s(T)$ given in Fig. 150. Unlike the restoring force, the electrostatic interaction increases continuously and this gives rise to a new instability of the transverse optical mode with the displacement vector directed along the [110] axis. The resultant transition is accompanied by an increase in all the values of ω_T. A similar analysis can be carried out also for the displacements along the [111] direction, which give rise to the third transition.

This analysis of ferroelectric phase transitions in diatomic crystals of the NaCl- or CsCl-type has been carried out by making some approximations. In particular, the introduction of anharmonic terms in the restoring force disturbs the "normality" of the modes and we must remember that only when the modes are normal can we ignore modes other than ω_T in the description of the properties of a crystal at phase-transition points. However, our discussion shows that the anharmonic terms have practically no

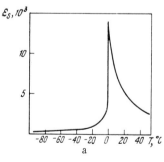

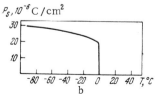

Fig. 150. Theoretical temperature dependences of the static permittivity ε_s (a) and of the spontaneous polarization P_s (b) in the region of a transition of BaTiO$_3$ from the cubic to tetragonal modification (Cochran [36]).

influence on the modes whose frequencies are higher than ω_T . Here again, we are assuming that only the frequencies with wave numbers close to zero change significantly at a phase transition.

Born and Huang [3] show that when an allowance is made for the retardation of the electrostatic interaction, the limiting frequency ω_T does not correspond to the infinite wavelength ($q = 0$) but to a wavelength small compared with the size of a crystal but large compared with the dimensions of a unit cell. For long wavelengths we now have two TO modes, one of which becomes identical with ω_L for $q = 0$, and the other vanishes. Hence, we may conclude that the instability of a crystal appears first in the case of the mode whose wavelength is comparatively large but smaller than the size of a crystal.

C. Lattice Dynamics and Properties of Barium Titanate. Cochran [36] has used the data on the lattice dynamics of diatomic crystals (see preceding subsection) and his own experimental data on the dielectric properties of cubic crystals in an analysis of some characteristics of transitions in $BaTiO_3$. He has considered the dimensions of five sublattices (the sublattices of barium and titanium and the three sublattices of oxygen). Taking into account the equivalence of two of the oxygen sublattices, the rank of the matrix of the force constants in equations of the (VI.89) type can be reduced to 4. This means that there should be only four transverse modes of different frequencies in $BaTiO_3$ at $q = 0$, and one of them is acoustical, whereas the other three are optical. The same is also true of the longitudinal modes. Thus, $BaTiO_3$ should have three "infrared-active" transverse vibration modes.

The problem of $BaTiO_3$ can be simplified still further by assuming that, in accordance with the structure data (Chap. II), its oxygen framework is practically undisturbed by a phase transition. This allows us to assume that the oxygen atoms are bound by relatively strong covalent bonds because, in the case of a transition involving displacements of other atoms along the [001] direction, the effective fields for the oxygen atoms along the line of displacement should be different. Structure investigations thus show that it is practically certain that all the oxygen cores move together in the lower-frequency TO mode. This makes it possible to reduce the rank of the matrix of the coefficients of this mode by unity. Moreover, taking into account the characteristics of the covalent bonds of the oxygen atoms via titanium (assuming that the titanium shell is more strongly bound to the shells of the surrounding oxygen atoms than to the titanium core), Cochran shows that the rank of the matrices of all the force constants (for all the modes) can be reduced from 4 to 3. The problem then simplifies and reduces to the problem of the dielectric properties of diagonal-cubic crystals solved by Cochran.

The theoretical atomic parameters are selected so as to satisfy the experimentally determined properties of $BaTiO_3$. Cochran uses the following parameters: $C^{**} = 4.57 \times 10^{-5}$ cgs esu $[\alpha^* = C^{**}(T - T_c)$, where α^* is a coefficient in the expansion of Eq. (VI.22)], $B = 7.81 \times 10^{20}$ cgs esu, $B' = 5.83 \times 10^{38}$ cgs esu, $R'_{11} = R'_{22} = 2.83 \times 10^5$ dyn/cm, $Z'_1 = 1.20$, $Z'_2 = 2.40$ (the subscripts 1 and 11 refer to barium atoms and the subscripts 2 and 22 refer to titanium atoms). Using these values, Cochran estimates the coefficients β and γ in the expansions of the (VI.22) type at the temperature of transition from the cubic to the tetragonal modification: $\beta = -10.5 \times 10^{13}$ egs esu, $\gamma = 2.30 \times 10^{-22}$ cgs esu, which are practically identical with the experimental values (§2 in the present chapter). Cochran also estimates the permittivity at T_c, which is $\varepsilon_s = 1.4 \times 10^4$ (Fig. 150a), and the spontaneous polarization at the Curie point, $P_s = 19.5 \times 10^{-6}$ C/cm^2 (Fig. 150b), which are very close to the experimental values. The temperature dependence of the spontaneous polarization, calculated by Cochran (Fig. 150b), is very close to the experimentally determined dependence (Fig. 113b). These results indicate that Cochran's theory explains quite satisfactorily many properties of $BaTiO_3$. Moreover, the parameters used in Cochran's calculations have reasonable values.

The most interesting new result of the theory of ferroelectrics, based on lattice dynamics, is the prediction of the absolute value of ω_T for perovskite-type materials. Using Eq. (VI.99), Cochran estimates this frequency to be $\nu_T = (2\text{-}3) \times 10^{11}$ cps $(\nu_T = \omega_T/2\pi)$. Moreover, Cochran analyzes his relationship

$$\frac{\varepsilon_s - \varepsilon_e}{4\pi} = v \sum_j \frac{\mathscr{P}_j^2}{\mathfrak{H}\omega_j^2},$$
(VI.100)

which, combined with an allowance for the fact that the relative displacements of atoms in an applied field are almost identical with the displacements in the low-frequency vibration mode (j = 2), yields

$$\varepsilon_s \, (\omega_2)^2_T = \frac{4\pi v \, P^2}{\sigma} \bullet \qquad\qquad (VI.101)$$

In the above equation $(\omega_2)_T$ and ε_s refer to the cubic modification (at any temperature above the transition point); the spontaneous polarization P and $\sigma = \sum_k m_k u_k^2$ (m is the mass of an atom and u its displacement) refer to the tetragonal modification. In connection with Eq. (VI.101) we must point out that if the anharmonic terms in the short-range forces are small (this has been demonstrated theoretically, as shown earlier), a crystal retains the values of P and u corresponding to j = 2 at the time of the transition and below the transition temperature. This means that Eq. (VI.101) describes quite satisfactorily a constant which is independent of the temperature below the phase-transition point. Using the following experimental values of the quantities occurring in Eq. (VI.101): $\sigma = 0.693 \times 10^{-40}$ g·cm², P = 6.6×10^4 cgs esu, $\varepsilon_s = 1.2 \times 10^4$, Cochran estimates that $v_T = 3.2 \times 10^{11}$ cps.

Theoretical analyses of the infrared absorption spectra on the basis of the lattice dynamics of perovskite structures have been carried out also by other workers. Thus, back in 1957 Last [50] concluded that perovskite structures of the $BaTiO_3$ and $SrTiO_3$ type should have three triply degenerate bands in the infrared part of the spectrum. The three normal modes suggested by Last correspond to stretching the Ti−O bond in the TiO_3 group (this is the highest frequency, equal to about 1.8×10^3 cps), bending of the Ti−O bond in the same group (this frequency is about 1.2×10^{13} cps), and vibrations of the cation−TiO_3 group (the lowest frequency), estimated to be about 6.8×10^{12} cps. Rajagopal and Srinivasan [58] have solved this problem taking into account the interaction only of the nearest atoms and ignoring the Coulomb interaction, and they concluded that the vibrational spectrum of $SrTiO_3$ should have four fundamental frequencies. According to Rajagopal and Srinivasan, Last ignored a frequency of about 1.3×10^{13} cps (445 cm⁻¹), which they ascribe to one of the vibrational modes of the TiO_3 group. Rajagopal and Srinivasan estimate the lowest frequency to be 2.2×10^{12} cps, which is approximately one-third of the value suggested by Last and an order of magnitude higher than the lowest value of v estimated by Cochran.

A thorough theoretical analysis of the infrared spectra of BaTiO$_3$ was carried out by Dvořák and Janovec [41]. They have calculated the frequencies of normal vibrations (for the wave vector q = 0) and have shown that a purely ionic cubic crystal of BaTiO$_3$ would be dynamically unstable. The condition of the dynamic stability of this crystal is achieved only due to the presence of some covalence of the bonds (as expressed in terms of the effective charges of ions). According to their estimates, barium titanate is stable if the effective charges of the titanium and oxygen ions are not higher than 0.162 of purely ionic charge. These values are considerably lower than the effective charge of 0.5, used in estimates of the spontaneous polarization discussed in § 2 of the present chapter. Dvořák and Janovec have found four normal vibration modes for cubic BaTiO$_3$ and, according to them (in contrast to the conclusions of Rajagopal and Srinivasan) there are only three infrared active modes, with frequencies of 1.07×10^{13}, 1.32×10^{13}, and 4.27×10^{13} cps. Their interpretation of these modes is different from that which will be discussed later, except for the lowest-frequency mode whose interpretation is similar to that given in the preceding paragraphs. Moreover, Dvořák and Janovec show that the lowest optical frequency depends considerably on the Coulomb interaction force. According to their estimate, this frequency is 1.72×10^{12} cps for BaTiO$_3$. This value is again considerably higher than that suggested by Cochran.

The frequency of the low-frequency dispersion of BaTiO$_3$, estimated by Cochran to be $(2-3) \times 10^{11}$ cps, lies in the millimeter wavelength range, which is difficult to investigate.

For this reason an experimental check of this theory has not been carried out until recently. Moreover, new investigations have recently been made in the infrared part of the spectrum. The first studies of BaTiO$_3$ powders and crystals were carried out by Last in 1957 [50] and by Yatsenko in 1958 and 1960 [28a, 28b] (see Chap. II). Last found two absorption bands at 1.2×10^{13} and 1.62×10^{13} cps. Yatsenko found four frequencies: 1.2×10^{13}, 1.72×10^{13}, 3.09×10^{13}, and 3.8×10^{13} cps. Dvořák and Janovec do not share the view of Last and Yatsenko that the frequencies 1.2×10^{13} and $\sim 1.7 \times 10^{13}$ cps represent internal vibrations of the TiO$_3$ group. Dvořák and Janovec regard the frequency 3.09×10^{13} cps as the first harmonic of 1.72×10^{13} cps and they consider the frequency 3.8×10^{13} cps to represent an independent normal frequency of vibrations of the TiO$_6$ octahedra.

Last has found two lines at 1.2×10^{13} and 1.8×10^{13} cps for SrTiO$_3$. Narayanan and Vedam [56] investigated the Raman spectra and found two more vibrational modes: one corresponding to the lowest frequency of 2.7×10^{12} cps and the other (1.3×10^{13} cps) to one of the vibration modes of the TiO$_3$ group. The most interesting of these is the first (low-frequency) mode, its occurrence having been confirmed in later investigations.

Barker and Tinkham [30] investigated the vibrational modes of SrTiO$_3$ in the infrared region by studying the reflection spectra in the frequency range 7.5×10^{10}-21×10^{13} cps (between 7.5×10^{10} and 2.3×10^{11} cps Barker and Tinkham used the klystron technique). They used their results to calculate the real and imaginary components of the permittivity ε. They found a very strong loss peak at 3.2×10^{12} cps at room temperature, which shifts in the direction of lower frequencies when the crystals are cooled (1.2×10^{12} cps at $-180°$C). According to Barker and Tinkham, the intensity of the vibrational mode, corresponding to the absorption peak, is fairly high and represents more than 90% of the low-frequency permittivity. This behavior of the low-frequency mode (reduction of the frequency with decreasing temperature) and its contribution to the static permittivity are of considerable interest in the theory of spontaneous polarization based on lattice dynamics because, according to numerous investigations, SrTiO$_3$ approaches a ferroelectric phase transition when its temperature approaches absolute zero.

The dispersion of the permittivity of BaTiO$_3$, SrTiO$_3$, and TiO$_2$ crystals was deduced by Spitzer et al. [62] from the reflection spectra in the frequency range 2.1×10^{12}-3.5×10^{13} cps. Spitzer et al. have found and investigated three room-temperature infrared bands for each of these crystals. The frequencies of these bands are 1.3×10^{12}, 5.4×10^{12}, and 1.5×10^{13} cps for BaTiO$_3$; for SrTiO$_3$ they are 2.7×10^{12}, 5.3×10^{12}, and 1.6×10^{13} cps. Of greatest interest are the low-frequency bands which are in agreement with the results of Narayanan and Vedam [56] and of Barker and Tinkham [30] obtained for SrTiO$_3$. It is worth noting that the low-frequency bands for the two titanates (one of which $-$BaTiO$_3$$-$ is ferroelectric) have very different frequencies, whereas the other bands do not differ greatly in frequency. This low-frequency mode is attributed by Spitzer et al. [62] to a strong frequency dependence of the permittivity (observed for these crystals) and to the high low-frequency value of ε. It is interesting to note that Spitzer et al. do not agree with the interpretations given by other workers. Thus, they attribute the frequencies of 1.5×10^{13} and 1.3×10^{12} cps of $BaTiO_3$ to the vibrations of the TiO_6 octahedra and the frequency of 5.4×10^{12} cps is assigned to the vibrations of cations relative to the TiO_6 octahedra.

Murzin and Demeshina [17] carried out similar investigations on polycrystalline samples of $BaTiO_3$ and $SrTiO_3$. They studied the reflection spectra in the frequency range 3×10^{11}-1.5×10^{14} cps in the temperature range 45-140°C. The reflection spectra of both compounds are found to have a band with a maximum at 1.6×10^{13} cps, as well as a broad plateau in the 3×10^{11}-1.4×10^{13} cps range. When the temperature is increased, Murzin and Demeshina find that the spectrum of $BaTiO_3$ exhibits an increase in the reflection coefficient in the frequency range 3×10^{11}-1.5×10^{12} cps as well as some change in the coefficient near 5.4×10^{12} cps. In order to determine the true spectral dependences of the optical and dielectric constants, the reflection spectra are analyzed using an electronic computer and the Kramers–Kronig integral relationship. These calculations indicate resonance vibrations of the crystal lattice of $SrTiO_3$ and near-relaxation vibrations for $BaTiO_3$. An increase in temperature shifts the loss maximum and the resonance frequency of the low-frequency vibrations of $BaTiO_3$ in the direction of lower frequencies. This is in agreement with the nature of changes in the low-frequency vibrations of a crystal in the ferroelectric region, deduced theoretically from lattice dynamics.

In conclusion, we must mention that although the experimental values of ν of the low-frequency mode, $\sim (1.2-2.7) \times 10^{12}$ cps, exceed by an order of magnitude the frequency deduced theoretically by Cochran from the dynamic theory of lattices, the experimental results can still be regarded as some justification of this theory. The dynamic lattice theory of ferroelectricity is supported also by the fall of the frequency of these vibrations on approach to the Curie point, as reported in several papers.

This discussion, like other published analyses, is concerned with cubic ferreroelectrics of the perovskite structure. However, there is no reason to suppose that the fundamentals of this theory cannot be extended to other crystals. We may assume that ferroelectric and antiferroelectric phenomena are, in general, associated with the lattice dynamics and that the high permittivity is always associated with the optical low-frequency mode. However, an analytic approach to the problem of low-symmetry crystals is very difficult or even impossible. Moreover, in some cases (for example, Rochelle salt), the symmetry of a crystal shows that there cannot be any purely transverse or purely longitudinal vibrations. Consequently, in such cases the frequency of the optical vibrations at $q \rightarrow 0$ will not coincide with the frequency of dielectric dispersion. Nevertheless, Rochelle salt satisfies, for example, the relationship $\omega^{-2} \propto \varepsilon_s$, where ε_s is the permittivity of a clamped crystal and ω is the lowest dispersion frequency. In this connection we must recall the results of investigations of the infared and Raman spectra of triglycine sulfate given in Chap. II. We have mentioned there that the frequencies of some of the lines increase with increasing temperature above the Curie point, whereas a reduction in their frequency would be more natural.

§5. Sublattice Polarization
and Phase Transitions
in Antiferroelectrics

Phase transitions in antiferroelectrics are also accompanied by the appearance or disappearance of spontaneous polarization. In the antiferroelectric modification of a crystal each unit cell of the paraelectric phase (subcell) is spontaneously polarized although the crystal as a whole shows no macroscopic spontaneous polarization. This is because the dipole moments of the subcells in the multiple unit cell compensate each other exactly. For this reason, it is usual to speak of the antipolarization of antiferroelectrics or of polarization of their sublattices ("substructures").

From the phenomenological point of view, an antiferroelectric modification is formed when the state with the antiparallel polarization of neighboring unit cells has a lower energy than the state with the parallel polarization. This allows us to consider antiferroelectrics as a subclass of ferroelectrics. Such a point of view has already been put forward in Chap. II, where we have stated that antiferroelectrics can be regarded as ferroelectrics with domain dimensions equal to one unit cell of the paraelectric modification.

A. Thermodynamic Description. The possibility of the existence of antiferroelectrics and some of their special properties were predicted by Kittel [48] before such compounds were discovered experimentally. For simplicity, we shall consider a crystal lattice which can be separated into two simple identical and interpenetrating sublattices a and b. Their polarizations (dipole moments per unit volume) will be denoted by P_a and P_b and the local fields acting on these sublattices will be denoted by E_a. Then,

$$E_a = E + f_1 P_a + f_2 P_b,$$
$$E_b = E + f_1 P_b + f_2 P_a, \qquad (VI.102)$$

where E is the external field; f_1 and f_2 are the Lorentz factors which can be calculated from the lattice geometry. We thus obtain

$$E_a = k P_a, \qquad E_b = k P_b, \qquad (VI.103)$$

$$\left. \begin{array}{l} k P_a = E + f_1 P_a + f_2 P_b, \\ k P_b = E + f_1 P_b + f_2 P_a; \end{array} \right\} \qquad (VI.104)$$

k is a coefficient related to the polarizability of the particles η by the expression k = $(N\eta)^{-1}$, where N is the number of particles per 1 cm^3. In a zero field (E = 0) the system (VI.104) becomes

$$\left. \begin{array}{l} (f_1 - k) P_a + f_2 P_b = 0, \\ f_2 P_a + (f_1 - k) P_b = 0. \end{array} \right\} \qquad (VI.105)$$

These equations have nonzero solutions when

$$\begin{vmatrix} (f_1 - k) & f_2 \\ f_2 & (f_1 - k) \end{vmatrix} = 0. \qquad (VI.106)$$

These solutions are

$$k = f_1 \pm f_2. \qquad (VI.107)$$

One of the solutions given by Eq. (VI.107) should correspond to the ferroelectric state. Adding the equation of the system (VI.104), we obtain

$$(P_a + P_b)(k - f_1 - f_2) = 2E; \qquad (VI.108)$$

the polarizability α is now given by

$$\alpha = \frac{P_a - P_b}{E} = \frac{2}{k - f_1 - f_2}. \qquad (VI.109)$$

The solution $k = f_1 + f_2$ corresponds to $\alpha \rightarrow \infty$, which indicates the existence of a macroscopic spontaneous polarization, i.e., it corresponds to the ferroelectric state. In this state $P_a/P_b = 1$. The solution $k = f_1 - f_2$ gives $P_a/P_b = -1$, which corresponds to the antiferroelectric state.

When the temperature is increased sufficiently, antiferroelectric crystals transform (like ferroelectrics) to the paraelectric state, i.e., the thermal motion destroys the orientation established by the internal fields. Transitions are also observed between the antiferroelectric and ferroelectric modifications. A thermodynamic discussion of these transitions can yield the principal relationships which govern them.

Following Kittel, we shall assume that near a transition point the free energy of a crystal consisting of two sublattices can be represented in the form of a series in powers of P_a and P_b right up to terms of the sixth order:

$$G - G_0 = \alpha_1^* (P_a^2 + P_b^2) + \alpha_2^* P_a P_b + \beta (P_a^4 + P_b^4)$$
$$+ \gamma (P_a^6 + P_b^6) + \ldots ; \qquad (VI.110)$$

here, G_0 has the value of the free energy in the case of zero polarization; α_1^*, α_2^*, β, and γ are the coefficients of the expansion, which depend on temperature. The external electric field E is assumed to be zero; the treatment is carried out ignoring the anisotropy and deformations. Not all the fourth- and sixth-order terms are included in Eq. (VI.110). These deficiencies of Kittel's theory were eliminated later by Smolenskii and Kozlovskii [23], but the results of Kittel still describe satisfactorily the basic properties of phase transitions and, therefore, we shall use Kittel's expansion.

In the absence of an external electric field an antiferroelectric satisfies the relationship $P_a = -P_b$ and, therefore, Eq. (VI.110) can be written in the form

$$G - G_0 = (2\alpha_1^* - \alpha_2^*) P_a^2 + 2\beta P_a^4 + 2\gamma P_a^6. \qquad (VI.111)$$

An analysis of this expression, similar to that given in §2 of the present chapter, yields some information on the dependence of the nature of a transition on the signs of the coefficients. The results of such an analysis show that, if $2\alpha_1^* - \alpha_2^* > 0$, G has a minimum at the point $P_a = 0$ (Fig. 138A); if $2\alpha_1^* - \alpha_2^* < 0$, G has a maximum at the same point, but it also has a minimum at some value $P_a \neq 0$ (Fig. 138B). Thus, when the sign of the quantity $2\alpha_1^* - \alpha_2^*$ changes from negative to positive with temperature, we should observe an antiferroelectric phase transition.

The nature of this transition is governed by the signs of the other coefficients. Let us assume that $\beta > 0$ and $\gamma > 0$. It follows that the only solution of the equation

$$\frac{\partial G}{\partial P_a} = 2(2\alpha_1^* - \alpha_2^*) P_a + 8\beta P_a^3 + 12\gamma P_0^5 = 0 \qquad \text{(VI.112)}$$

which satisfies $2\alpha_1^* - \alpha_2^* > 0$ is $P_a = 0$. Let us assume that near the transition point

$$2\alpha_1^* - \alpha_2^* = \lambda(T - T_c), \qquad \text{(VI.113)}$$

where T_c is the transition temperature. At $T > T_c$ the solution of Eq. (VI.112) is $P_a = 0$. When the temperature is lowered so that $T < T_c$ and $2\alpha_1^* - \alpha_2^* < 0$, the solution of Eq. (VI.112) can be $P_a \neq 0$:

$$P_a^2 = \frac{-2\beta + \sqrt{4\beta^2 - (2\alpha_1^* - \alpha_2^*) 6\gamma}}{6\gamma}. \qquad \text{(VI.114)}$$

Near the transition point but at $T < T_c$, we have

$$P_a^2 = -\frac{2\alpha_1^* - \alpha_2^*}{4\beta}. \qquad \text{(VI.115)}$$

Using Eq. (VI.113), we obtain

$$P_a^2 = \frac{\lambda(T_c - T)}{4\beta}. \qquad \text{(VI.116)}$$

Thus, if $\beta > 0$ and $\gamma > 0$, we have a phase transition of the second kind.

Let us now assume that $\beta < 0$. Then, in the case of fairly small positive values of $2\alpha_1^* - \alpha_2^*$ the free energy varies with P_a

as follows: it increases from a minimum at zero polarization, then decreases to a minimum at some value $P_a \neq 0$, and then again increases (Fig. 138C). At some temperature (corresponding to a small but positive value of $2\alpha_1^* - \alpha_2^*$) the minimum at $P_a \neq 0$ becomes less deep than the minimum at $P_a = 0$ and the system changes suddenly from the state with $P_a = 0$ to the state with $P_a \neq 0$. This is a phase transition of the first kind.

Let us now calculate the change in the spontaneous polarization in such a transition. It follows from the equality of the thermodynamic potentials before and after the transition that

$$(2\alpha_1^* - \alpha_2^*) P_a^2 + 2\beta P_a^4 + 2\gamma P_a^6 = 0, \tag{VI.117}$$

and, using Eq. (VI.112), we obtain

$$\left. \begin{aligned} P_a^2 &= \frac{\alpha_2^* - 2\alpha_1^*}{\beta}, \\[2ex] P_a^4 &= \frac{2\alpha_1^* - \alpha_2^*}{2\gamma}. \end{aligned} \right\} \tag{VI.118}$$

Let us now consider in more detail the phase transitions of the first and second kind. We shall discuss first the behavior of the spontaneous polarization P and of the polarizability α near a phase-transition point of the second kind, and we shall calculate the specific heat discontinuity at such a point. In this case, we can use the expansion for the free energy restricted to terms of the fourth and lower orders:

$$G - G_0 = \alpha_1^* (P_a^2 + P_b^2) + \alpha_1^* P_a P_b + \beta (P_a^4 + P_b^4). \tag{VI.119}$$

The change in the spontaneous polarization has already been determined in the preceding paragraph. We shall now calculate the polarizability.

When a weak electric field E is applied to a substance in the antiferroelectric state, we obtain

$$\left. \begin{aligned} P_a' &= P_a + \frac{\Delta P}{2}, \\[2ex] P_b' &= P_b + \frac{\Delta P}{2} \end{aligned} \right\} \tag{VI.120}$$

(the prime indicates that the polarizability is measured in the presence of a field E); since $\partial G / \partial P_a = E$, we obtain

$$2\Delta E = 2\alpha_1^* P_a' + \alpha_2^* P_b' + 4\beta P_a'^3, \tag{VI.121}$$

$$\alpha = \frac{\Delta P}{\Delta E} = \frac{1}{2\left(\alpha_2^* - \alpha_1^*\right)} \qquad \text{at} \quad T < T_c. \tag{VI.122}$$

Because at the Curie point $2\alpha_1^* - \alpha_2^* = 0$, it follows that

$$\alpha\big|_{T=T_c-0} = \frac{1}{\alpha_2^*}. \tag{VI.123}$$

In the paraelectric state, ignoring $P_a'^3$, we have

$$\alpha = \frac{2}{2\alpha_1^* + \alpha_2^*}, \tag{VI.124}$$

$$\alpha\big|_{T=T_c+0} = \frac{1}{\alpha_2^*}. \tag{VI.125}$$

Thus, at an antiferroelectric phase transition of the second kind the permittivity varies continuously and is finite. We recall that, in the case of ferroelectric transitions, the permittivity also shows no discontinuity at a phase transition of the second kind, but it does become infinite at the transition point; in practice, the permittivity is simply very high at this point. We have already seen that the permittivity at an antiferroelectric Curie point need not reach high values.

We shall now calculate the specific-heat discontinuity. Assuming that the quantities α_2^* and β in the expression for the thermodynamic potential are independent of temperature, we obtain

$$S = -\left(\frac{\partial G}{\partial T}\right)_{P_a} = -(P_a^2 + P_b^2)\left(\frac{\partial a_1^*}{\partial T}\right)_{P_a}, \tag{VI.126}$$

$$\Delta c_p = T_c\left(\frac{\partial S}{\partial T}\right)_p = \frac{T_c}{\beta}\left(\frac{\partial \alpha_1^*}{\partial T}\right)_T \left(\frac{\partial \alpha_1^*}{\partial T}\right)_{P_a} \tag{VI.127}$$

(here p denotes the pressure).

We shall now consider phase transitions of the first kind in antiferroelectrics. The change in the spontaneous polarization at a phase transition of the second kind has already been determined. The polarizability below the transition point is

$$\alpha\big|_{T=T_c-0} = \frac{1}{4\alpha_1^* - \alpha_2^*}; \qquad\qquad \text{(VI.128)}$$

the polarizability immediately above the transition point is

$$\alpha\big|_{T=T_c+0} = \frac{2}{2\alpha_1^* + \alpha_2^*}. \qquad\qquad \text{(VI.129)}$$

Thus, the polarizability changes discontinuously during a transition of the first kind but it need not assume large values. This also applies to ferroelectric transitions. The difference between the antiferroelectric and ferroelectric transitions is that, in the former case, the polarizability cannot be high in transitions of either kind.

A phase transition of a crystal from the antiferroelectric state need not give rise to a paraelectric phase. Transitions are also possible between antiferroelectric and ferroelectric modifications. An analysis shows that such transitions are possible only for certain relationships between the absolute values and signs of the coefficients in the expansion (VI.110). Such an analysis shows, first of all, that a transition of this type can take place only if $\alpha_1^* < 0$. When the coefficients satisfy the inequality

$$0 > \alpha_2^* > \alpha_1^*, \qquad\qquad \text{(VI.130)}$$

the ferroelectric phase is stable and the antiferroelectric phase is metastable. The reverse is true when the following condition is satisfied:

$$0 < \alpha_2^* < -\alpha_1^*. \qquad\qquad \text{(VI.131)}$$

Since α_1^* and α_2^* depend on the temperature and pressure, these inequalities may be interchanged, giving rise to a transition between an antiferroelectric and a ferroelectric modification.

Let us assume that at some temperature and pressure $\alpha_1^* < 0$ and a crystal is in the ferroelectric state. Let us also assume that the temperature is varied in such a manner that the quantity $2\alpha_1^* - \alpha_2^*$ increases. After passing through the point $\alpha_2^* = 0$, the crystal remains ferroelectric because a potential barrier has to be overcome in order to go over into the more stable antiferro-

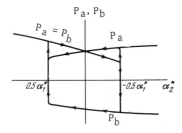

Fig. 151. Dependences of the spontaneous polarizations P_a and P_b on the coefficient α_2^* for $\beta = 0$ and $\alpha_1^* < 0$.

electric state. The transition does not take place until the point $\alpha_2^* = -f$ is reached, at which the antiferroelectric state is formed by a phase transition of the first kind (Fig. 151). Similar "supercooling" is observed also in a transition from the antiferroelectric to the ferroelectric state. Thus, the temperature dependence of the total polarization exhibits a hysteresis.

Let us now consider the behavior of the polarizability at transitions between the ferroelectric and antiferroelectric states. We shall assume that a very weak electric field ΔE is applied to the system. The free energy of the system then becomes

$$G - G_0 = \alpha_1^* (P_a^2 + P_b^2) + \alpha_2^* P_a P_b$$

$$+ \beta (P_a^4 + P_b^4) - \Delta E (P_a + P_b). \tag{VI.132}$$

The conditions for the potential minima give

$$\left.\begin{aligned}
\Delta E &= 2\alpha_1^* P_a + \alpha_2^* P_b + 4\beta P_a^3, \\
\Delta E &= 2\alpha_1^* P_b + \alpha_2^* P_a + 4\beta P_b^3.
\end{aligned}\right\} \tag{VI.133}$$

In the ferroelectric state the polarization P is found from the relationship

$$P = P_a + \frac{\Delta P}{2} = P_b + \frac{\Delta P}{2}; \qquad P_a = P_b; \qquad P_b = -\frac{2\alpha_1^* + \alpha_2^*}{4\beta},$$

and hence

$$\alpha_f = \frac{\Delta P}{\Delta E} = -\frac{2}{2\alpha_1^* + \alpha_2^*}. \tag{VI.134}$$

The polarizability in the antiferroelectric state has been given already [see Eq. (VI.122)]:

$$\alpha_{af} = \frac{1}{2\left(\alpha_2^* - \alpha_1^*\right)}.$$

We shall now determine the polarizability at the critical points. We thus find

when $\alpha_2^* = \alpha_1^*$,

$$\alpha_{af} = \infty \qquad \alpha_f = -\frac{1}{3\alpha_1^*},$$

when $\alpha_2^* = -\alpha_1^*$,

$$\alpha_{af} = -\frac{1}{4f} \qquad \alpha_f = \frac{1}{f}. \tag{VI.135}$$

Thus, the polarizability becomes infinite at the point of transition from the antiferroelectric to the ferroelectric state and it decreases by a factor of 4 at the point of transition from the ferroelectric to the antiferroelectric state. The latter result applies also to a transition of the first kind from the ferroelectric to the paraelectric state. The change in the polarizability is even greater if higher-order terms are included in the expansion of the free energy.

It is shown in Chap. V and in § 2 of the present chapter that the application of an external electric field increases the ferroelectric–paraelectric transition temperature if the paraelectric modification exists at higher temperatures. This behavior of a ferroelectric can be easily understood from the observation that the application of an electric field increases the polarization of a crystal and, therefore, thermal motion at a higher temperature is required to destroy the enhanced polarization. The application of an electric field to an antiferroelectric below the Curie point reduces the temperature of transition to the ferroelectric state (in which P_a has the same direction as P_b). This means that the application of an electric field reduces the antiferroelectric –ferroelectric phase-transition temperature if the ferroelectric phase exists at lower temperatures. However, if the high-temperature modification of an antiferroelectric crystal is paraelectric, the shift of the Curie point is no longer self-evident. However, considering the antiferroelectric phase as more ordered than the fer-

Point Group Symbols*

Crystallographic System	Notation System Shubnikov	Notation System International	Schoenflies
Triclinic	$\frac{1}{2}$	$\frac{1}{1}$	C_1 $C_i = S_2$
Monoclinic	2 m $2:m$	2 m $2/m$	C_2 $R_{1h} = C_5$ C_{2h}
Orthorhombic	$2:2$ $2 \cdot m$ $m \cdot 2:m$	222 $mm2$ mmm	$D_2 = V$ C_{2v} $D_{2h} = V_h$
Rhombohedral	$\frac{4}{4}$ $4:2$ $4 \cdot m$ $4:m$ $\overline{4} \cdot m$ $m \cdot 4:m$	$\frac{4}{4}$ 422 $4mm$ $4/m$ $\overline{4}2m$ $4/mmm$	C_4 S_4 D_4 C_{4v} C_{4h} $D_{2d} = V_d$ D_{4h}
Hexagonal	$\frac{3}{6}$ $3:2$ $3 \cdot m$ $\overline{6} \cdot m$ 6 $3:m$ $6:2$ $6 \cdot m$ $6:m$ $m \cdot 3:m$ $m \cdot 6:m$	$\frac{3}{3}$ $3/2$ $3m$ $\overline{3}/m$ 6 $\overline{6}$ 622 $6mm$ $6/m$ $\overline{6}2$ $6/mmm$	C_3 $C_{3i} = S_6$ D_3 C_{3v} D_{3d} C_6 C_{3h} D_6 C_{6v} C_{6h} D_{3h} D_{6h}
Cubic	$3/2$ $3/4$ $3/\overline{4}$ $\overline{6}/2$ $\overline{6}/4$	23 432 $\overline{4}3m$ $m3$ $m3m$	I O I_d I_h O_h

*The Shubnikov notation is used throughout this book; the table above gives the International and Schoenflies symbols for the convenience of readers. Keep this page folded out if you require quick conversion from the Shubnikov to the other systems. The different notation systems are also given in Table 3 on pp. 12-13 in Vol. 1.

roelectric modification and bearing in mind the observation that the application of a field brings the antiferroelectric modification closer to the ferroelectric state, we may conclude that the application of an electric field should reduce the antiferroelectric −paraelectric transition temperature. This is indeed observed experimentally.

An external electric field can, in principle, transform any antiferroelectric into a ferroelectric, i.e., it may rotate the dipole moments of one sublattice so that they face in the same direction as the dipole moments of the other sublattice. This can always be done when the high−temperature modification is not ferroelectric but paraelectric.† The field E_{cr} at which this transition takes place is known as the critical field. A thermodynamic analysis shows that the critical field E_{cr} can be expressed in terms of coefficients in the expansion for the free energy:

$$E_{cr} = \frac{4}{3\sqrt{6\beta}} (\alpha_1^* - \alpha_1^*)^{3/2}.$$ (VI.136)

The critical field of antiferroelectrics is responsible for their polarization in strong alternating fields, in which the dependence $P(E)$ is in the form of double hysteresis loops (see Chap. VII).

The critical field of a given antiferroelectric depends on its temperature or, more exactly, on the difference between its temperature and the transition point. The critical field governs the special field−induced transition from the antiferroelectric to the ferroelectric state. This transition is of the first kind and is accompanied by the evolution of a latent heat. Therefore, such a transition is described by an analog of the Clapeyron−Clausius equation (VI.36):

$$\frac{dE_{cr}}{dT} = \frac{S_f - S_{af}}{P_f - P_{af}},$$ (VI.137)

where the subscripts "f" and "af" refer to the ferroelectric and antiferroelectric phases, respectively. Bearing in mind that S_f =

---

†If the high−temperature phase is ferroelectric, the antiferroelectric− ferroelectric transition can be regarded as a result of the field-induced displacement of the Curie point in the direction of lower temperatures.

$S_{af} = \Delta Q/T$ and that $P_f - P_{af} \approx P_s$ (P_s is the spontaneous polarization), we obtain

$$\frac{dE_{cr}}{dT} = \frac{\Delta Q}{TP_s}. \tag{VI.138}$$

Assuming that ΔQ is the latent heat per mole, Eq. (VI.138) can be given in the form

$$\frac{dE_{cr}}{dT} = \frac{\Delta Q}{TP_s N v}, \tag{VI.139}$$

where N_v is the molar volume.

Assuming that ΔQ, P_s, and v are constants and integrating with respect to T, we obtain

$$E_{cr} = \left(-\frac{\Delta Q}{P_s N v}\right) \ln T + \text{const.} \tag{VI.140}$$

Using T_{cr} to denote the temperature at which $E_{cr} = 0$, we have

$$E_{cr} = \left(-\frac{\Delta Q}{P_s N v}\right) \ln\left(\frac{T_{cr}}{T}\right). \tag{VI.141}$$

Near T_{cr} the logarithm can be expanded as a series and only the first term need be retained. We then finally obtain

$$E_{cr} = \frac{\Delta Q}{P_s N v} \frac{T_{cr} - T}{T}. \tag{VI.142}$$

Equation (VI.142) has been confirmed experimentally.

The influence of hydrostatic pressure on the transition temperatures of ferroelectrics has been discussed in detail in §3 of Chap. V. Qualitative observations on the influence of hydrostatic pressure on the transition temperatures of antiferroelectrics can be stated as follows. Let us assume that hydrostatic compression increases the spontaneous polarization of the antiferroelectric subcells. This increase signifies also an increase of the stability of the antiferroelectric state. In this case, the temperatures of the antiferroelectric–ferroelectric and antiferroelectric–paraelectric phase transitions should increase. However, if hydrostatic compression reduces the spontaneous polarization of the subcells, the temperatures of the antiferroelectric –ferroelectric and antiferroelectric –paraelectric transitions should decrease.

B. Molecular Models. The theory of the appearance of the spontaneous polarization in various ferroelectrics, based on microscopic models (§3 in the present chapter), can be applied – in principle – to antiferroelectric crystals. The formation of the antiferroelectric state requires the appearance of spontaneous polarization in the subcells and such an orientation of the subcells which would yield full compensation of the subcell dipoles. The first of these conditions is equivalent to the "polarization catastrophe" (interpreted in terms of the electronic or ionic polarizabilities) within the limits of a single subcell. The second condition is satisfied when the energy of the dipole interaction of antiparallel dipole chains is lower than the energy of the interaction of parallel dipole chains. (The electrostatic interaction energy of charges and dipoles makes a negative contribution to the energy of a crystal.)

Analyses of specific (particularly, cubic) structures have led different authors to different conclusions on the stability of the ferroelectric and antiferroelectric states. Thus, according to Cohen [37], the inclusion of ionic displacements shows that the antiferroelectric modification of $BaTiO_3$ should be more stable than the ferroelectric phase. Kinase [47] and Takagi [66] reach the opposite conclusion. Taking into account the partial overlap of the electron shells of ions, Takagi shows that the ferroelectric state of $BaTiO_3$ is more stable than the antiferroelectric state.

Takagi [65] has considered earlier a lattice of the CsCl type with constant point dipoles at the lattice sites and a polarizable ion at the center at a cell. He has found that the transition should be antiferroelectric if the polarizability of the central ion is small, and ferroelectric if this polarizability exceeds a certain threshold value. This model predicts a finite polarizability at the antiferroelectric transition point and an infinite susceptibility at the ferroelectric transition point. In both cases the transitions should be of the second kind.

Nagamiya [55] has applied Slater's model (used to describe the transition in KH_2PO_4, as discussed in §3 of the present chapter) to antiferroelectric $NH_4H_2PO_4$. According to Nagamiya, the entropy of the transition in $NH_4H_2PO_4$ at $-125°C$ should be $0.8\,cal \cdot$

mole$^{-1}\cdot$deg^{-1}, which is reasonably close to the experimental value of 1.05 cal$\cdot$mole$^{-1}\cdot$deg^{-1}. However, Nagamiya is unable to demonstrate that this model predicts a phase transition.

Stephenson and Adams [63] have applied Slater's model to $Ag_2H_3IO_6$ and have obtained a transition entropy close to the value they have found from experimental measurements. However, their approximation does not make it possible to distinguish between various ferroelectric and antiferroelectric states.

Jaskiewicz and Konwent [44] discuss the distribution of dipoles in the structure of perovskite due to displacements of A ions. They show that this displacement cannot produce a dipole distribution corresponding to the ferroelectric modification. When A ions are displaced we can only have a distribution of dipoles corresponding to the antiferroelectric modification. According to Jaskiewicz and Konwent, their results can be applied to the antiferroelectric $PbZrO_3$.

Zhdanov [10] discusses in detail the dipole structures corresponding to the antiparallel and parallel distributions of dipoles and estimates the energies of systems of point dipoles for various cases. The results obtained by Zheludev [70] may be useful in the analysis of the dipole structures of specific antiferroelectrics.

The theory of crystal lattice dynamics has not yet been applied to antiferroelectrics. However, there are indications that phase transitions in antiferroelectrics can be explained by the instability of some normal vibration modes. In particular, Woods et al. [69] show that, in some cases, a CsCl-type crystal may show an instability of a transverse mode if the vector $\mathbf{q}$ is not equal to zero (as in the case of ferroelectrics) and is governed by the reciprocal-lattice coordinates $(1/2, 0, 0)$. This type of instability gives rise to the antiferroelectric modification.

References

1. P. W. Anderson, in: Physics of Dielectrics (Proc. Second All-Union Conf., Moscow, 1958) [Russian translation], Izd. AN SSSR, Moscow-Leningrad (1960), p. 290.

2. N. N. Bogolyubov, Problems of a Dynamical Theory in Statistical Physics [in Russian], GITTL, Moscow (1946); English translation in: Studies in Statistical Mechanics, 1:5-515 (1962).

3. M. Born and K. Huang, Dynamical Theory of Crystal Lattices, Oxford University Press (1954).
4. S. Boguslavskii, Zh. Russ. Fiz.-Khim. Obshch., Fiz. Otd., 47(5):247 (1915).
5. W. F. Brown, Jr., "Dielectrics," in: Handbuch der Physik (ed. by S. Flügge), Vol. 17, Part 1, Springer-Verlag, Berlin (1956), p. 1.
6. Yu. N. Venevtsev, V. N. Lyubimov, S. P. Solov'ev, A. S. Viskov, and I. S. Zhdanov, Abstracts of Papers presented at Symposium on Ferromagnetism and Ferroelectricity, Leningrad, 1963 [in Russian].
7. V. L. Ginzburg, Zh. Éksp. Teor. Fiz., 15:739 (1945).
8. V. L. Ginzburg, Usp. Fiz. Nauk, 38:490 (1949).
9. V. L. Ginzburg, Fiz. Tverd. Tela, 2:2031 (1960).
10. G. S. Zhdanov, Crystal Physics, Oliver and Boyd, Edinburgh (1965).
11. V. L. Indenbom and M. A. Chernysheva, Zh. Éksp. Teor. Fiz., 32:697 (1957).
12. W. Känzig, "Ferroelectrics and antiferroelectrics," Solid State Phys., 4:1 (1957).
13. V. I. Klyachkin, Izv. Akad. Nauk SSSR, Ser. Fiz., 24:1176 (1960).
14. V. Kh. Kozlovskii, Zh. Éksp. Teor. Fiz., 30:766 (1956).
15. V. Kh. Kozlovskii, Izv. Akad. Nauk SSSR, Ser. Fiz., 21:352 (1957).
16. I. V. Kurchatov, Ferroelectrics [in Russian], Moscow (1933); abridged French translation: I. V. Kourtschatov, Le champ moléculaire dans les diélectriques (le sel de seignette), Hermann, Paris (1936).
17. V. N. Murzin and A. I. Demeshina, Fiz. Tverd. Tela, 6:182 (1964).
18. R. E. Pasynkov, Izv. Akad. Nauk SSSR, Ser. Fiz., 21:340 (1957).
19. G. I. Skanavi, Dokl. Akad. Nauk SSSR, 59:231 (1948).
20. G. A. Smolenskii and V. A. Isupov, Ferroelectrics (Review) [in Russian], Institut poluprovodnikov, AN SSSR, Leningrad (1958).
21. G. A. Smolenskii and N. V. Kozhevnikova, Dokl. Akad. Nauk SSSR, 76:519 (1951).
22. G. A. Smolenskii and V. Kh. Kozlovskii, Zh. Tekh. Fiz., 23:445 (1953).
23. G. A. Smolenskii and V. Kh. Kozlovskii, Zh. Éksp. Teor. Fiz., 26:684 (1954).
24. L. N. Syrkin, Kristallografiya, 1:274 (1956).
25. H. Fröhlich, Theory of Dielectrics, 2nd ed., Oxford University Press (1958).
26. V. Y. Khozyainov, Abstracts of Papers presented at Symposium on Ferromagnetism and Ferroelectricity, Leningrad, 1963 [in Russian].
27a. L. P. Kholodenko, Zh. Éksp. Teor. Fiz., 31:244 (1956);
27b. L. P. Kholodenko, Kristallografiya, 1:393 (1956);
27c. L. P. Kholodenko, Izv. Akad. Nauk SSSR, Ser. Fiz., 21:368 (1957).
28a. A. F. Yatsenko, Izv. Akad. Nauk SSSR, Ser. Fiz., 22:1456 (1958);
28b. A. F. Yatsenko, in: Physics of Dielectrics (Proc. Second All-Union Conf., Moscow, 1958) [in Russian], Izd. AN SSSR, Moscow (1960), p. 314.
29. W. Ackermann, Ann. Physik, 46:197 (1915).
30. A. S. Barker, Jr. and M. Tinkham, Phys. Rev., 125:1527 (1962).
31. C. A. Beevers and W. Hughes, Proc. Roy. Soc. (London), 177:251 (1941).
32. S. Boguslawski, Physik. Z., 15:283, 569 (1914).
33. S. Boguslawski, Physik. Z., 15:805 (1914).
34. M. Born, Physik. Z., 23:125 (1922).

35.   M. Born, Rev. Mod. Phys., 17:245 (1945).

36.   W. Cochran, Adv. Phys., 9:387 (1960).

37.   M. H. Cohen, Phys. Rev., 84:369 (1951).

38.   A. F. Devonshire, Phil. Mag., 40:1040 (1949).

39.   A. F. Devonshire, Phil. Mag., Suppl., 3:85 (1954).

40.   A. F. Devonshire, Phil. Mag., 2:1027 (1957).

41.   V. Dvořák and V. Janovec, Czech. J. Phys., B12:461 (1962).

42.   R. H. Fowler, Proc. Roy. Soc. (London), A149:1 (1935).

43.   J. H. Gibbs, Phys. Rev., 94:292 (1954).

44.   A. Jaskiewicz and H. Konwent, Acta Phys. Polon., 21:509 (1962).

45.   E. T. Jaynes, Ferroelectricity, Princeton University Press, New Jersey (1953).

46.   E. T. Jaynes and E. P. Wigner, Phys. Rev., 79:213 (1950).

47.   W. Kinase, Progr. Theoret. Phys. (Kyoto), 13:529 (1955).

48.   C. Kittel, Phys. Rev., 82:729 (1951).

49.   J. Larmor, Proc. Roy. Soc. (London), 99:1 (1921).

50.   J. T. Last, Phys. Rev., 105:1740 (1957).

51a. W. P. Mason, Phys. Rev., 72:854 (1947);

51b. W. P. Mason, Piezoelectric Crystals and Their Applications to Ultrasonics, Van Nostrand, New York (1950).

52.   W. P. Mason and B. T. Matthias, Phys. Rev., 74:1622 (1948).

53.   B. T. Matthias, Phys. Rev., 75:1771 (1949).

54.   T. Mitsui, Phys. Rev., 111:1259 (1958).

55.   T. Nagamiya, Progr. Theoret. Phys. (Kyoto), 7:275 (1952).

56.   P. S. Narayanan and K. Vedam, Z. Physik, 163:158 (1961).

57.   J. Pirenne, Physica, 15:1019 (1949).

58.   A. K. Rajagopal and R. Srinivasan, J. Phys. Chem. Solids, 23:633 (1962).

59.   M. E. Senko, Phys. Rev., 121:1599 (1961).

60.   J. C. Slater, J. Chem. Phys., 9:16 (1941).

61.   J. C. Slater, Phys. Rev., 78:748 (1950).

62.   W. G. Spitzer, R. C. Miller, D. A. Kleinman, and L. E. Howarth, Phys. Rev., 126:1710 (1962).

63.   C. C. Stephenson and H. E. Adams, J. Am. Chem. Soc., 66:1409 (1944).

64a. Y. Takagi, Proc. Phys. Math. Soc. Japan, 23:44 (1941);

64b. Y. Takagi, J. Phys. Soc. Japan, 3:271 (1948).

65.   Y. Takagi, Phys. Rev., 85:315 (1952).

66.   Y. Takagi, Proc. Intern. Conf. on Theoret. Phys., Kyoto and Tokyo, 1953, publ. by Science Council of Japan, Tokyo (1954), p. 824.

67.   H. Takahashi, Proc. Phys. Math. Soc. Japan, 23:1069 (1941).

68.   A. R. Ubbelohde and I. Woodward, Proc. Roy. Soc. (London), A185:448 (1946).

69.   A. D. B. Woods, W. Cochran, and B. N. Brockhouse, Bull. Am. Phys. Soc., 4:246 (1959).

70.   I. S. Zheludev, Proc. Indian Acad. Sci., A57:361 (1963).

Index*

---

* pp. 1-336, inclusive, are in Volume 1; pp. 337-620 are in Volume 2.

xxiii